The Pictorial Encyclopedia of
Birds

The Pictorial Encyclopedia of

Birds

J. Hanzák

Edited by Bruce Campbell

American Consultant: Ned R. Boyajian

PAUL HAMLYN · LONDON

Designed and produced by Artia

Published 1967 in Great Britain by
Paul Hamlyn Ltd.
Drury House, Russell Street, London WC2

Printed in Czechoslovakia by Svoboda Prague
S 2249

Foreword

Bird-watching today is an international hobby. Gone are the times when British or American readers were content to study only the birds of their own country; and for many the whole world is now their ornithological oyster. Even those who do not travel far wish to know about the bird life of other countries and continents. The object of the Pictorial Encyclopedia is to present between one pair of covers a survey of the wild birds of the world, and of those which have been domesticated, with a succinct text and photographic illustrations as varied as possible.

The birds are arranged in general conformity with the modern scientific classification, which needs some explanation. The first classifications, of birds, as of other animals and plants, depended on outward resemblances which may be quite misleading; for example, the flightless Great Auk was externally not unlike a penguin, but anatomically and in other respects bears no close relationship; and the thick-billed sparrows of Eurasia were at one time placed with the finches because of superficial resemblance, but are now classified with the weavers.

Modern classification, in fact, depends primarily on anatomical and physiological resemblances, which indicate probable evolutionary descent, as do patterns of behaviour, which are being increasingly studied for their bearing on relationships. Recently the analysis of proteins by electrophoresis has suggested another approach to the problem, and few ornithologists believe that today's classification is likely to be definitive.

The unit of systematic classification is the species, the members of which generally interbreed with each other and produce fertile offspring. This is not an absolute rule – rules in nature are seldom absolute – but it holds good in the main for wild populations, and is therefore a distinction with biological meaning, whereas all other divisions or taxa (singular: taxon) are basically the results of subjective human judgments.

Closely related species are placed in the same genus (plural: genera); for example the Raven, Crows and Rook or the Mistle Thrush, Song Thrush, Fieldfare, Redwing and Blackbird. The next major step upward is to the family, for example, the Old World warblers or the cuckoos, and families are grouped in orders, which make up the entire class Aves or Birds. But some authorities consider these distinctions are not nice enough, so we get two subclasses and many superorders, suborders, superfamilies, subfamilies, tribes, subgenera and superspecies. The most widely used is the ultimate subspecies or geographical race. When they meet its members interbreed freely with those of another race of the same species and produce fertile progeny, but it is from the isolation of subspecies that we believe full species are evolved. A good example of a border-line case is the Red Grouse; for a long time it was regarded as a species unique to Britain and Ireland, but it has now been reunited with the European Willow Grouse, although this form turns white in winter and has white wings even in summer.

The present system of scientific names dates from the 1st January 1758, the year in which the great Swedish naturalist, Carl von Linné or Linnaeus, published the tenth edition of his *Systema Naturae*, in which he consistently used two names in Latin form for each species of plant and animal. The first name indicates the genus (a taxon first defined by Linnaeus) and is spelt with an initial capital letter; the second is the specific name and is spelt nowadays with a small initial letter. By agreement no generic name is repeated in the entire animal kingdom, but specific names, e.g. *vulgaris* (common) recur constantly. These scientific names are always in Latin form and if the specific is an adjective it must agree with the gender of the generic name. So *Turdus torquatus* is the correct name of the Ring Ousel but *Saxicola torquata* is correct for the Stonechat. Sometimes the generic and specific names are the same, as for the Wren *Troglodytes troglodytes*.

A third name is added to denote the subspecies or race. The typical or first race to be described repeats the specific name, so we get mouthfuls like *Troglodytes troglodytes troglodytes* for the type race of Wren or *Coccothraustes coccothraustes coccothraustes* for the Hawfinch. Where specific and subspecific names are the same it is usual just to use the initial letter of the specific thus: *Troglodytes t. troglodytes*. After the scientific name it is the practice in works of reference to give the name of the authority who first described each species or race. This is usually abbreviated and it is remarkable how many times L. or Linn. (both short for Linnaeus) still appears. If the name of the authority is in brackets, it means that he originally placed the bird in a different genus. Sometimes the date of publication is added, or even the title of the work in which the first description appears. But in the Encyclopedia only the most widely accepted generic and specific names are given at the first mention of each species.

Because English speaking peoples are found all round the world, widespread species of birds have tended to be given more than one English name, e.g. American loons are British divers. Sometimes the same English name is used for two different species; the American and European Robins are the classic examples of this. Widely used alternatives are given throughout the Encyclopedia, but some species which are confined to non-English speaking countries may have no English name in common use.

The sequence in which the birds of the world are arranged has been altered many times. Today there is general agreement to arrange the orders in a sort of progression from the most primitive to the most highly evolved. Opinions on details of this sequence vary considerably, and some juxtapositions are quite arbitrary. In general this Encyclopedia follows the sequence adopted in *Birds of the World* by Oliver L. Austin, but departs from it on occasion in the interests of presentation.

All the 27 orders recognized by Austin are represented in the Encyclopedia and the vast majority of the 155 families. Omission is usually because no adequate photographs exist. Of necessity photographs of stuffed specimens or of birds in captivity have been used for a few species, but the photographic resources of the world have been scoured for studies of species in the wild, and the Encyclopedia is notable for the number of pictures of birds from the eastern parts of the great Eurasian landmass. No species is mentioned in the text without a supporting photograph, apart from one or two birds which are externally identical to others that are shown.

Bruce Campbell

Introduction

During the long period of their evolution birds have adapted themselves to life in a great variety of environments, and their shape, the form of their bills, feet and other parts of the body, their colouration and habits show enormous diversity. Despite this, all birds have several features in common which distinguish them from other vertebrates. Birds are most closely related to the reptiles and there is no doubt that birds and reptiles in their present form trace their evolution back to common ancestors, many of whose characters they have retained to this day. Like most young reptiles, birds are hatched from eggs, and in both the skin is without glands, the skull is attached to the spinal column by a single joint, and the arrangement of the excretory and reproductive organs as well as the growth of the embryo show a marked resemblance. The study of extinct forms provides further evidence of the connection between the two classes.

The first creatures resembling present-day birds date from the Mesozoic Era more than 150 million years ago. Their fossil remains were found in the Jurassic slate formation near Solenhofen and Eichstätt in Bavaria; the three existing specimens belong to the genus Archaeopteryx and combine the features of birds and lizards. The tail, which is as long as the body, has twenty free vertebrae and the tail feathers are arranged in two rows on either side, one pair to each vertebra. The skull is that of a bird, but the bill is provided with teeth. The fore limbs are covered with flight feathers, but have three free fingers terminating in claws; it is the possession of feathers, a specialized product of the skin, that distinguishes birds as a class. These crow-sized birds were probably capable of gliding flight, but they were equipped with clawed fingers and were also able to climb.

Another extinct bird, found as a fossil in the North American Chalk (60 to 120 million years old) is *Hesperornis regalis* [2], a flightless bird which stood nearly 6 ft tall and resembled the diver of today. *Archaeopteryx* [1] was a land bird, but the skeleton of Hesperornis suggests that this creature was well adapted to movement in water and was probably very clumsy on land, crawling on its belly by pushing with its legs, which were located at the very end of the body. It probably fed chiefly on fish, which it dived for, and caught with jaws which may have had teeth. Living in similar localities was another primitive bird, *Ichthyornis victor* [3], which resembled a small gull or tern. It was a good flier which according to the latest opinion did not possess teeth and was generally much more like present-day birds. Both forms had a much reduced tail. At a later date – in the early Tertiary Period – there appeared representatives of orders existing to this day.

The main reason for the success of birds as a class is undoubtedly their power of flight, for apart from insects and bats and a few other small vertebrates, they have no rivals in the air. There are two theories as to how the transition from life on land to life in the air came about. The first stage, according to one view, was gliding to the ground from an elevated perch with the aid of the feathered fore limbs and tail. According to the other theory, which cannot be entirely excluded, flight resulted from attempts to use the primitive wings when making a rapid escape from pursuers on the ground, by leaps covering short distances which led finally to momentary flapping flight. From these beginnings, there evolved birds of many specialized types, including some which lost the power of flight and became purely land or water creatures. It is clear from the basic wing structure of the flightless species that they have developed from forms which were able to fly.

All birds are distinguished from other vertebrates by several common characteristics which have evolved to facilitate travel through the air, against the pull of the earth's gravity. The wings of flying birds provide a very large surface area, while their construction keeps their weight down to a minimum; for example, the long bones supporting them are hollow tubes. The bodies of birds, too, are very light; there is no urinary bladder, and the toothless bill and the legs add little to the weight. The wings are powered by a thick layer of muscles attached to the keel of the breastbone.

Birds, like mammals, are warm-blooded creatures,

and the fact that they are not dependent on the temperature of their environment makes it possible for them to inhabit very cold and forbidding regions. The average body temperature of birds is 41° Centigrade (106° Fahrenheit), which is higher than in mammals. As in mammals, the bird heart consists basically of two parts, each with two chambers. The first part collects the used blood returned from the veins of the body, and pumps it through vessels in the lungs where it takes up a fresh supply of oxygen; the oxygenated blood returns to the second part of the organ, which pumps it out into the body's arteries. Flight puts a great strain on the heart, which in birds is much larger and more powerful than in other vertebrates. In small birds the pulse rate is about 500 beats a minute. The size of the heart and the rapid pulse are signs of the higher rate of body metabolism.

Feathers were probably first evolved as protection against loss of body temperature, for they are very good insulators. They are a product of the skin, just like the scales of a reptile or the fur of a mammal, and are composed of a horny substance. The structure of the feather is complicated. A skin-bud or pimple gives rise to the shaft of the feather whose base is called the quill – the hollow part which was once cut and used as a pen. The greater, elongated part of the shaft, called the rachis, is bordered on both sides by a series of lamellae or barbs carrying a similar double series of barbules; these form the vane or web, which in the wing and tail quills is the actual supporting surface. The barbules give rise to barbicels or cilia, which terminate in hooklets. These catch in the margins of the next row to form a firm surface which when pulled apart immediately comes together again. The 'oar' feathers (remiges) of the wings and the steering feathers of the tail (rectrices) are the specialized forms which regulate flight. Feathers are of two main types; the connected web is found only in the contour feathers, which give the body its shape. In these feathers the shaft (rachis) is sometimes accompanied by a secondary "aftershaft". The second type is the down-feathers; these have short, soft tubes with rays and barbs which do not possess hooklets and are therefore not connected. These down-feathers form the coats of the young and a soft, thick layer which lies underneath the contour feathers of adults and helps to maintain the body temperature. Only in the Horned Screamer, the penguins and the Ostrich and its relatives do the contour feathers grow continuously over the whole body surface; in all other birds they grow in certain definite tracts called pterylae, the intervening spaces being termed apteria. Powder-down feathers are a special kind of down-feather which never develop beyond the early stage and continually disintegrate at the tip into powder; this powder covers the feathers and prevents them from becoming damp. They are to be found in parrots, toucans, bowerbirds and herons, usually growing in two patches on the flanks. The webless "bristle-feathers" at the gape of many birds serve a sensory function. A full-grown feather is non-living; its colour is produced by various pigments or else is due to the internal structure of the feather itself which gives the effect of colour to the observer; for example, the iridescence on a pigeon's neck. If the colour changes without a concurrent change of plumage, this is usually caused by the rubbing off of the margins which differ in colour from the remainder of the feathers, but may be due to changes in diet, especially in captivity.

Feathers suffer from wear and tear and for that reason are shed regularly and replaced by new ones – this is called moulting and is caused by periodic stimuli from certain glands, combined with changes in temperature and the amount of light. Most songbirds and many other types moult twice a year. In summer or autumn, following nesting, the bird changes its whole plumage; the wing quills and steering feathers are usually shed successively so that the bird does not lose the power of flight. But swans, geese and ducks go through a flightless period in late summer, which has been made use of to catch them for marking purposes. Contour feathers are also discarded successively and replaced by new ones. Such a moult is called a complete moult, whereas a partial moult, which occurs in spring before nesting, affects only the smaller contour feathers. Many species of birds have two differently coloured garbs a year – the brighter, or nuptial dress following the partial spring moult, and the duller winter plumage, following the complete moult.

Birds devote much time to caring for their feathers; many kinds coat theirs with a special secretion produced by an oil gland located among the feathers near the root of the tail.

Instead of teeth, birds possess a bill or beak, covered by a horny sheath, with a sharp tip and edges, which are occasionally serrated. It cannot chew food like the teeth of mammals, but only crack, peck, pluck, tear, split, scoop up, sift, or simply grasp. Bills vary widely in shape, depending on the purpose for which they are intended. They are also used when preening the feathers. The base of the bill is sometimes covered by a special type of skin called the cere.

The digestive system of birds is adapted to the large supply of energy that must be readily available for flight; that is why they are so voracious. As a rule,

1

small birds require proportionately much more food than large ones. The daily amount consumed by humming birds, kinglets and wrens, for example, equals more than their body weight, sometimes even twice as much. The senses of smell and taste seem to play little part in a bird's selection of its food. Only a few groups are able to grasp food with the claws (tits, birds of prey, crows) and only parrots can transfer it to the beak. On passing through the gullet, the food is generally retained for a time in an enlarged section called the crop, where it is sometimes softened before passing on to the stomach. In some birds (pigeons, gallinaceous birds) the crop is markedly developed, in others (owls and insect-eaters) it is absent or only imperfectly developed. The stomach comprises an antechamber (proventriculus), where protein digestion is effected with the aid of hydrochloric acid, and the gizzard (ventriculus), whose strong muscular walls, often assisted by stones, grit or sand swallowed for that purpose, grind up the food. The power of the gizzard muscles is remarkable; they pulverize the strong shells of molluscs swallowed by eiders and even the porcelain cups accidentally swallowed by ostriches. Their

mechanical action does the work of the teeth in mammals. The gizzard is greatly developed in birds feeding on seeds and grain, whereas in those which take soft foods it is the antechamber which plays the main role. Undigested matter such as fur, scales, bones and the chitinous remains of insects, is regurgitated as pellets. Further digestion and the absorption of fats, carbohydrates and proteins occur in the intestines. In some birds, at the point where the small intestine joins the large intestine, there is a pair of blind sacs (caeca) where further digestion takes place with the aid of bacteria. The intestine is somewhat enlarged at the end and is at this point joined by the termination of the excretory and reproductive passages. Faeces, urine and reproductive cells all pass out of the body through the same vent. Urine is passed out with the faeces as compact, white matter. The process of digestion in birds is very rapid, especially in those species which consume soft foods such as fruit.

The reproductive organs of birds also show great efficiency in structure; immediately after the breeding period they shrink markedly in size, to regain their former dimensions when it is again time for mating,

9

2

increasing by 200 to 300 times the size when dormant. The embryo does not develop inside the body of the female, but in an egg. Of the two ovaries the right one is usually rudimentary and the left is shaped like a cluster of grapes comprising, during the breeding period, eggs of various sizes and in various stages of development. When mature, the eggs fall off from the clump into the funnel-shaped mouth of the oviduct and are fertilized in its uppermost part before addition of the egg-white and formation of the membranes, which takes place during their passage down the duct. These membranes are formed very rapidly—within the period of one day in domestic fowl, for instance. The vital parts of the bird's egg are the yolk and the blastodisc, which is the actual embryo-forming portion and is the largest to be found among the vertebrates. The egg therefore comprises yolk (the inner nutritive portion), yolk sac, albumen or white, shell membrane and shell, which is composed chiefly of calcium. At the rounded end of the egg there is an air space and the membrane does not adhere to the shell at this point.

The determination of a bird's sex is often possible only by means of dissection; but in certain species it is possible to distinguish the male from the female by the colour of their feathers or by other secondary sexual characteristics such as lobes, combs, wattles or bare skin on the head, spurs on the feet, etc. As a rule, the male is more brightly coloured than the female, sometimes the colouration is identical, and in rare instances the female may be the more brightly coloured of the two.

The respiratory tract has several peculiarities of structure. Just behind the tongue there is a narrow opening into the larynx, the upper part of the trachea or windpipe, which is formed by a continuous succession of bony rings connected by membrane. The vocal cords are not situated in the larynx, where they are generally found in mammals. Birds produce sounds by means of a special organ, called the syrinx, which is usually located at the point where the trachea branches into the bronchial tubes; the complexity of its structure varies, being most highly developed in song-birds. The lungs are porous and fairly small. The bronchial tubes pass through the lungs and terminate in additional large, thin-walled sacs larger in volume than the lungs themselves. Basically there are three pairs which branch out into various parts of the body, including some of the bones. Little is known about the exact function of these air sacs, but there is no doubt that they serve as reservoirs of air for breathing while in flight.

The bird's sensory organs also show adaptations to its specialized way of life. Some are fully developed, others are not. Of primary importance for fast-flying birds is the sense of sight, which is keenest in the birds of prey and in owls. Hearing is also very good and birds are able to register even slight rustling sounds and determine their exact location. The anatomical equipment for the sense of smell exists in most birds, but there is little evidence that they make use of it.

Birds are quick to react to all environmental stimuli, but their behaviour is governed mainly by inherited instinct, and not by intellect, though many species have some learning ability. But if a bird is transferred to a new and completely strange environment, it is usually quite at a loss, lacking the necessary intelligence to adapt itself to the situation. Caring for the young is often given as an example of parental love, any many species will certainly defend their nests, eggs or babies with apparent devotion. But a bird is often unable to tell the difference when one of its eggs is replaced by that of another kind, or even by some foreign object; it cannot count its brood if they become scattered, it may be deceived into feeding a dummy nestling, and may desert its young if food becomes scarce, because from the standpoint of natural selection it is better for the adult to survive and nest again when conditions are more favourable. The forms of expression used by birds lead to auto-

matic but very definite modes of behaviour and are psychologically very complex. Birds normally communicate with one another by means of simple sounds serving to express contentment or fright, or to warn of approaching danger. These are innate forms of expression and have nothing in common with human language; their equivalents are man's instinctive cries of fright, surprise, etc. During the mating season the males of many species utter or make special sounds which are heard mainly or only at this time. Belonging to this group are the melodies of the male song-birds which serve to establish the nesting territory, to ward off other males, and as a means of courting the female. Some birds replace vocal sounds by mechanical noises caused, for example, by rapid pecking (woodpeckers), the vibration of certain feathers (Common Snipe), or by making a clatter with the bill (storks). During the mating season these vocal manifestations may be accompanied by specific movements, both in the air and on the ground, whose effect is heightened by the

3

16   Eye ring
15   Crown
17   Iris   Forehead   18
Nostril   19
Bill   20
14   Nape
13   Ear region
Upper mandible   21
Tip of bill   22
12   Neck
Lower mandible   23
Lores   24
11   Upper back
Chin   25
10   Shoulder coverts
Throat   26
9   Upper wing coverts
8   Middle wing coverts
7   Lower wing coverts
Crop   27
6   Lower back
5   Secondaries
Breast   28
4   Rump
Leading edge   29
3   Primaries
Primary covert   30
2   Upper tail covert
Flank   31
Belly   32
1   Tail feather
Shank   33
Tarsus   34
Under tail covert   39
Inner toe   35
Hind toe   38
Middle toe   36
Outer toe   37

colouration and form of the bird's feathers, for example, the 'train' of the peacock. These movements are all directed towards one purpose – the winning of the female – and are an expression of sexual excitement. Birds may mate permanently or only for a single nesting; it is not uncommon to find polygamous cocks, and in some species hens may mate with a succession of cocks.

A bird's nest serves as a receptacle where the eggs are laid and hatched, and also as a place where the nestlings remain until they are able to fend for themselves. The nest may be a simple depression or hollow, it may be shallow, cup-shaped or spherical with a domed roof, a work of art woven of twigs, made laboriously of mud or even a structure cemented with the secretions of the salivary glands. The nest is usually built by the female alone or with the aid of the male; sometimes he makes several cock's nests and his mate chooses one and lines it. The number of eggs is more or less constant for the females of each species, and even in the several species of a systematic group. Thus, for example, the fulmars and other sea-birds lay one egg, pigeons, cranes, bustards and large eagles two, gulls three, shore-birds four and most song-birds 4 to 6 eggs at one time. Larger numbers are laid by the game birds and ducks, and some birds nest two or three times in the season. The embryo in the egg requires a specific temperature in which to develop and so needs to be warmed by the parent birds; they place the bare brood-patches on their skin in direct contact with the eggs. The male and female may take turns on the eggs, the female alone may incubate or, much more rarely, the male alone. Some 'parasitic' birds, such as the cuckoos and cowbirds, leave the hatching of their eggs and care of the young to other 'host' species. Occasionally other means are used to warm the eggs, e.g. the megapodes bury their eggs in mounds of leaves and humus where heat is generated by the process of decay.

Birds can be divided roughly into two separate groups according to the degree of development in the young on hatching. In the one group the young are hatched in a helpless condition, without feathers or covered only with a light down, and are fed by their parents or inhabit the nest for a considerable time; these are known as nidicolous or altricial species. In the other group, called nidifugous or precocial, the nestlings are hatched with a cover of down and in a condition that enables them to leave the nest and feed themselves almost immediately,

a typical contour feather, with connected web; **b** barbules, barbicels and hooklets, magnified to show how web is formed; **c** down feather.

the parents merely guiding and watching over them; the time spent in the nest is very brief, sometimes only a matter of hours. The embryonic stage of this latter group is longer than that of nidicolous birds of the same size, as more time is required for the development of the central nervous system.

The most distinctive characteristic of birds as a class is their power of flight, possessed by all birds of the present day with the exception of the ostrich group, the penguins and a few other species. There are two main forms of flight: flapping, and soaring or gliding. The first is effected by the beating of the wings, i.e. by the action of muscles, and is the chief form of flight for "travelling". The smallest species, mainly humming birds, employ a rapid whirring motion reminiscent of the flight of insects, enabling the bird to hover in one spot as well as moving from one place to another. In soaring or gliding flight, the bird does does not flap its wings but keeps them outstretched so that they function as supports in gliding or, especially in the case of species with large wing surfaces, for swooping and soaring. Gliding, as we have seen, was probably the earliest form of flight. The speed of flight is frequently overestimated. Most birds can attain quite high speeds (the crow 30 miles per hour, the finches slightly more, the starling over 45 miles per hour). Great speeds have been measured in ducks (about 75 miles per hour), and swifts (100 miles per hour), and the Peregrine Falcon can reach up to 165 miles per hour when attacking or swooping. Birds when migrating fly at heights of 3,000 to 6,000 feet and quite small species have been recorded up to 23,000 feet on radar screens.

Birds are creatures seemingly free to wander at will over the earth's surface. But, in fact, they are bound to certain areas, especially to their nesting grounds which vary in size but have definite though invisible boundaries. Resident birds may not go more than a short distance beyond these borders even when the nesting season is over except when food is scarce, others range far afield, and a third group, known as migrants, leave their nesting grounds in late summer or early autumn as soon as they have reared their young and often long before the weather turns cold. They generally make their way to distant regions where the climate and conditions of life are more favourable. Insectivorous birds can thus assure themselves of sufficient food during the winter months. Many birds which breed in the North Temperate Zone are migratory in the northern part of their range of distribution and resident further south. The winter quarters are sometimes ecologically much like their nesting grounds, though the birds do not nest there as well.

Many of the mysteries surrounding the movements of birds have now been explained by ringing or banding and by observations using radar. One question which has yet to be satisfactorily answered is how birds are capable of such excellent orientation that they are able to make the long journey home or to their winter quarters without being shown the way or having made the trip before. It is now generally believed that birds which migrate by day navigate by the sun; and there is a good deal of evidence that night migrants use the stars in the same way. This ability to navigate is inherited, which would explain why young birds can migrate unguided. Birds which have made the journey before are able to recognise landmarks; this accounts for the return of swallows to the barn where they have nested in previous years.

The distribution of birds throughout the world is now fairly well known, though it is still possible that new species may be discovered in some little visited jungle or forest. Ornithologists are not agreed on the exact number of species in existence, as it is sometimes difficult to determine whether certain forms are independent species or only races. The most reliable estimates suggest that there are about 8,650 species of birds, the greatest numbers occurring in South America and Africa. This number may well decrease as certain species are exterminated either directly by man, or indirectly through changes wrought in their natural environment. Some species also show evidence of having passed the peak of their evolutionary development, and their numbers are declining because they are unable to adapt themselves to changing conditions; and we know that others have become extinct in recent times from natural causes. But at last interest in the conservation of birds has been aroused throughout the world and many species may yet be saved for the enjoyment and study of future generations.

Contents

15

4

Kiwis

The kiwis (Apterygiformes) comprise only three living species, all confined to New Zealand. These birds are about the size of a domestic fowl, with short, stout legs terminating in four toes, and a long bill with nostrils at the very tip. The body is covered with simple vaneless feathers resembling long, thick hair. They are nocturnal birds and their search for food is

5

governed mainly by their keen sense of smell, their eyesight being very poor. The wings are small and stunted, and they are incapable of flight. Kiwis usually lay only one egg (rarely 2), which is enormous, weighing up to 1 lb, i.e. between one fifth and one quarter of the weight of the female. The cock performs most of the duties of incubation, which takes from 75 to 80 days.

The **Common Kiwi**, *Apteryx australis* [4], was at one time abundant in New Zealand and on Stewart Island, where it was considered a great delicacy by the natives. With the inroads of civilization its numbers rapidly declined and in some districts it is now extremely rare. Kiwis inhabit wooded country with dense undergrowth where they hunt food in much the same way as snipe and where they dig holes to hide in or for nesting. The male is smaller and weighs about 3 lb, the female 5 lb.

In the southern regions of New Zealand lives the **Little Spotted** or **Little Grey Kiwi**, *Apteryx oweni* [5], which differs from the Common Kiwi by its delicate transverse markings.

6

Ostriches
The order Struthioniformes contains only one surviving species—the largest bird in existence, the **Ostrich** or **Camel-bird,** *Struthio camelus* [6–8]. This is a flightless bird with rudimentary wings believed, however, to be descended from forms capable of flight; the wing's basic structure is the same in principle as that found in flying birds, and the wing quills are well developed even though stunted or in the form of soft feathers. The loss of

7

the ability to fly, caused apparently by the increase in body weight, resulted also in atrophy of the flight muscles and the absence of a keel on the breastbone. The legs, on the other hand, are very strong, enabling the bird to run at great speed for long distances. The structure of the legs points to the fact that this bird frequents broad open plains and deserts.

The ostrich was at one time widely distributed throughout Africa, but today its occurrence is limited to the parts south of the Sahara. It is extinct in Asia. The head, almost the whole neck and the legs are either bare or covered with down, the other parts of the body with feathers – black in the male and brownish grey in the female. The wings and tail of the male are adorned with magnificent white plumes which were once highly valued as ornaments. The foot has only two toes. The ostrich feeds chiefly on plants but its large bill indicates that it has no difficulty in capturing even small vertebrates. It swallows small stones to help the stomach in grinding up its food. The courting cock presents a spectacular sight as he performs his ceremonial dance, swaying his head, ruffling his feathers, buckling his legs, bristling and spreading his wings and puffing up his neck [7]. The adult bird weighs more than 200 lb and is taller than a man. The female lays 10–12 eggs in one season, each weighing $2\frac{1}{2}$–$3\frac{1}{2}$ lb. Picture 9 shows an ostrich egg (left), a domestic hen's egg (centre) and the egg of the extinct Aepyornis of Madagascar, related to the kiwis of today, which weighed up to 26 lb.

8

9

Rheas

The plains of South America, from north-east Brazil and east Bolivia through the whole of Argentina to the Rio Negro, are inhabited by the **Common Rhea** (sometimes called the South American Ostrich), *Rhea americana* [10], belonging to the order Rheiformes. This bird is smaller than the ostrich, standing about $4\frac{1}{2}$ ft high and weighing approximately 45 lb, and also differs in its colouration. After moulting the ornamental plumes are bluish grey, the neck yellow-brown, the upper parts blackish. The female lays about 10 eggs, each weighing $17\frac{1}{2}$–21 oz. The cock performs the duties of incubation, which are no easy task as one nest contains the eggs of several hens. The Rhea, or Nandu, just like the ostrich, is capable of great speed, equalling that of a galloping horse.

Cassowaries and Emus

The order Casuariformes comprises two families: the Casuaridae, or cassowaries, and the Dromiceidae, or emus, strong stout birds with quite rudimentary wings and very characteristic feet. Cassowaries weigh about 220 lb and possess unusually strong legs [13]. The feathers are generally dark, the head is bare, with a helmet which is larger in the male than in the female; the neck is also naked and usually wattled. Growing from the rudimentary wings are from three to five long wiry, vaneless quills in place of the usual flight feathers. These birds inhabit the wooded country of New Guinea, Obi Island, the Aru Islands, New Britain, the north of Queensland and Ceram. They run with great swiftness and can deliver strong kicks. The eggs are green, of rough texture and weigh more than 17 oz. The hen deposits from 3 to 6 eggs in the nest in a depression in the soil, and the cock incubates alone. The **Australian Cassowary,** *Casuarius casuarius* [11, 12], stands up to 5 ft high and the head carries a high helmet. There are three toes, the inner one possessing a long sharp claw – a formidable weapon capable of causing serious injuries [13]. The feathers are dark, almost black, the neck is bare, the throat blue and the hind neck scarlet, with two long wattles in front.

12
13

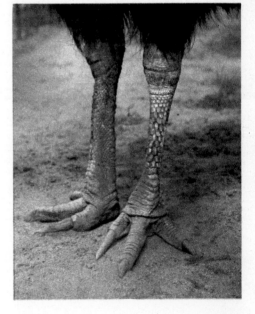

14

The sole representative of the family Dromiceidae is the **Emu,** *Dromiceius novaehollandiae* [14], of Australia and Tasmania. It is related to the cassowaries but lacks the helmet and wattles; the head and neck are feathered. It stands up to 5 ft or more high. The plumage is brown, the head black. The short rudimentary wings hang unused. Emus inhabit the open plains. The 7–12 dark green eggs laid by the female are incubated almost exclusively by the male.

Tinamous

The tinamous (Tinamiformes) are a unique group of birds. Ornithologists do not agree as to where this order should be classed, and its position is still the subject of debate. The birds resemble game-birds in shape and colouring and have a keeled breast-bone, but in other characters they resemble ratite birds. They are generally the size of a small fowl with a small head, slender neck and comparatively long legs. The sexes are alike externally, and in most species both are reddish brown with dark spots and bands, an excellent camouflage which is their best protection, because they tire quickly in flight. The female is polygamous and the male alone incubates and tends the young. The tinamous are nocturnal birds, remaining concealed during the day.

They are found from northern Mexico to Patagonia in a variety of habitats from above the tree line to lowland rain-forests and grassy plains. There are about 60 species.

The **Great** or **Pampas Tinamou** or **"Perdiz grande"**, *Rynchotus rufescens* [15], inhabits the pampas of Argentina, southern and south-eastern Brazil, avoiding the forests. It is capable of flying a distance of some 750–1,300 yards three times in succession. Members of the genus Nothura have a shorter beak, the **Spotted Tinamou** or the **"Perdiz comun"**, *Nothura maculosa* [16], resembling the quail with its light brown colouring and dark brown and black markings. These birds are found in south Brazil and Paraguay.

15

16

Divers or Loons

All four divers or loons (order Gaviiformes) are water-birds. They have legs set very far back and webbed toes, and are excellent swimmers and divers. The dense, oily plumage is impermeable to water and serves to retain their body heat. The wings are narrow, but divers fly fast, usually in a straight line; some undertake long migrations. The bill is long and pointed–well adapted for catching fish. The adult breeding plumage, from the second or third year, is black or grey with white underparts. In winter the upper parts become duller, predominantly grey. The two eggs, brown with darker spots and blotches, are laid in a simple nest on the ground. During the breeding season, the birds inhabit lakes in the northern forests and tundras of both worlds. In migration and in winter they range south to northern Africa and Japan, and in North America to Mexico, mostly along the coasts.

The handsomest of them all is the **Black-throated Diver** or **Loon,** *Gavia arctica* [17, 18], which weighs about 4½ lb and is about 26 inches long. The head and hind neck are ashy grey, the throat an intense black. On a black area in the region of the shoulder

blades there are large white spots crossed by black stripes. In winter the upper surface is a uniform grey, the underparts white. This colouring is characteristic of the young birds in the first and second year. The Black-throated Diver nests on the lakes of northern Europe, Asia and western America. It can stay under water for as long as two minutes, travelling a distance of over 500 yards during that time.

The **White-billed Diver** or **Yellow-billed Loon,** *Gavia adamsi* [19], is the largest species of this order, weighing up to 9 lb and measuring up to 30 inches. In spring, the head and neck of adults are intense black with white spots, interrupted with black on the sides of the neck. The back is black with square white marks. The breeding range of this diver extends from north-western Canada and northern Alaska to Novaya Zemlya in Siberia. Unlike other divers it winters near the breeding grounds, ranging south only to northern Japan and south-eastern Alaska.

The **Red-throated Diver** or **Loon,** *Gavia stellata* [20], the smallest diver, is shown in its dappled grey winter feathers. In breeding plumage the throat is reddish brown. It breeds in the northern regions of both worlds.

21

Grebes

The grebes (Podicipediformes), like divers, are water-birds, but instead of having a connected web, each of the toes is fringed separately. They build floating nests directly on the water and their eggs when laid are unspotted chalky white. Some species have ornamental nuptial plumes on the head in the form of collars, horns or ears. When leaving the nest grebes cover the 3 to 10 eggs with wet vegetation, to hide or keep them warm. The chicks are able to swim shortly after hatching, but they are often carried about on their parents' backs until they are quite large. They feed chiefly on fish. With the exception of the arctic regions, the grebes, comprising the single family Podicipedidae, are to be found throughout the world. The **Great Crested Grebe,** *Podiceps cristatus* [21, colour plate I], inhabits the waters of Eurasia, Africa, Australia, Tasmania and New Zealand. It is easily distinguished from the ducks by its slender neck and dagger-like bill, and in spring

by the ruff and two "horns" on the head [22]. Its upper parts are blackish brown, and the underparts are silvery white. The winter plumage is much simpler [23]. A ceremonial courtship, comprising several stages all of which take place on the water, precedes actual nesting. The female lays 3–6 chalk-white eggs [24] which gradually acquire a brownish hue from the rotting vegetation, hatching after a period of 25 days. The adults carry the chicks concealed among their back feathers, and can even dive with the young aboard. The Great Crested Grebe is not fond of flight, but when airborne it flies fast and straight. Northern grebe populations winter in Africa and southern Asia.

23

24

29

25

26

The **Eared** or **Black-necked Grebe,** *Podiceps nigricollis* [25, colour plate II], is about 1 ft long. In spring the head and neck are black with reddish yellow ear-tufts; the flanks are reddish, the underparts white and the upper parts black. It is distributed throughout almost the whole of Europe, extending far into Asia, and is found also in the Far East, South Africa and western North America. It feeds chiefly on water insects and nests in colonies which may contain several hundred nests. The female lays 3–5 eggs. As with most birds, repeat clutches, produced if the first eggs have been destroyed, contain a smaller number of eggs [26].

The **Little Grebe,** *Podiceps ruficollis* [27], is 11 inches long. In its breeding plumage the front of the

neck is chestnut, the corners of the bill are yellow-green, the feathers on the upper parts dark brown and a little paler below. It is to be found even in small, overgrown ponds in Europe, Asia, Africa and Indonesia, and most of the Old World Pacific islands. It is not gregárious, preferring to build its nest in a concealed spot among reeds or other water plants. The clutch contains 3–6 eggs [28]. Immediately on hatching the young chick conceals itself under the adult's wing or among the back feathers [27] where it remains several days, occasionally venturing on to the water by itself. In winter grebes migrate south from their northern quarters. In more southerly climes both migrant and resident species are found during the winter.

29

Penguins

One of the most distinctive of all bird orders, excellently adapted to life in water, are the penguins (Sphenisciformes), comprising the one single family, Spheniscidae. The body is streamlined, the head elongated, and the stout beak ends in a sharp point. The thick, close-packed feathers, smooth and well-oiled, serve not only as an insulating layer but also to lessen the friction caused by the bird's passage through the water. The short, powerful flippers have long lost the power of flight and are used as paddles; in some species they make up to 120 strokes a minute.

i **Great Crested Grebe** *Podiceps cristatus*

ii **Black-necked Grebe** *Podiceps nigricollis*

iii **Great Frigate-bird** *Fregata minor*

The webbed feet act as rudders. Penguins attain great speeds under water to catch the fish they feed on. When coming out of the water, e.g. on to an ice floe, the penguin often pops up like a cork, jumping to a height of up to 6 feet. Movement on land is clumsy and the penguin combines shuffling along on its feet with propelling itself over the surface on its belly, attaining a pretty fast pace in this manner. The feet, placed well aft, with four toes connected by a web, are comparatively small. Penguins spend the greater part of their lives in the water, emerging only during the breeding period when they converge in

32

dense colonies on dry land or shore ice. The birds moult during the nesting season, either at the beginning or the end. In penguins this process is remarkable because the plumage is shed in bulk instead of gradually, and it takes from 10 to 24 days to grow out. During this time the bird cannot enter the water and so cannot obtain food. Small species of penguins lay two eggs, larger species only one. They either build a simple nest or else keep the egg warm in a fold of the belly, the egg resting on top of the feet. The 15 species of penguins are to be found in certain regions of the Antarctic, on the islands of the Antarctic Seas, extending from Cape Horn to New Zealand, northwards approximately to the Tropic of Cancer. Only two species occur outside this range, one nesting on the western coast of South America, the other on the Galapagos Islands on the equator. The **Emperor Penguin**, *Aptenodytes forsteri* [29], is about 4 ft long and weighs about 90 lb. It is bluish grey with a white breast and belly. The crown, nape,

cheeks and chin are black and there is an orange spot on each side of the neck. It inhabits the waters of the Antarctic, extending northwards as far as South Orkney and Kerguelen, but nesting in winter only at certain spots on the shore ice of the coast of Antarctica. Its breeding cycle is of unusual interest. In early April, which is autumn in the Antarctic, the birds gather at their regular nesting grounds. The courtship and laying of the eggs takes place in the days of the severest frosts. After it is laid the egg is immediately taken charge of by the male, who places it on his feet and covers it with a fold of his belly skin, remaining in this vertical position throughout the 63 days of the incubation period while the female heads for the sea to break her fast. At the end of this time the female returns to care for the young. When feeding, the chick puts its head into the parent's crop to get its meal. The juvenile plumage is thick and fine [31], the adult plumage [30] being acquired after the moult in December.

The **King Penguin,** *Aptenodytes patagonicus* [32–35], a close relative of the Emperor, has a similar life history. It is a smaller bird, with a black head with yellow-orange spots on each side. Its nesting grounds are on various islands off the coast of the Antarctic continent.

36
37

38

Belonging to the medium-size group is the **Adelie Penguin**, *Pygoscelis adeliae* [36, 37], weighing about 13 lb and measuring 28 inches in length. The upper parts are blue-grey, the head black and the under parts white. It nests on the shores of Antarctica and adjacent islands, and also in the South Shetlands and South Orkneys. The birds arrive at their rocky nesting grounds in late October as the first heralds of spring. They build shallow nests of small pebbles set close together. The females begin laying eggs in November and incubation lasts about 35 days, so that the young hatch at the beginning of the antarctic summer. The parents sit on the eggs in the normal manner of birds, as do most other penguin species. As a rule, there are two chicks to a nest [36]; their growth is rapid and they soon join their parents in the open water. These birds are unusually trusting creatures with something almost human in their behaviour.

Various islands in the colder parts of the south temperate zone, including Tierra del Fuego and neighbouring islands, the Falklands, Tristan da Cunha, Gough Island and some of the New Zealand group are the nesting grounds of the 2-ft-tall **Rockhopper Penguin**, *Eudyptes crestatus* [38, 39]. This species has a golden-yellow streak above the eye terminating in a crest on either side of the crown. The nesting season is from August to December, and the nest is a small depression in the ground in which the female lays 1 or 2 eggs.

38

39

39

40

Often seen in zoos is the **Jackass Penguin**, *Spheniscus demersus* [40], which inhabits the coast of South Africa and neighbouring islands. It is 26 inches long and has a black band across the breast. Very similar but slightly smaller is the **Humboldt Penguin**, *Spheniscus humboldti* [41], the only species found on the coast of Peru and north Chile. At one time it was an important source of guano.

Tube-nosed Swimmers

The tube-nosed swimmers or tubinares (order Procellarii-formes) are all sea-birds comprising about 100 different species. Characteristic features are the horn-sheathed bill, the tubular structure of the nostrils and the webbed feet. These birds spend most of their lives in the air and on the water, coming to land only during the nesting season; they nest in colonies. All are excellent fliers. The many species range from birds the size of a swallow to albatrosses. They feed principally on sea animals which they pick up on the water's surface.

The **Fulmar** or **Northern Fulmar,** *Fulmarus glacialis* [42], makes its home on the subarctic shores of the Atlantic and Pacific Oceans, ranging south in winter to the coasts of France, Japan, California and eastern Canada. It is about the size of the Herring Gull and is coloured grey above and white below, occurring also in a darker, uniformly smoky grey phase. It nests on the steep rocks of the coast. The parents take turns sitting on the egg at intervals of 2 to 4 days; incubation takes 40 to 60 days. The young mature slowly, leaving the nest after 6 to 8 weeks and probably do not breed until the sixth year. Picture 43 shows two birds in the dark form of the Pacific race—*Fulmarus glacialis rodgersi.* The Fulmar belongs to the family Procellariidae, which comprises 53 species.

41

42

43

44

45

42

Another member of this family is the **Manx Shearwater,** *Puffinus puffinus* [44], 14 inches long, an inhabitant of the North Atlantic, chiefly on the European side. It is dark brown above and white below, with legs of delicate grey and pink. It nests in burrows or under stones, laying a single white egg which the parents take turns to incubate for a total of over 50 days. The offnest bird flies great distances to feed. The fluffy chick, eventually deserted by its parents, fledges in about 60 days. This species has been the subject of experiments in orientation and homing, and about 150,000 individuals had been ringed in the British Isles by the end of 1966. One British-ringed bird has been recovered off the coast of Australia.

Among the southernmost of the world's inhabitants, besides the Emperor Penguin and the Great Skua, is a representative of the family Procellariidae, the **Snowy Petrel,** *Pagodroma nivea* [45], with black eyes and bill and dark grey legs, which measures about 14 inches in length. It nests on the shores of Antarctica and neighbouring islands up to about latitude 50°S.

The **Storm Petrel,** *Hydrobates pelagicus* [46], only 6 inches long, is the best-known member of its family, the Hydrobatidae. Like the Manx Shearwater, it is a bird of the North Atlantic and Mediterranean, often seen flying behind ships in a characteristic zigzag fashion, now fluttering, now gliding, sometimes coming down to water level to patter along the wave-tops; hence the derivation of its name, from St. Peter walking upon the waters. Storm Petrels fly in this manner to collect their food; they feed mainly on plankton floating near the surface. They nest in colonies in burrows, under stones and boulders, even in stone walls. Both parents sit in turns on the single egg for about 40 days and the nestling takes 60 days to fledge. Storm Petrels, like other sea-birds, may be driven far inland by gales at sea, usually in autumn.

46

43

47

The family of albatrosses (Diomedeidae) comprises only 13 species. The **Wandering Albatross**, *Diomedea exulans* [47], has a wing span of over 11 ft and is the largest of all living flying birds. It glides magnificently, and is a tireless companion of ships sailing in the southern seas between latitudes 60°S and 30°S. The adults are predominantly white with black wing tips; the young are brown until they attain a span of about 4½ ft. The courtship display is remarkable. The male and female stand facing each other, wings extended, necks outstretched and heads swaying from side to side, touching each other on the neck and breast with their bills, and laying their short tails on their backs. The female lays only one egg, which weighs about 1 lb. The incubation period lasts up to 81 days.

The **Waved** or **Galapagos Albatross**, *Diomedea irrorata* [48], nests only on Hood Island. This species has a fairly long beak and is dark in colour, with a whitish head and neck and considerable barring.

Pelicans and allies

The pelicans and their allies (order Pelecaniformes) are as a rule large birds which, though divided into six distinct families, have several characteristics of anatomy in common. The most important is the foot, in which all four toes are connected by webs, this being used to advantage in swimming and in some species for diving. The diet consists mainly of fish and other water animals. All pelicans have a gular or throat pouch which is without feathers. They are strong fliers and some species glide magnificently. The feathers are stiff and dense, a typical feature of these specialized water-birds. The eggs are unspotted. The young hatch blind and naked and are fed by regurgitation by the parents. One or more of the 52 species of this order are to be found on all the larger expanses of water throughout the world.

The tropicbirds (Phaëthontidae) are the smallest family in this order, both in size and numbers. There are only three species, very similar in appearance; of these the **Red-billed Tropicbird,** *Phaëthon aethereus* [49], is found in the tropical zone of the Atlantic, Indian and Pacific Oceans. About $1\frac{1}{2}$ ft long, the tropicbirds have two central tail feathers which may trail another foot behind them, the resemblance to a marlin-spike leading to their other name of Bo'sun Bird. They seldom rest on the water but catch their food of fish and squids by plunging from a height. They nest in colonies and lay one dark egg.

45

The pelicans (family Pelecanidae) are all large birds.
The **Eurasian White Pelican,** *Pelecanus onocrotalus* [50], measures 56–68 inches – about the size of
a swan. Its plumage is white, with black wing tips
which are visible in flight. In the nuptial plumage
both male and female have a fairly large crest, and
the feathers on the breast are tinged with pink. The
lores and eye-rims are naked and flesh-coloured. The
feet are also reddish. The White Pelican has a sporadic distribution in eastern Europe (Danube delta,

Bulgaria, Sea of Azov), central Asia and southern Africa.

The closely allied **Dalmatian Pelican,** *Pelecanus crispus* [51, 52], is larger; it has a naked eye-rim, and is silvery grey above and greyish white below with brownish wing quills. The feet are dark grey. It nests in several parts of south-east Europe, in Asia Minor, Persia, and across central Asia as far as Mongolia. Pelicans sometimes unite in bands to catch fish by forming a line and beating the water with their wings

as they advance toward the shore, thus forcing the fish into the shallows. They catch the fish with their beaks, stowing them in the distensible pouch which they use as a dipnet. The young, usually three in number, are reared in large nests built among the reeds. The **Australian Pelican**, *Pelecanus conspicillatus* [53], measuring about 5½ ft, is distinguished from the preceding two birds by its black shoulders and tail and its grey-brown crest. It is the only species of pelican found in Australia and New Guinea.

52

53

iv **Black-crowned Night Heron** *Nycticorax nycticorax*

v **Eurasian Bittern** *Botaurus stellaris*

vi **Great Adjutant Stork** *Leptoptilus dubius*

The **Pink-backed Pelican,**
Pelecanus rufescens [54], makes
its home in Africa. It has a
reddish back, with red-tinged
flanks and under tail-coverts.
The feet are yellowish. It
breeds from Capetown to
Gambia and Ethiopia and also
occurs in southern Arabia.

The **Spotted-billed Pelican,** *Pelecanus philippensis*
[55], of southern Asia and the
Philippines, is distinguished
by its grey wing quills. The
bill is flesh-coloured with blue
blotches.

54

55

49

The **American White Pelican,** *Pelecanus erythrorhynchus* [57], is mainly white with black primaries and some yellow on the chest and wing-coverts. During the breeding season it develops a triangular horny excrescence on the middle of the culmen. The cheeks, unlike those of the other species, are feathered. The bird weighs up to 20 lb and has a wing span of nearly 10 ft. It nests on lakes from British Columbia and Mackenzie to central California and North Dakota. It winters south to Mexico, east to Florida. Whereas in the white pelicans brown plumage is to be found only in the young, the **Brown Pelican,** *Pelecanus occidentalis* [56] is coloured brown throughout its whole lifetime, only the head and sides of the neck being white; during the nesting season the back of the neck is a dark chestnut. The bird measures 40–50 inches and weighs 15 lb. It flies with its neck drawn back upon its shoulders like all pelicans, and it is the only pelican which catches fish by plunging down from the air; it strikes the water with a tremendous splash, disappearing below the surface only for a moment. The Brown Pelican nests in large colonies in scattered localities on the coasts of the New World from South Carolina and central California to northern Chile and north-eastern Brazil, with as many as two nests to a square yard. Large colonies, however, can be located only where fish are to be found in abundance, for the quantity of food required to feed the young (the brood is usually 2 or 3) is by no means small. The Brown Pelican is a valuable source of guano in Peru.

The cormorants (family Phalacrocoracidae) are medium-sized water-birds with dark plumage. They have long necks and long, narrow, hooked beaks. The short legs are located well back on the body. Cormorants, comprising some 30 different species, are to be found throughout the world, both on the sea-coast and on inland waters. Their diet consists mainly of fish, which they catch by diving from the surface (except one species which dives from the air). Underwater they propel themselves by paddling with both feet together, the wings held half-open and the tail acting as a rudder. They have no air sacs under the skin and their bones are less pneumatic, so that they float lower on the surface of the water than their relatives. Cormorants are known to dive to depths of over 60 ft, though only in rare instances.

The **Common** or **Great Cormorant**, *Phalacrocorax carbo*, is the size of a goose (3 ft). The plumage of adult birds is black with a greenish gloss, and with white chin and cheeks; in Old World birds the throat is bare, yellow. From January on, narrow white feathers appear on the front of the neck and the head, and white patches on the flanks [58]. Young birds are brownish with a white belly. This species is found in Europe, Asia, Africa, north-east Canada, Australia and New Zealand. In North America it is strictly a coastal species, nesting in north-east Canada and wintering to the central states on the US Atlantic seaboard. Throughout the rest of the continent, south to the northern Caribbean, it is replaced by the **Double-crested Cormorant**, *Phalacrocorax auritus*, a very similar but smaller species which shows no white in its plumage and has a more orange throat. The Common Cormorant is becoming rarer. Its numbers have been greatly depleted in many regions by man. It nests in colonies on the sea-coast as well as on inland lakes and rivers; in the interior of Asia also on lakes situated almost 10,000 feet above sea-level. The nest is built either on cliffs or in the branches of tall trees [59]. The clutch consists of 3 to 5 blue-green eggs, which both parents incubate in turns. The young are fed first with regurgitated food and later with fresh fish from the throat pouch. which is also used to provide them with water.

The much smaller (20-in.) **Pygmy Cormorant**, *Phalacrocorax pygmaeus* [60, 62], is greenish-black, spotted white in summer, with a reddish brown head. The bill is shorter than in the preceding species. Colonies are to be found only on inland waters and its range of distribution extends from east Europe through Asia Minor all the way to east Persia and

58

59

51

60

62

and the West Indies, from sea-level to high in the regions of the Mississipi. It also nests on the islands of the Gulf of Mexico.

Closely related to the cormorants are the anhingas or darters (family Anhingidae), slim birds with unusually long, thin necks and small heads. They are skilful divers, with webbed feet, thick compact feathers and a compressed, serrated beak. Darters are noted for their speed under water, where they propel themselves with their feet, aided to some extent by their wings. The long neck is held folded back in an S against the shoulders in preparation to strike. Larger fish are impaled with the beak as with

central Asia; the westernmost boundary of the nesting grounds is Hungary.

The small **Bigua** or **Mexican** or **Olivaceous Cormorant,** *Phalacrocorax olivaceus* [61], is found on the coast and by rivers and lakes from Tierra del Fuego northwards to the southern coast of Louisiana

61

a spear. On being brought to the surface the fish is tossed into the air and then swallowed. Like cormorants, darters have no air sacs and their bones are not very pneumatic, which enables them to dive more easily. When hunting, or if danger threatens, they float below the water's surface with only head and neck showing like a periscope. Besides fish their diet includes numerous other water creatures. Anhingas nest in trees and bushes bordering freshwater lakes, river and swamps; they are rarely found on the sea-coast. The range of the **Anhinga, Snakebird** or **Darter,** *Anhinga anhinga* [63, 64], extends from the south-eastern and south-central United States to Argentina. When courting it displays its

65

ornamental feathers and expands its pouch. If danger threatens, the young will leave the nest when only two weeks old, already showing marked skill in diving. As a rule, however, they remain in the nest from 5 to 8 weeks. All the four species which occur in the tropical and subtropical regions of both worlds are much alike in colour and differ even less in their way of life. They are 30–36 inches long and weigh about 2 lb.

The boobies and gannets (family Sulidae) comprise nine species of large birds with straight, sharp bills and long wedge-shaped tails. Also characteristic are the short, stout legs with four toes connected by webs. They have a small bare area on the throat and naked skin around the eye. The family inhabits chiefly the warmer seas but is also to be found in the temperate zones.

The **Northern Gannet** or **Solan Goose**, *Sula bassana* [65], with white plumage and black wingtips, is the size of a goose. It nests in large colonies on the cliffs of the North Atlantic coasts and is only found inland if forced there by storms. In winter it ranges south to the western Mediterranean and the southern states on the Atlantic seaboard of the USA. It cruises above the water's surface in gliding flight, flapping its wings occasionally, but when it sights a shoal of fish, its main food, it plummets down with its beak stretched forward. It swims rapidly underwater using its feet and half-opened wings and can dive to depths of 60 ft and more. The plumage is the same in both sexes and the young are brown, dappled in a lighter shade. Gannets and boobies have air sacs under the skin which help to soften the impact as the bird, diving from a height of 40–60 feet, hits the water. These sacs also occur in pelicans.

Frequently encountered near the shores of tropic seas are the frigate-birds (family Fregatidae) which are recognizable in flight by their remarkably long wings (in some species the wingspan measures over $7\frac{1}{2}$ feet) and long, deeply forked tails. The long slender bill is sharply hooked at the tip. The males have brightly coloured throat pouches. Though all four toes are webbed they are not used for swimming, and the birds spend most of the time in the air. Their adroitness in flight provides them with two methods of procuring food – catching it from the surface of the sea or pirating it from gulls, cormorants or pelicans by harassing them till they disgorge their prey, which the frigate-bird catches in mid-air as it falls. Frigate-birds nest colonially on trees, shrubs and rocks, feeding the single white-headed offspring from beak to beak as shown in the picture of the **Great Frigate-bird,** *Fregata minor* [66, col. plate III]. This bird is marked by a yellow-brown band across the wings, otherwise it is coloured black; the female has a white throat and breast [67]. It inhabits the tropic zone of the Pacific, Atlantic and Indian Oceans. A very similar bird, the **Magnificent Frigate-bird,** *Fregata magnificens,* occurs along the coasts of tropical America and in the South Atlantic. It is quite common in summer in southern Florida, though it does not nest there, and is also occasionally seen on the Gulf and west coasts of the United States during storms.

Herons and allies

Members of the order Ciconiiformes are all large wading-birds with long legs and necks. Most species, especially those which feed on fish, have a long pointed beak; those whose diet consists of crustaceans and worms have a long, thin, downward-curved bill or one that is shaped like a spoon. The species which feed on carrion have bare necks and heads. The long neck consists of 16–20 vertebrae and is extremely flexible. The plumage is comparatively thin and simple in pattern and colour. Although the preen gland is well developed, an important role in the care of the plumage is played by the patches of powder-down feathers which continually fray at the tip into powder. These birds, comprising seven families and 114 species, are distributed throughout the whole world, with the exception of several far-flung islands.

The herons and bitterns (family Ardeidae) number 62 species. The mainstay of their diet is fish; they shoot their necks out like a coiled spring, grasping the fish with their beaks. In flight the neck is bent into an S, unlike the storks, which fly with neck outstretched. Frequently encountered in regions abounding in lakes and rivers is the **Common** or **Grey Heron,** *Ardea cinerea* [68–71], a bird the size of a small stork. It is grey above, with a white neck dotted with dark longitudinal spots in front and with elongated plumes on the neck. Running above the eye to the back of the head is a wide, black band. Adults have a small crest on the nape. The **Great Blue Heron,** *Ardea herodias,* a widespread American species ranging from Canada to Argentina, is virtually identical in appearance and habits.

Common Herons generally nest in colonies, often together with other species. The nests are often located close to the surface of the water, though they may also be found in the top branches of tall trees or among reeds and on cliffs by the sea. The nesting site is selected by the male, who then starts his courting. After he has found a mate, the two build the nest together [68]. The courting, building of the nest and alternating of the two on the nest is accompanied by various ceremonial displays in which stance, ornamental feathers and voice play the chief roles. The clutch comprises 3–5 blue-green eggs which are incubated by both the male and the female [69], in 4–6-hour shifts for 25–28 days; after hatching

they continue to shelter the young from inclement weather. Strong downpours and cold take the greatest toll of the young. At first, the parents feed their offspring by placing regurgitated food directly into their beaks, later they regurgitate on the edge of the nest only slightly macerated food which the chicks pick up for themselves. The young birds remain in the nest for seven or eight weeks, while acquiring a coat of feathers closely resembling but rather browner than that of the adults [70]. Central European herons generally spend the winter on the Mediterranean but have also been found in west and east Africa. During mild winters they may not even

71

leave their nesting grounds. After the breeding season is over they can be seen standing completely motionless in shallow waters singly or in groups, waiting for their prey to come near, or they may sit hunched near the water, resting [71]. In the autumn they can be seen in the fields waiting beside the holes of fieldmice. The Common Heron is a native of Europe, ranging through central and southern Asia, and is found also in Africa including Madagascar.

The **Purple Heron,** *Ardea purpurea* [72], is somewhat smaller than the Common Heron. It is predominantly reddish brown; adult birds are grey above, young ones reddish, with underparts a paler shade. The range of distribution of the two species is similar, but that of the Purple Heron is less northerly, extending only to Bohemia and the Netherlands. In southern and eastern Europe it is a common inhabitant of reed-grown waters. It favours open country

73

74

and nests in pairs or small colonies among reed,
sometimes also on trees. Immediately on their return
from their winter quarters, the adult birds seek
suitable spot for their nest among the old reeds of the
previous year. The nest of sticks and reeds soon
holds 4–5 pale blue eggs which both parents incubate
for a period of 24–28 days. The young fledgling
herons [73] will leave the nest to hide in the reeds
danger threatens. Both young and old can freeze into
a position with body, neck and bill pointed skyward
[74], in which they are less visible among the reed.
The diet of Purple Herons consists chiefly of fish.
Found in the same habitat is the small (18-in.-long)
buff **Squacco Heron,** *Ardeola ralloides* [77]. This
bird hunts its prey, chiefly insects, not only in
shallow, reed-grown waters, but also in fields and pastures far from any body of water. It nests colonially

75

76

77

usually in company with other
herons, in trees [78], reeds or
in low-growing tangles of
vegetation. The nest is made
either of twigs or reeds, depending on the site. The
spring plumage is warm buff,
the wings, tail, breast and
belly white, the darker mantle
possessing long hair-like
plumes which cover the tail
and are spread wide when the
bird is engaged in courting or
is agitated [75, 76]. It nests in
southern Europe, south-west
Asia and all Africa except the
Sahara, wintering in Africa.

The **Little Egret,** *Egretta garzetta* [79, 80], is a beautiful bird with snow-white plumage, a black bill and black legs with yellow feet; it is about 22 inches long. During the breeding season adult birds have

lengthened crest feathers and long plumes on shoulders and breast. These "aigrettes" may be up to 10 inches in length and were at one time a very popular fashion item which caused the slaughter of hundreds

of thousands of these lovel
birds. The Little Egret nest
colonially on bushes [81
and trees in swamps, as wel
as in treetops [82] in humid
forests along with other bird
of this family. When huntin,
it thrusts one foot slightly
forward, moving it quickl
back and forth amidst th
dense growth of aquatic vege
tation and, with a dartin;
movement of the head, catche
with its beak the fish it ha
stirred up. It occurs in south
and south-east Europe, south
and south-east Asia, part c
Africa, Indonesia an
Australia.

80

81

64

Very similar to the Little Egret is the somewhat larger **Snowy Egret,** *Egretta thula* [83], whose range extends from the central United States to Argentina. In the days when their beautiful feathery plumes were used to adorn women's hats the **Great White Heron,** *Casmerodius alba* [85], called the **Common** or **Great Egret** in America, was on the verge of extinction. Thousands of adult birds were shot on their nests for the money their plumes would bring both in south-east Europe and in America. This species nests in south-east Europe, south and south-east Asia, Indonesia, Africa, Australia and, distinguished as a separate race, from the United States to Argentina. It was only thanks to the active protection introduced in Europe and America that this bird is still to be seen today, even in places such as the Danube delta and the lakes of Hungary where it was once very abundant. In North America it has recovered its former numbers and is a common bird throughout its range. It is a large bird, larger than the Common Heron, with snow-white plumage. During the breeding season it may have as many as 50 ornamental crest feathers, each up to 20 inches in length. In Old World birds, the bill is black at this time of year and yellow in winter; American birds have yellow bills at all seasons. Both have black legs throughout the year. The Great White Heron nests in reeds [84], shrubs and trees.

At first glance, the **Cattle Egret,** *Bubulcus ibis* [86], is reminiscent of the lighter-hued Squacco Heron, but it is somewhat larger and has a shorter beak. In the breeding season it has long reddish brown plumes on head, shoulders and throat. Unlike the other birds of this family, it is not dependent on water, frequently foraging for insects in fields, meadows and on the plains. It has a habit of consorting with cattle, moving fearlessly around their feet and at times perching on the animals' backs, feeding on the insects they stir up or dislodge. The bird nests in colonies, preferring the company of Little Egrets and Night Herons. The Cattle Egret was originally a native of southern Europe, northwest Africa, Africa south of the Sahara, the Near East and southern Asia. Around 1930 a group of these birds appeared in British Guiana (now Guyana), having flown across the Atlantic of their own accord or perhaps forced by storms. Their numbers increased from year to year and their range spread to the Caribbean islands; in 1950 they were found nesting in Florida, in 1958 they were reported in Colombia, and their distribution is still spreading through the New World, as well as in Australia.

86
87

88
89

The **Black-crowned Night Heron,** *Nycticorax nycticorax* [87, colour plate IV], is a very handsome bird, especially in its breeding plumage. There is no difference in appearance between the male and female. Both are black above and white below, the wings and tail a pale grey. The legs, with long toes, are bright yellow or pink, the bill black. Adult birds have three long, narrow, plumes which extend down the back from the nape. In their first year the young are brownish, dappled a paler hue [91]. Night Herons are not in fact nocturnal birds, but they do most of their foraging at twilight and just before dawn. When feeding the young, however, they forage during the day as well. They nest in large colonies, either with birds of their own species or with other members of the family. In the nest of twigs the female lays 3–5 eggs [89], the down-covered nestlings hatching after 21 days [88]. As with most members of this family eggs are laid and the young hatch in one- to two-day intervals because the female incubates from the time the first is laid, so that there is a marked difference in their size. The parents first feed the chicks with partially digested food regurgitated into the bill, later with regurgitated fish and frogs which are its main diet. This species is widely distributed throughout North and South America, Africa, southern and central Europe, and Asia; the European populations are migratory and winter in Central Africa. In the New World only the more northerly nesting birds migrate.

The closely allied **Yellow-crowned Night Heron,** *Nyctanassa violacea* [90], is distinguished by the black and white pattern on the head, the rest of the body being of a dark colour; it is 28 inches long—somewhat larger than the Black-crowned Night Heron. It breeds from the east-central United States to Peru and Brazil, and winters in the southern part of its range.

90
91

69

92

The **Eurasian Bittern**, *Botaurus stellaris* [92, colour plate V], illustrated sitting on its nest among the reeds, is a bird rarely seen but more frequently heard; its booming note, resembling the lowing of cattle rather than the call of a bird, carries a long way during the mating season in spring. It measures about 28 inches. When danger threatens, it stretches to its full height, freezing into a reed-like pose with the beak pointing skyward. It is capable of remaining like this for some time, its tawny, darkly streaked and longitudinally striped plumage blending well with its surroundings [93]. Like other members of this family, when faced with immediate danger it opens its bill wide, especially the mandible with its gular pouch, regurgitating its prey in moments of extreme fright, apparently to lessen its weight [94]. Bitterns forage primarily in reed-beds, leaving their shelter only when migrating. They inhabit Europe, the warmer parts of Asia and South-west and South Africa. The **American Bittern**, *Botaurus lentiginosus*, is similar in appearance but smaller, and has a different call, which sounds like a stake being pulled from mud. It occurs throughout North America, wintering to Panama.

93

94

The **Little Bittern,** *Ixobrychus minutus,* is one of the species of this family with different male and female plumage, as can be seen in picture 95, which shows the female preparing to take the place of the incubating male. This bittern is a small bird (14 in.), occurring in some numbers on small and large bodies of water whose shores are covered with the reeds and marshy vegetation in which it nests. In spring the characteristic call, a repeated "roo", is heard in the vicinity of the nest, though the bird can be seen only when it flies across the water's surface while foraging. In flight the light patches of the male stand out clearly against the dark colour of the wings and back. The female is brown on the back. The Little Bittern nests from June to July, laying 5–6

eggs, the young being reared by both parents. After only a few days the young birds show a remarkable ability to hold on to reeds with their long, slender toes [96], so that they leave the nest for brief explorations of the vicinity from the age of 7–12 days. The species nests from temperate Europe and Asia to Turkestan and west India, and in Africa and Australia. In August and September the central European population migrates to Africa, returning to its nesting grounds in April and early May. The **Least Bittern,** *Isobrychus exilis,* which ranges from northern Canada to Argentina, is the American counterpart of this species. Both sexes of Least Bittern resemble the male Little Bittern. There is also a rare dark, rich chestnut phase.

9

Allied to the night herons is the **Boat-billed Heron**
Cochlearius cochlearius [97, 98], which is also
nocturnal bird. The plumage is black, grey and
white, but its most outstanding features are the broad
bill, 3 in. long and 2 in. wide, and the long, wide
black crest. The comparatively large eyes indicat
its nocturnal habits. It ranges from the coastal low
lands of north-west and north-east Mexico south
generally, to southern Brazil. It is a solitary feeder
preying on fish, crabs, mice, worms and other small
animals. During the breeding season it claps and
rattles its bill to accompany the loud, harsh sound c

9

its voice. The clutch comprises 2–4 white, brown-speckled eggs. The Boat-billed Heron nests alone or in colonies with other herons. Some ornithologists place this species in a family of its own, Cochlearidae, others group it with the true herons.

The family Balaenicipitidae also comprises only one species—the **Whalehead** or **Shoe-bill Stork**, *Balaeniceps rex* [99]. This bird stands 39–47 in. high, on long legs, and has a fairly short neck, a large head and a broad, ungainly bill, 8 in. long and shaped like a shoe. It is difficult to account for this shape, as the diet is similar to that of numerous other birds. Per-haps it is useful for probing in the mud for lung-fish—its favourite food. Besides fish it also feeds on frogs, turtles, young crocodiles and small mammals. This pale-grey bird inhabits the papyrus swamps of the upper White Nile and its tributaries in central East Africa.

The **Hammerhead**, *Scopus umbretta* [100], the single representative of the family Scopidae, is brownish in colour, about 20 inches long, and resembles a stork or ibis. It is distinguished from these birds by its high, compressed bill and the wide, thick crest, which is carried horizontally. The neck is slightly curved in flight. Its voice is also different from that of its allied species, the call sounding like "witwit". The Hammerhead is widely distributed in tropical Africa, Madagascar, and Arabia, where it is found near water in pairs or small flocks. The nest is an enormous, dome-shaped structure 5–6½ ft in diameter, built by the male and female over a period of several months. It is generally placed in bushes or low trees and is made of sticks plastered in place with mud, and with roots, grass, rushes, leaves, sometimes even bones, pieces of leather, etc., so that when finished it is hard and firm. The hole at the side leads to a small compartment containing 3–6 eggs. The bird does not crawl into the nest, but flies straight in.

99

100

101

The family of storks (Ciconiidae), comprising 17 species, all characterized by long legs, is widely distributed throughout the world, though only two species are found in Europe and only three in the Americas. Storks have long, broad wings and are excellent fliers capable of sailing to great heights on upward convection currents. In flight the neck is held outstretched. Adult storks are mute, producing only a hissing sound and expressing themselves by rattling their bills. The young utter various sounds but as they grow older they lose the use of their voice muscles. They lack the serrated middle claw found in all the other families of the order Ciconiiformes, and the powderdown.

The **White Stork,** *Ciconia ciconia* [101–104], is the best known member of this family. Its plumage is black and white, the bill and legs red in adult birds, black in the young. At one time it nested in Europe on rocky cliffs and in trees [102], as it still does in some parts of the world to this day. In central and western Europe, where it is regarded as a symbol of good luck and the bearer of babies, it is a favourite of country folk and has acquired the habit of building its nest on chimneys and rooftops. This has probably been influenced also by the fact that villagers frequently put baskets and cartwheels on the roofs to attract them [101]. The stork is not given to nesting alone; as many as nine incubating birds may be found in a ngle tree. Whether nesting on rooftops or in trees, orks are generally found in localities where there is 1 abundance of water to provide them with a fficient supply of frogs, their chief source of food. he bird forages on fields and meadows [104] as well by lakes and streams. Besides frogs it also feeds on olluscs and crustaceans. In March or April the ales, followed by the females, leave their winter uarters to return to their old nests which, if necesry, they will defend in bloody battle against truders. They either build new nests or repair the d ones, adding on to them every year so that in time ey become high, towering structures weighing veral hundredweight. Each bird then welcomes its ate with great ceremony, raising its head, placing it its back, and shooting it forward, all the while ttling its bill, raising its tail and spreading its wings. he birds also clap their bills when greeting their ates or to warn the young of danger, though this is metimes done by hissing. The clutch consists of -6 white eggs. Both parents incubate, sitting on the gs 30 days until the young hatch, afterwards ielding them from cold, rain and excessive heat. he birds remain in the nest for two months. At the

102

age of 70 days they are already independent but do not breed till the fourth of fifth year, when they attain full maturity. Before their departure for their winter quarters in South Africa, storks sometimes gather to form large flocks. When taking flight they make a few short jumps before rising in the air (103). The White Stork nests in north-west Africa, Europe, Asia Minor, central Asia and in the Far East.

103

The **Black Stork,** *Ciconia nigra* [105, 106], a wild
bird inhabiting deep forests, is slightly smaller than
the White Stork and is distinguished by glossy black
plumage with white underparts. The bill and legs of
adult birds are red. During the nesting season the
Black Stork is seldom seen in open country. It is
sometimes found high up in the mountains, in Asia
even at altitudes of 7,000 ft where it breeds on rocky
cliffs. When migrating to central and southern Africa
it follows the same routes as the White Stork, either
via Gibraltar or across the Dardanelles. the Bos-
phorus, Turkey, Israel and Egypt, avoiding the
Mediterranean. Its breeding habits are similar to
those of the White Stork; the down of the nestlings is
pure white [105]. The Black Stork nests in Spain and
from eastern Europe throughout the temperate zone
of Asia to the shores of the Pacific. It has also begun
to nest in South Africa in this century.

of the tallest species of storks is the **Saddle-**
ed Stork, *Ephippiorhynchus senegalensis* [107,
], which stands up to 58 in. high. It is distin-
hed by a large crimson bill with a black band and
angular yellow frontal shield, and has black legs
reddish joints. The colouring is black and white
head, neck, tail and wing-coverts black, the
aining plumage and the flight feathers white. It
ds in tropical Africa, generally by rivers, building
arge nest in the tops of tall trees. Grasshoppers are
avourite food.

107
108

77

109

The largest stork of the New World is the **Jabiru,** *Jabiru mycteria* [109, 110], which inhabits the tropical forests of South and Central America from Argentina to southern Mexico. It is 52–55 in. long, and has a tremendous, heavy, upward-curving bill. The plumage is white, the naked head and neck black with a reddish ring around the base of the throat. It is found near lakes and shallow swamps where it forages for food. Although it resembles the marabous it is not a scavenger. It builds a huge nest in tall trees.

Like the vultures, marabous help rid Africa and southern Asia of carrion. These birds all have naked heads and a ruff of feathers surmounting the shoulders. The largest is the **Greater Adjutant Stork,** *Leptoptilus dubius* [111, colour plate VI], which occurs from central India to Borneo. It is greenish black above; the bill, 18 in. long, has a slight

112

downward curve. The wingspan is more than 10 ft. Another scavenger of tropical Africa is the **Marabou (Adjutant) Stork,** *Leptoptilus crumeniferus* [112], a tall, shy bird, swift enough to catch live prey with its huge bill. When feeding on carrion it thrusts its bare, flesh-coloured, black-spotted head deep inside the body cavity of the dead animal. Hanging below the throat is a pointed, distensible pouch which is not used to hold food but is connected with the breathing system and may serve as a cushion for the bill when the bird is resting.

The **Lesser** or **Javan Adjutant,** *Leptoptilus javanicus* [113], sharing the same distribution range as *Leptoptilus dubius*, is distinguished by a horny plate on the head and bristles on the crest. The plumage is black above and the greater wing-coverts lack the white border. It is about 3 ft long.

113

Closely related to the storks are the "shell ibises" of which the **Open-bill,** *Anastomus oscitans* [115], an Indian and Indochinese species, is distinguished from its brown African cousin by its white plumage with grey-black wing quills and tail feathers. The bill of these birds is compressed and the jaws bent in the front part, so that when they are closed there remains a fairly wide gap between them. The shape of its bill enables the bird to open mollusc shells and extract these animals, which are its favourite food. It also feeds on fish, frogs, insects and worms. The Open-bill nests colonially on shrubs and trees.

The family of ibises and spoonbills (Threskiornithidae) contains 28 species of medium-sized birds smaller than the storks. They fly with the neck straight out in front. Like storks, they have no pow-

114

116

der down patches or voice-box, except in a few rare instances. Ibises have a face bare of feathers, the head and neck also being naked in some birds, and a long, down-curved flexible bill, round in cross-section, which they thrust into the mud when foraging for food.

The **White-headed Stork** or **Asian Wood Ibis,** *Ibis leucocephalus* [114], of India, south-west China and northern Malaya, has crown, cheeks and bare throat coloured creamy to orange yellow, the wings, breast-band and tail black. The wing-coverts have a conspicuous white border.

Living in Africa and Madagascar is the closely allied **Yellow-billed Stork** or **African Wood Ibis,** *Ibis ibis* [116], in which only the front of the head is naked, and the smooth face coloured red. The white plumage is tinted red, the wing quills and tail are black. It

nests in small colonies on rocky cliffs and in trees
and feeds on small animals for which it forages i
shallow and swampy meadows.

One of the handsomest species is the **Scarlet Ibi**
Eudocimus ruber [117], with its vivid scarlet pluma
and black wing tips. It lives in large coastal coloni
chiefly in the tropical zone of South America fro
north-east Venezuela to Brazil. In captivity t
feathers lose their vivid colouring, becoming i
creasingly paler with each successive moult. Th
clutch comprises 4–5 blue-white, brown-spotte
eggs. Both sexes incubate for 21 days. The youn
birds are coloured brown and white. In the coloni
the nests are very close to one another; several ma
be found in the top of a single tree. The Scarlet Ib
often breeds colonially with the **American Whi**
Ibis, *Eudocimus albus* [118], sometimes even in mix
pairs, which has caused some ornithologists to co
sider the Scarlet and White Ibises as two differen

117
118

119

oloured variants of one species. The **White Ibis,** as its name implies, is white with black wing tips, the bill, legs and bare face being red. It is found from the south-eastern United States to southern South America, mostly in coastal areas. At one time these birds nested in large colonies in the areas they inhabit. Today, however, in many parts of South America, flocks of thousands are much less numerous and are fast on the way to being wiped out if no protective measures are taken.

The **Sacred Ibis,** *Threskiornis aethiopicus* [119], of tropical Africa was the bird revered by the ancient Egyptians. In ancient times these birds lived much farther north, vast numbers of them appearing in Egypt when the Nile flooded its banks, so that people linked the two phenomena together. Moreover, the Ibis was to them the god Thoth, whose duty it was to record the life-story of every human being. Thousands of mummified birds were found buried, in urns or piled in layers on top of each other, in the pyramids

120

121

and tombs of the pharaohs. The Sacred Ibis is 30 in. long; the bare head is coloured black, as are the bill, feet and tips of the primary flight feathers. The divided inner secondaries and scapulars are iridescent black. These black ornamental feathers are absent in the **Black-headed** or **Asian White Ibis,** *Threskiornis melanocephala* [121], of southern and south-eastern Asia.

The **Glossy Ibis,** *Plegadis falcinellus,* measuring only 22 in., has brown plumage with a lovely bronze sheen. The young are a dull, dark brown with delicate white markings on the head and neck; in adults the head is a uniform colour [120]. The birds breed in large marshes, building their shallow nests in the reeds or on bushes in the centre of the swamp. The male forages for food, bringing it to the nest where he gives it to the female who then feeds the young. This ibis has a discontinuous distribution in southern Europe, south-east and south Asia, Australia, South

Africa, the south-eastern United States and the West Indies. In the western United States and through most of continental tropical America it is replaced by the **White-faced Ibis,** *Plegadis mexicanus,* which differs only in having a narrow white ring round the base of the bill in the breeding season.

The **Black Ibis,** *Ibis papillosus* [122], inhabits India, Burma, Siam and Cambodia. It is brown with an olive-green gloss above and a white shoulder patch and measures about 28 in. The head and throat are bare, and the crown and nape are covered with red scaly warts.

123

Closely related to the ibises are the six species of spoonbills, which resemble small storks. In these, the bill is long, straight and flattened, dilated at the tip into a "spoon" with grooved inner edges. Spoonbills catch their prey by wading along, with bill half-open and partly immersed, swinging their heads from side to side in a quarter circle. Their diet consists primarily of crustaceans, insects, fishes, worms and frogs. Male and female spoonbills do not differ in external appearance.

The **Spoonbill**, *Platalea leucorodia* [123–125], of Eurasia, smaller than the stork, breeds in southern, rarely in central and western Europe, south-west, south, central and eastern Asia. The plumage of the adult bird is white, tinged with ochre at the base of the neck in front; during the breeding season it develops a fine crest at the nape [125]. This species nests in the same places as the Glossy Ibis and other herons and bitterns, in whose company it is often found either in bushes [123] close above the water, or on islands, or sometimes in reeds. Although they are gregarious, these are rather quiet birds which attract no attention to themselves. Only when the young are being fed is the air filled with the sound of their low voices. Both sexes incubate the 3–6 eggs and following hatching, after 21–25 days, both procure food for the young. These have fairly strong, slightly curved, soft bills at first and not till the fifth week does the downward curve begin to be visible. The young birds shove their wide bills down the throats of the adults for their food, which the latter regurgitate. After about 28 days they leave the nest, remaining nearby and forming a flock of juveniles with those from neighbouring nests. They fledge after 49 days. The bill of the young spoonbill pictured in flight [124] already resembles that of the adult though it is

neither as wide nor as long. Ibises and spoonbills fly like storks with the head straight out in front. The spoonbills of Europe winter in Central and East Africa, those of Asia in India and China. These birds are threatened by the spread of civilization and continuing land improvement, and their numbers are rapidly decreasing despite protective legislation.

125

126

Also disappearing from the scene is the lovely **Roseate Spoonbill,** *Ajaia ajaja* [126], which formerly nested in colonies numbering thousands of pairs from the Gulf Coast of the United States to Argentina and Chile. In the north, measures have been taken to protect the birds in their breeding grounds, but they are a migratory species flying to tropical America in winter, and are killed en route or in their winter quarters, where conservation measures are fewer. This spoonbill is rose-pink with carmine wing-coverts, white neck and back; the bare head is yellowish green, the bill greenish blue with a grey and black base, and the legs crimson. It breeds in large, mixed colonies with other herons, laying 3–5 dirty white, brown-marked eggs in nests high up in mangroves.

Every visitor to the zoo is attracted by the beautiful flamingos (family Phoenicopteridae)–four species of graceful long-legged, long-necked birds. The flamingos still pose a puzzle as regards classification. Like ducks and geese, they shed all their flight feathers together when moulting, the bill is furnished with little plates on the margins, they are attacked by Mallophaga, external parasites also found in the Anseriformes, this being why some systematists class them with water-fowl; others believe them to be an independent order. However they show many resemblances (e.g. in the way they feed their young) to the herons and storks. The bill is unique, quite unlike that of any other bird. It is fairly high at the base and abruptly bent down in the middle, the mandible (lower jaw) being larger than the maxilla (upper). Whereas in most birds the former is the more movable of the two jaws, in flamingoes the opposite is true. The margins of the bill are lined with small plates and the thick tongue has about 20 similar tooth-like projections on either side which serve to sieve water and mud while retaining the food–plankton, small molluscs, crustaceans, algae, protozoans, etc. – as ducks do for example. When feeding, however, the upper jaw is bottom-most, and the lower jaw above it and pumping against it [129]. The small animals caught on the horny lamellae when the water and mud are sieved are scraped off by the projections on the tongue and swallowed. The feet, with webbed anterior toes, trail behind in flight, the necks being held straight out in front. Though they are not fond of swimming, flamingos sometimes forage for food up to their bellies in water. The rose-tinted plumage slowly becomes pale in captivity, probably due to the dirt or to some deficiency in the diet.

Flamingos prefer salt or brackish waters. They build their nests close together, in shallow water or on muddy shores, of soft mud which soon hardens. These simple, flattened, cone-like structures are used only for one season. In the hollowed out, saucer-like top the female lays one or at most two white eggs which both sexes incubate alternately, folding their long legs beneath them. The young hatch after 30–40 days, remaining in the nest for four days. They are covered with white down and have a straight bill which starts curving downwards only after the third week. At first, the adults feed the nestlings a protein

128

129

secretion from the crop, then regurgitated food containing plankton for 14 days, after which the young fend for themselves, forming flocks with those from other nests. Their feathers are an unattractive grey colour. When not foraging for food, flamingos generally rest on one leg with the head tucked among the shoulder feathers.

The best known and most widespread species is the **Greater** or **Roseate Flamingo,** *Phoenicopterus ruber* [127], which is divided into three distinct geographical races: *Phoenicopterus ruber roseus* [128], white with a pinkish tinge, found scattered over western Asia, north and central Africa, with groups in southern Spain and southern France; *Phoenicopterus ruber ruber,* light vermilion, breeding in small numbers in Central America, the Bahamas, the northern coast of South America and on the Galapagos Islands; and *Phoenicopterus ruber chilensis,* sometimes called the **Chilean Flamingo,** whose green-grey feet have red joints, breeding from

Peru and Uruguay to Tierra del Fuego.

Picture 131 shows *Phoenicopterus ruber roseus* in the foreground, two specimens of *Phoenicopterus ruber ruber* behind, and *Phoenicopterus ruber chilensis* at the extreme right. In the genus Phoeniconaias, the upper jaw lies between the edges of the lower jaw; in Phoenicopterus it overlaps. The **Lesser Flamingo,** *Phoeniconaias minor* [129, 130], distinguished by a dark carmine bill, is found in large numbers on the salt lakes of Africa south of the Sahara. Some Greater Flamingos join these flocks.

Waterfowl

The screamers form an independent family (Anhimidae) belonging to the order of water-fowl (Anseriformes). They differ from most other birds in that their feathers are distributed uniformly over the body without any bare patches (apteria). The head and bill, resembling those of a game-bird, and the spurs at the bend of the wing distinguish them from the other family of this order, the Anatidae, which includes the swans, geese and ducks.

The **Horned Screamer,** *Anhima cornuta* [132, 133], is found in tropical South America, usually near water. It is 32 in. long, and is a strong flier even though heavy and robust in build. It is blackish brown, with a paler crown and white belly. A long slender horn, up to 6 in. in length, adorns the forehead, and there are two sharp horny spurs at the bend of the wing.

The closely related **Crested Screamer,** *Chauna cristata* [134], has a black and light-coloured ring round the neck and weighs about 6½ lb. It is found in the swamps and by the rivers of South America.

The **Black-necked Screamer,** *Chauna chavaria* [135], of northern Colombia and Venezuela is somewhat smaller. The neck is black and the white cheeks stand out in sharp contrast; it, too, has a crest. It inhabits jungle lakes where it may often be seen walking on the floating masses of vegetation.

With few exceptions almost all of the 200 species of ducks are good swimmers, some being excellent divers which can submerge directly from the surface of the water. Their flight, with neck outstretched, is rapid and strong, though some ducks require a longer run before becoming airborne. The most characteristic feature is the bill, which is broad and flat, covered on the outside with a sensitive membrane and inside with little horny plates, which serve as a sifting apparatus. With the bill and tongue, which has tooth-like projections on the edges, they can sift the finest food particles from the water. The duck family inhabits salt and fresh waters throughout the world, with the exception of the Antarctic.

133

134

93

135

The subfamily Anserinae includes the swans, geese and whistling ducks. In all, there is very little external difference between the sexes. The birds moult only once a year and the young, as in all the other species of water-fowl, leave the nest on hatching. Swans are the largest of the Anatidae. They fly and swim well. They do not dive, but merely submerge the head and neck, sometimes also the forward part of the body, when foraging for food, which is mainly vegetable, but with some worms and insects.

The **Mute Swan**, *Cygnus olor* [136, 137], is raised in captivity for its great beauty; domesticated birds are frequently seen on small lakes in parks and private grounds. The male, or cob, in particular, is an impressive sight when disturbed: he pulls his S-curved neck on to his back and raises his bent wings to make himself appear larger. Full-grown adult birds may weigh as much as 22 lb. The adult bird has white plumage and an orange bill with a black knob. The young (cygnets) are grey-brown. Wild populations may be found here and there in northern Europe and discontinuously throughout central Asia to the lower reaches of the Amur River in eastern Asia. In the United States, feral Mute Swans, descendants of birds escaped from captivity, are fairly common in the coastal areas of the middle Atlantic states. The Mute Swan occupies some of the same habitats as the Whooper Swan, the two species sometimes nesting together. The nest is built in reeds or on islets by the female (pen), with material supplied by the cob.

138

The **Whooper Swan,** *Cygnus cygnus* [138, 140], differs from the Mute Swan in having a lemon-yellow and black bill with no basal knob. The neck is not curved but is generally held erect. The Whooper breeds in northern Europe and Asia; the related **Trumpeter Swan** of north-western North America, considered by some ornithologists as a separate species, *Cygnus buccinator*, differs only in having an all-black bill. **Bewick's Swan,** *Cygnus bewickii* [139], is much smaller and has only about one third of the

139

140

bill coloured yellow. It breeds in the northernmost parts of Europe and Asia. Perhaps of the same species is the **Whistling Swan,** *Cygnus columbianus*, in which the yellow of the bill is confined to a narrow streak. It breeds from north-east Siberia across the American Arctic, wintering throughout the western USA and also in great numbers on Chesapeake Bay. The **Black Swan,** *Cygnus atratus* [141, colour plate VII], living on the lakes and rivers of southern Australia, is black with white wing quills. The red bill has a pale band at the tip but no basal knob. The neck is unusually long and curved in an S.

Southern South America is the home of the **Black-necked Swan,** *Cygnus melancoryphus* [142], whose ecology is much like that of the European swans. The plumage is white; adult birds have a bluish grey bill, yellow at the tip and red at the base, with a high red knob.

141

142

143

144

Geese are less dependent on water than the other members of this subfamily. They are more agile on land where they feed mainly on fields and meadows, grass and grain forming the mainstay of their diet. Geese are smaller than swans, have longer legs, shorter necks and thicker bills terminating in a nail. Like the swans they fly and swim excellently.

The **Grey Lag Goose**, *Anser anser* [143], inhabits the calm, still waters of central and northern Europe, is over 3 ft long and weighs nearly 8 lb. It is coloured grey-brown, vermiculated below, with pale forewing

145

ible in flight. These geese are migrants which
nter in southern and western Europe and Asia,
metimes also in North Africa.

e female builds the nest and incubates alone; but
 male remains close by, as if to keep guard. The
st is generally made of reeds or other aquatic vege-
ion and may be surrounded by water on all sides.
  Scotland these geese nest among heather and
hes on islands or by the shores of lochs (lakes).

The 4–6 or more eggs rest on a soft layer of grey down
which the goose tears from her belly to line the nest
[144].

The European farmyard geese are descendants of
the Grey Lag. The process of domestication can be
traced to the Egyptians as long ago as 2200 B.C. The
several breeds are raised chiefly for their meat, fat
and feathers, the white form predominating as its
feathers have a higher market value [145–147].

147

The **White-fronted Goose,** *Anser albifrons* [148, 149], of the northern tundras is a somewhat smaller, closely allied species. During the migrating season and in winter it is regularly found in central Europe and the British Isles, and across western North America to northern Mexico. Adult birds are distinguished by a white spot on the reddish bill and dark bars on the belly which are absent in the young. Also inhabiting the mountainous regions of the Eurasian tundras is the **Lesser White-fronted Goose,** *Anser erythropus* [150, 151]. It resembles the White-fronted Goose, but it is distinguished by a larger white blaze extending from the base of the bill up

148

149

to and above the eye, and a yellow rim encircling the eye. The **Bean Goose,**
Anser fabalis [152], nests from Greenland through northern Europe all the
way to the Far East. It is distinguished from the preceding species by its
black bill with orange band, and its generally darker colouration. As soon
as the waters of the subarctic freeze over, flocks of these wild geese start

151

153

their journey south. The Bean Goose winters in large numbers on the sea-coast and on the freshwater lakes and rivers of central Europe and Asia. Very few visit Britain, where the closely related **Pink-footed Goose,** *Anser brachyrhynchus,* is much commoner. They feed by day on plains and fields, retiring at night to sand-banks or mud-flats. Shooting these birds when they leave their resting place is a favourite sport with hunters. Wild geese often fly in typical V-formations [153].

The **Snow Goose,** *Anser caerulescens* [154], apa from the black flight feathers, greatly resembles t small farmyard goose. It occurs in two basic colo variations – white with black wing tips, and dark wi white head [155]. Also shown is a young bird in t juvenile plumage of the dark phase [157]. This speci breeds in arctic America and the north-easternmo tip of Asia, ranging in winter to California, northe Mexico, Louisiana and Virginia.

The **Emperor Goose,** *Anser canagicus* [156], bree

158

159

on the islands of the Bering
Strait, the coast of Chukot
and south-west Alaska, wandering slightly south in winter.
It resembles the dark phase
of the Snow Goose but is
handsomely scaled black and
white.

Ross's Goose, *Anser ross*
[158], is smaller than the Snow
Goose but has a similar
colouration. The bill is very
short. This is a rare bird which
breeds in a limited area along
the Perry River in the centre
of the north Canadian coast
migrating south-west to pass
the winter in inland California. It is estimated that the
species numbers 8,000 birds.
Its northern nesting ground
were first discovered in 1942.
The **Bar-headed Goose,**
Anser indicus [159], still occurs
in abundance on the lakes of
central Asia from Tien Chan
to Ladakh and Koko Nor. It
is smaller than the Grey Lag
and is distinguished by the
two black bars on the back of
the white head. It frequently
nests in large colonies. In their

160

161

162

winter quarters in India these geese sometimes congregate in large flocks.

Geese of the genus Branta are coloured chiefly in various combinations of black and white, the bill always being black, and do not honk like the grey goose. The largest is the **Canada Goose,** *Branta canadensis* [161, 162], measuring up to 40 in. It is greyish brown above with pale wavy markings, the head and neck black, the cheeks and throat white. It is a native of North America, breeding in Canada and the northern United States and ranging south to Mexico and the Gulf coast in winter. Because of its size the Canada Goose is a favourite sporting bird and has been successfully introduced to several other countries, chiefly Great Britain and Sweden. The nest is built in tall grass or beneath low shrubs, rarely in trees.

Races occurring in Alaska and neighbouring territories have a white ring between the black neck and breast [160].

163

164

The **Barnacle Goose,** *Branta leucopsis* [163], is
smaller handsome bird (23–28 in.) with white fore
head, cheeks and throat. It is grey above, not grey
brown like the Canada Goose. It breeds in easter
Greenland, Spitzbergen, Lofoten and souther
Novaya Zemlya, wintering south to the coasts (
northern Europe, and is generally found in larg
flocks; it nests near the coast on rocky cliffs, often i
small colonies. The Barnacle Goose is a wary bi
which makes a great deal of noise, its call somewh
resembling the barking of a dog.

The **Brant** or **Brent Goose,** *Branta bernicla* [164
a much smaller bird than the Canada Goose,
coloured grey-black and white, with a white necl
patch the shape of a half-moon. It breeds on the coas
of America and Eurasia and outlying islands fa
above the Arctic Circle; it winters in more souther
regions, in Europe along the North Sea coastlir
where numbers are to be seen during migration, mar
of them staying there throughout the whole winte
In North America it winters to the coasts of Californi
and Virginia.

The **Red-breasted Goose,** *Branta ruficollis* [165, 166], measures up to 22 in. and is a striking bird coloured black and white, with chestnut ear-coverts, foreneck and chest. It inhabits the taiga and tundras of the Yamal peninsula in Siberia down to the lower reaches of the Khatanga. It is a very sociable bird, and its clear call "tschak-woi" is frequently heard in the flocks. It winters in central Asia but is occasionally seen in Europe at this season.

165

166

167

The domesticated form of the Chinese Goose [168, 169], is much larger than the wild breed, weighing from 11 to 12 lb, sometimes specially fed up to 26 lb, as compared with the latter's 7½ lb. It is further distinguished by the frontal knob at the base of the bill. This bird was first domesticated in China, it is believed, almost 3,000 years ago. Pure white strains [170] are also bred.

The **Magpie Goose,** *Anseranas semipalmata* [171], of Australia stands somewhat apart from the other members of this family, in that its toes are webbed only at the base. It frequents swamps and shallows

The southern regions of eastern Siberia, from the upper reaches of the Ob and Tobol rivers east to Sakhalin and south to northern China, are the home of the **Chinese Goose,** *Cygnopsis cygnoides* [167]. The crown, nape and feathers on the upper parts are dark brown, the cheeks and throat white, the underparts pale brown. It is about the size of a farmyard goose, but with a longer bill. Its call resembles that of the Grey Lag but is louder. It is found mainly on the banks of fast-flowing streams overgrown with shrubs. The Chinese Goose is a migrant species with winter quarters in China and on Hondo Island.

168

169

and dislikes swimming. It is a white bird with black neck, chest, tail, flight feathers and "pantalets".

Another distinct group closely resembling geese are the whistling ducks or tree ducks (Dendrocygna), eight species of small, long-legged water-fowl with an upright stance, found in warm-temperate and tropical regions in both the Old and New Worlds. The note is a clear whistle and hunters usually call them whistling ducks. Some species frequently perch on trees and a few even nest in tree-cavities.

The **Plumed** or **Eyton's Tree Duck,** *Dendrocygna eytoni* [172], of Australia and Tasmania has remark-

171

170

ably long feathers on the flanks which extend over the folded wing. The upper parts are olive-brown, the chest and neck whitish grey, the flanks rusty, barred with black.

172

173

The **Black-billed** or **Cuban Tree Duck,** *Dendro-cygna arborea* [173], of the Bahamas and Antilles is mostly mottled brown, with black, white-spotted flanks and a small, barely visible crest. It inhabits forest swamps but rarely swims on the water.

The **White-faced Tree Duck,** *Dendrocygna viduata* [174], is distinguished by its white face and a white patch on the neck. The nape and abdomen are black, and the flanks are barred with black. This bird occurs in South America, Africa and Madagascar.

174

The **Black-bellied** or **Red-billed Tree Duck,** *Dendrocygna autumnalis* [176], is a common species in its range of distribution—from southern Texas to Brazil and northern Argentina. The upper parts and breast are reddish brown, the belly an intense black, the wings grey, white and black. It nests in hollow trees or marshes laying 12–16 eggs which are incubated chiefly by the male.

Closely allied to the tree ducks is the **Coscoroba Swan,** *Coscoroba coscoroba* [175], which differs from the true swans in having feathered lores. It is white with black wing tips, red bill and feet, and measures about 3 ft. It inhabits the lagoons of Argentina, Chile and the Falkland Islands.

The **Cape Barren Goose,** *Cereopsis novae-hollandiae* [178], of south-east Australia and Tasmania, differs from the other ducks and geese in having a short, blunt bill with a large yellow-green cere ex-

tending almost to the tip [177]. Though included among the shelducks it looks very like a goose. The plumage is a sober ashy grey with dark spots on the wing-coverts and a white patch on the crown and forehead. The bird weighs $7\frac{1}{2}$ lb and measures $2\frac{1}{2}$ ft in length. It inhabits the islands off the southern coast of Australia. It breeds in the cold months, July to August; in captivity in Europe even in winter. It is not fond of water, preferring to stay on dry land where it feeds and rests.

179

180

The genus Chloephaga comprises geese of smaller size occurring in South America and closely allied to the shelducks and the Cape Barren Goose. All are predominantly land birds, foraging for their food—plants and seeds—on meadows and pastureland, and all moult twice a year. The sexes differ in the voice and sometimes also in colouration. The two sexes of the **Andean Goose,** *Chloephaga melanoptera* [179], are alike in external appearance. Both are white with black wings and tails, the lesser wing-coverts spotted black. They nest in the mountains of Peru and across to northern Chile and northern Argentina, frequently close to snow fields. In autumn they migrate to lower altitudes. The **Ashy-headed Goose,** *Chloephaga poliocephala* [180], has a grey head and upper neck, rust-brown chest and nape, and brownish grey back. The white underparts are barred with grey on the flanks. The feet are black in front, yellow behind. The bird breeds in Chile, Argentina, Patagonia and the Falkland Islands. In the Andes foothills it occurs in abundance on grassy sites, chiefly pastures. The **Magellan** or **Upland Goose,** *Chloephaga picta* [181], the most numerous member of the genus, shows great variation in its colouring. It is grey above, white below, barred with black, either entirely or at least in part. The female is generally brown, also with transverse black bars on the underparts. It occurs in South America in two distinct races, one in the Andes, the other on the extreme southern coasts. Nesting birds are so numerous in some localities, for example the Falkland Islands, that they endanger the food supply of sheep, so that landowners destroy the clutches to prevent their over-population. In the autumn the southern birds migrate a little way up the coast, the mountain birds to lower altitudes.

The **Abyssinian Blue-winged Goose,** *Cyanochen cyanopterus* [182], occurs in the mountains at altitudes above 8,000 ft. Both sexes are grey-brown with pale markings, the wing-coverts lead-blue. This bird shows a marked resemblance to its American cousins in both habits and colouration.

181

182

The **Egyptian Goose,** *Alopo-chen aegyptiacus* [183], is often bred in captivity. It nests in the whole of Africa except the Sahara. It has fairly long legs, pale yellow-brown feathers vermiculated with black, the wings being green, black and brown, the upper tail-coverts white. Both sexes are coloured alike, but the female is some-what smaller than the male. It builds its nest in bushes and trees, often also on the ground. The southernmost tip of the African continent is the home of the **South African** or **Cape Shelduck,** *Tadorna cana* [185], a bird somewhat larger than the Mallard. The male is rust-coloured with a grey head, white upper wing-coverts and green speculum. The female is similarly coloured but with a white face. It frequents swamps and river-banks and nests in holes in the ground.

183

184

The **Ruddy Shelduck,** *Tadorna ferruginea* [184], is similar in size and colouring, but with a pale rust-coloured head. The male has a narrow black collar. It breeds from southern Spain and the Balkan peninsula eastwards across Asia all the way to the Amur River; also in North Africa. It winters in India, southern China, Arabia, Egypt and north-west Africa. Occasionally it finds its way to central Europe. It builds its nest in an abandoned burrow or digs one for itself.

The **Radjah Shelduck,** *Tadorna radjah* [186], of north and north-west Australia, New Guinea and the Moluccas, with two geographical races, is distinguished by its white head and narrow black breast band. The **Common Shelduck,** *Tadorna tadorna* [187], is one of the most brightly coloured of ducks – especially the drake in full plumage, which is a combination of white, red, green and brown. At the base of the carmine bill there is a large knob. The feet are pink. The duck is similar but lacks the basal knob. The

187

188

Common Shelduck frequents coastal areas for it prefers brackish waters. It breeds from Spain, the British Isles and Scandinavia through the Eurasian temperate zone all the way to Manchuria, wintering in North Africa and southern Asia. It nests in burrows in the ground or under thick vegetation. Every year, during the moult, birds from the western European coast gather on the sandy island of Knechsand at the mouth of the River Weser.

All Anatinae moult twice during the summer. For part of this period they have no flight feathers—this applies to swans and geese as well—and remain in hiding as much as possible. The two sexes may look more or less alike when the drakes are in their "eclipse" plumage; this aids concealment. But there is a marked difference between the nuptial dress of the drake and that of the duck. There are also other differences between the two in voice and behaviour, which are much more pronounced than in the geese. Although these birds are predominantly monogamous, the drake performs few if any of the duties of incubation and caring for the young, but some stay quite near the nest, which contains any number from 4 to 14 eggs.

In summer, dabbling or surface-feeding ducks sleep throughout much of the day on large, calm bodies of water, taking off from the surface at dusk to make their way to small pools and streams or to harvest fields in search of food. In winter they feed more

189

190

during the day. Though good swimmers the adults usually dive only when injured.

The **Mallard** or **Wild Duck,** *Anas platyrhynchos,* the most common species of duck, ranges throughout the whole of Eurasia excepting the most northerly and southerly regions, and almost all of North America, north to the Arctic Circle. It is also found on the waters of north-west Africa. The difference between the plumage of the sexes is very marked, especially in winter and spring when the drake is in his nuptial dress [192], with the central tail feathers curled upwards. The speculum in both sexes is a metallic purple with margins of white. The Mallard spends much of its time on the water, but the nest may be located some distance inland, usually on the ground beneath bushes, amidst nettles and grass, rushes, sometimes in trees in the forks of branches, or in nests abandoned by other birds. The duck tends the young alone.

The nest [189] is lined with a thick layer of down, and the clutches consist of 8–14 pale green eggs, which the duck carefully covers with grass or down whenever she leaves it.

The ducklings, coloured smoky-grey and yellow, leave the nest as soon as they are dry [190], being from the first very agile. They follow the mother wherever she goes [188] and when one goes astray it calls with a plaintive, high-pitched note. They are adept at diving when danger threatens.

During the day Mallard often rest on the water, flying off to forage for food in the fields and smaller streams with the coming of twilight [191]. Plants are the mainstay of the diet but during the breeding season they eat some animal food. Throughout their range numbers may have been affected by reclamation of swamps, but large flocks may still be seen in Europe in autumn, when half a million may be present in Britain. In North America they are still abundant.

191

192

Over the centuries several domesticated types were bred from the Mallard, being reared chiefly for their meat and eggs. Ducks were first domesticated in China and were introduced to Europe at the beginning of the Christian era.

Some, such as the **Rouen** [196], keep the colouration of their wild ancestors; the most familiar are the white or

193

194

yellow-white types such as the **Pekin** [193].

Also common are the ornamental types of domesticated ducks with a crest of down feathers on the nape [194]. **Indian Runners** [195] are distinguished by a slender body and almost upright stance, feet placed well aft, and a long, raised neck. They are good egg-layers, laying as many as 150–230 in a year.

195

196

The drake **Common Teal**, *Anas crecca* [197], has during winter and spring a dark brown head with a broad green band on the side, a pinkish breast and a grey body with a horizontal white stripe on the side; in eclipse he is coloured much like the duck, which is duller, plain mottled brown. Teal are much smaller than Mallard and nest throughout most of Europe, north and central Asia, occasionally wandering to North America in winter. The drake **Green-winged Teal**, *Anas carolinensis*, is identical except that the white streak is replaced by a vertical white crescent on the fore flank. The females of the two species are identical. The Green-winged Teal breeds throughout western North America, ranging in winter east to the Atlantic coast and south to Central America. Most

Teal migrate south in winter. This is an abundant species in Europe, belonging, like the Mallard, to the tribe of dabbling ducks, which obtain their food by sifting water through their bills [199].

The **Baikal Teal**, *Anas formosa* [198], is somewhat larger. The drake has a striking colour pattern on the head, a combination of black, yellow and green, and sickle-shaped black and white secondaries. The bright nuptial dress of the drake contrasts sharply with the duller plumage of the duck. These teal nest in north-east Asia, wintering in China and Japan.

The **Falcated Teal**, *Anas falcata* [200], has a similar distribution. The drake is strikingly patterned; its chestnut head has a green tuft at the back, the throat is white and there is a white patch on the

forehead. The breast is white
with black markings, the long,
sickle-shaped inner secondaries are black and white.
The duck resembles that of
the European Teal. May be
seen in Europe and Alaska on
migration or in winter.

The **Gadwall,** *Anas strepera*
[201], is fairly common, with
unobtrusive colouring, like
the Mallard in size and build.
The drake's head and neck
are brown, finely spotted with
black and white, otherwise
the plumage is predominantly

200

201

202

203

grey. The feathers beneath the
tail are black and those in
front of the black and white
speculum are chestnut. The
duck has a yellow-brown
stripe down the length of the
upper bill. The Gadwall inhabits Europe and temperate
Asia, migrating south in winter. It also breeds throughout
western North America and
locally on the Atlantic coast,
wintering south to Mexico.

A familiar bird in northern
Eurasia is the **Wigeon,** *Anas*
penelope [202], a handsome
species somewhat smaller than

204

205

206

the Mallard. The drake has a reddish head with a buff forehead and crown and a bluish bill; otherwise he is coloured grey and white. The duck is reddish brown with black markings and white under parts. The Wigeon is a migrant which winters in Britain and Ireland, on the Mediterranean and in southern Asia. In autumn and winter it frequently strays to the coasts of southern Canada and the northern United States. Its route leads through central Europe where it can frequently be seen in autumn and early spring. It grazes on land much more than Mallard or Gadwall.

The **White-cheeked** or **Bahama Pintail,** *Anas bahamensis* [203], with race in the Galapagos Islands and eastern South America, also breeds in central Chile and the West Indies. It is brown spotted with black, the crown and nape dark brown. The throat, sides of the head and cheeks are white. The blue-grey bill is red at the base. The sexes are nearly alike and both have a long, pointed tail.

The somewhat smaller **Brown** or **Chilean Pintail,** *Anas georgica* [205], with a race in South Georgia, has black and brown plumage, and is distinguished by a yellow bill with a black ridge. This species also has pointed tail feathers. It occurs in South America, chiefly in the mountainous regions.

The **Common Pintail,** *Anas acuta* [204], is slightly less robust than the Mallard. The nuptial dress of the drake is very handsome. The head and nape are brown, interrupted on either side by a white line which runs down into the

122

207

hite neck. The back and nks of the male are grey, e breast white and the under il-coverts black. The middle il feathers are pointed as in e last two species. The duck s unobtrusive plumage and ffers from the Mallard in ving a longer, more slender ck. The Pintail inhabits orthern Europe, a large part Asia and western North merica. It sometimes breeds central Europe as well. A igrant, in winter it is one of e most common species on e upper reaches of the Nile. North America it is wide- read in winter from ashington and New York uth to Mexico.

the **African Cape Teal** or **ink-billed Duck,** *Anas pensis* [206], the sexes are ike in external appearance. heir general colour is grey ith darker spots, the back d wings pale brown; the rge green speculum has a hite margin. The pink bill is irly large. Cape Teal fre- uent large and small bodies water, often being seen on t lakes.

208

209

he **Garganey,** *Anas quer- edula* [207], is a little larger an the Common Teal. It habits temperate Europe d Asia and is most abundant here there is plenty of quatic vegetation. It is not und high up in the moun- ns. During the breeding ason, the drake is distin- ished by a broad white band either side of the brown ad and by long black and hite shoulder feathers. The eculum in both sexes is en bordered with white.

s North American cousin e **Blue-winged Teal,** *Anas* *scors* [208], has a grey head th a white crescent in front

2

212

213

of the eye. It breeds on bodie of water in open plains and wooded regions from Canac to Mexico, wintering Columbia; its habits are sim lar to those of the Europea Teal.

The unusual **Shovele** *Anas clypeata* [209], is di tinguished by a broad, spoo shaped bill which serves well in foraging for food ar sieving plankton. The dra is brightly coloured, with black and green head, whi chest and reddish brow underparts; the duck resen bles the duck Mallard. I range covers almost the who of Europe and northern As and North America, mostly the west, from the northe United States to northe Canada. It winters from wes ern Europe to central Afric in southern Asia and throug most of North America Central America. The nest built near water [210].

In comparison with dabbli ducks, the diving ducks lower in the water and the movements on land are mo cumbersome. When di turbed or foraging for fo they dive without difficult rarely using their wings, b only their feet to propel ther selves forward.

The **Common Eider,** *Soma-ria mollissima*, inhabits the islands and coasts of the northern seas and is of circumpolar distribution. It is famous for the down with which it lines its nest and which is harvested to be used for pillows and, of course, eider-downs [211]. Eiders frequently nest on barren islets without any shelter, often in large numbers, forming colonies. The incubating female shows little fear even when approached by man [212].

These ducks are adept at diving to comparatively great depths. The mainstay of the diet is molluscs and crabs. Eiders have social courtship displays, during which the cooing calls of the drakes sound almost like humans talking. The adjoining picture [213] shows a male in breeding plumage—white with black, the white of the chest tinged with pink. The bill is deep and massive.

The **Red-crested Pochard,** *Netta rufina* [214], is about the same size as the Mallard. The drake has a red bill and chestnut head with a large crest and high forehead. The neck, chest and underparts are black, the flanks a paler colour. The female is light brown, the back and crown darker, the cheeks pale grey. It occurs chiefly in southern Europe and the central zone of Asia, nesting sometimes also in central Europe.

The **Common Pochard,** *Aythya ferina* [215], is a typical representative of this tribe of ducks. The drake has a chestnut head with a grey-blue bill, while the upper and underparts are grey with darker markings. The base of the throat and chest are black. The

214

215
216

217

duck is grey-brown [217].
nests on smaller shallo
bodies of water among thi
reeds and other vegetatio
[216], diving for its foo
chiefly plants, to depths
3–5 ft. It breeds in Europe a
across Asia to Lake Baikal a
is a migratory species. A virt
ally identical species, t
Redhead, *Aythya america*
breeds throughout weste
North America, wintering
the coast of Texas and nor
ern Mexico and, in smal
numbers, east to the Atlant
The **Ferruginous Duc**
Aythya nyroca [219], has
similar range of distributio
The drake is chestnut, wh
on the belly and under t
tail. It is distinguished by t
pale eye and blue-grey b
The duck is a paler colo
with a brown eye. Unlike t
Common Pochard, in win
it is usually to be seen in sm
groups rather than lar
flocks. It, too, nests near wat
among rushes.
The **Tufted Duck,** *Ayth*
fuligula [218], though
brightly patterned, is an el
gant bird. The drake is bla
the underparts and flan
white. Both sexes have a sm
overhanging crest, which
more apparent in the dra
The duck is brown with a p

218

219

elly and sometimes a pale area at the base of the bill.
n flight it displays a broad white band down the
ngth of the wings. This duck inhabits northern
urope and Asia, except the northernmost tundras.
ince the end of the 19th century it has been spreading
s range into central Europe and is a common sight
n shallow, reed-grown waters. Like the Common
ochard, it builds its nest among reeds, often in the
ompany of gulls and terns. The clutch is of 6–14

greenish eggs. The North American counterpart of
this species is the **Ring-necked Duck,** *Aythya
collaris,* which nests in the north and west and winters
to Florida and Costa Rica. It lacks the crest of
Aythya fuligula, but is otherwise virtually identical.
In localities where there is an abundant food supply,
chiefly water snails, one can often observe whole
flocks of diving ducks of various species–Pochards,
Tufted Ducks, Ferruginous Ducks [220]

The male **Maned** or **Australian Goose,** *Chenonet
jubata* [222], of Australia has a brown head and
whitish breast mottled with brown, the remaind
of the body being grey, and black below. The fem
is paler with darker spots and with dark and p
stripes on the side of the head. It breeds in wood
regions near rivers, building its nest in the grass li
true geese.

The **Wood Duck,** *Aix sponsa* [221, colour pla
VIII], the only species which can rival the beauty
the Mandarin, is also strikingly coloured and has
long crest. The head of the drake is dark, glossy gre
with white markings, the sides of the head and ne
purplish green with a blue sheen. The duck is simi
to that of the Mandarin and, like it, nests in tre
holes. It frequents the lakes and inland streams
North America, wintering south to southern Mexic

vii **Black Swan** *Cygnus atratus*

viii **Wood Duck** *Aix sponsa*

ix **Goshawk**
Accipiter gentilis

x   **Common or Grey Partridge** *Perdix perdix*

The male of the **Mandarin Duck,** *Aix galericulata* [223], is particularly handsome, though small in size. The chestnut "fan" formed by the decurved innermost secondary is striking. The sides of the head are whitish, the crown and crest a metallic green, the breast reddish purple. The duck is brownish, grey above, the eye set in a white band. This ornamental duck inhabits the Far East in the region of the Amur River, Japan and Formosa; it has been successfully introduced to southern England. It is adept at making its way among tree branches and is a shy bird which keeps to the thick vegetation bordering the banks. The Mandarin and the Wood Duck are both prized by duck fanciers.

223

224

The **Comb Duck,** *Sarkidiornis melanotos* [224], is distinguished by the blunt protuberance at the bend of its wing, while drakes have a caruncle at the base of the bill. The two sexes are alike in colouration. The head and neck are white mottled black, and the black of the back, wings and tail has a greenish purple metallic sheen. The underparts are white, the flanks grey or brownish. This duck lives in the tropical

225
226

regions of the Old World and in South America; it nests in holes in trees. During the day it forages for food on the ground; at night flocks of these birds roost in treetops. The **Muscovy Duck,** *Cairina moschata* [225], is the ancestor of the widely distributed domestic Muscovy Duck which occurs in various coloured forms [226]. The original wild form inhabits tropical Central and South America. It is coloured black

227
228

with a greenish purple sheen and white wing-coverts. The frontal and eye-rim caruncles of the drake are red. It frequents forest swamps and ponds and roosts in trees. During the breeding season the drake has a distinctive, unpleasant body odour.

The **Spur-winged Goose,** *Plectropterus gambensis* [228], of Africa is a large bird, up to 40 in. long, and, with its long legs, is more like a goose than a duck. It is black with a green sheen above, the underparts and sides of the head are white. There is a knob at the base of the upper bill. The face is bare and crusty. It frequents marshes, sometimes in large numbers, and nests in reeds, bushes and tree-holes. It is agile on land, occasionally roosting on trees.

The **Labrador Duck,** *Camptorhynchus labradoricus* [227], is an extinct species about which little is known;

229

131

230

231

it inhabited the North Atlantic coast up to the year 1875. The two birds (drake and duck) shown in the picture are very highly prized specimens of the National Museum collection in Prague.

The **Common Goldeneye,** *Bucephala clangula* [229], is a somewhat smaller duck than the Mallard. The drake is black above, white below, and has a white patch at the base of the bill. The duck's head is chocolate-brown and the neck is ringed with a pale band [230]. It breeds in the northern regions of the Old and New Worlds, moving south for the winter. Courting begins in the bird's winter quarters. The drake spreads his tail and lays his head on his back, the bill jutting upward, then with a rapid movement he thrusts the bill and neck forward at the same time uttering a bell-like note. Picture 231 shows Goldeneyes performing their courtship. The nest is placed in holes of trees, the down-covered ducklings frequently jumping from great heights to land on the water's surface or on the ground [232].

233

The **Harlequin Duck,** *Histrionicus histrionicus* [233], is grey and reddish with white patches on the side of the head. It occurs in Iceland, the coast of Greenland, north-east Siberia, Alaska and northern Canada, and south in the western mountains to northern California and Wyoming. It winters along the coast to Japan, northern California, New Jersey.

Of the seven species of saw-billed ducks, the one shown here is the duck of the **Goosander,** *Mergus merganser.* This bird is larger than the Mallard and

234

235

the drake in his nuptial dress is distinguished by the large black head with a green sheen, and a long red bill. The back and part of the wings are black, the large speculum white. The neck, chest and belly are white with a pinkish tinge. In the duck the head is brown, the upper parts blue-grey, the underparts white [235]. The Goosander inhabits the northern regions of both hemispheres, nesting in cavities in trees or in crevices and under boulders, and wintering south to the southern parts of the northern temperate zone. It feeds mainly on fish, the long narrow bill being well adapted to grip slippery surfaces.

The **Red-breasted Merganser,** *Mergus serrator* [236], is somewhat smaller than the Mallard, measuring about 2 ft in length. Like the Goosander it has a long slender bill. The drake differs in having a long double crest on the nape. The green-black head is separated from the reddish brown, black-flecked breast by a broad white collar. The back is black, the flanks marbled with grey, and the white wing patch is crossed by two black bars. The duck is similar to that of the Goosander. The Red-breasted Merganser has a similar range of distribution to the preceding species, but extending somewhat further north. Sometimes both species will be found nesting in the same place. In winter it frequents the ice-free waters of the southerly regions of its range; in North America it tends to be a more coastal species.

236

Marked difference in plumage is also shown by the smallest of the mergansers—the **Smew,** *Mergus albellus* [237], which breeds on the forest lakes and streams of northern Scandinavia as far as Kamchatka in Siberia; it measures only 16 in. The drake is white with black markings, the smaller female grey with red-brown head and nape.

The scoters are three species of robust sea-ducks in which the breeding plumage of the drakes is pre-dominantly black. The drake of the **Common** or **Black Scoter,** *Melanitta nigra* [234], is entirely black without any white patches; the duck is dark brown with pale throat and cheeks. Adult drakes have a yellow horny knob at the base of the yellow upper bill. These birds dive to great depths to forage for the molluscs which are their favourite food. They breed on the lakes of forest tundras, by moorland pools and on northern coastal waters, wintering south to middle temperate sea coasts.

237

238

Birds of Prey

All birds of prey (order Falconiformes) are distinguished by a downcurved bill. This bill shape is also characteristic of the owls and the parrots, but the maxillae (upper bills) of owls and parrots are sickle-shaped, whereas in the hawks and their allies they are hooked. In addition to this there are differences in the skeleton. The outer toe of an owl's foot is reversible, in parrots it is permanently reversed, but in birds of prey the three toes point forward (with the exception of the Osprey which also has a reversible outer toe). The sharply hooked, downcurved bill, and the long-toed, clawed foot are signs of the hunting which is the chief means whereby these birds procure their food. Most raptors are carnivorous, feeding mainly on warm-blooded animals but also on fish, reptiles and amphibians, and insects and other invertebrates, but some prefer carrion and some are vegetable feeders. The various types of raptors demonstrate the close relationship between the shape of the wing, the way they seek their food and the method of flight. Long, narrow wings are characteristic of birds which capture their prey high

in the air or over open country; the flight is rapid and direct. Short, rounded wings, facilitating sharp turns in the air, are found in raptors which swoop to sudden attack in country where the range of vision is limited, as below treetop level in woodlands. Birds with long and broad wings sail in long soaring flight seeking their food on the ground, as a rule, or feeding on carrion. The stomach is thin-walled and rather large, which is typical of carnivores. Hawks have a crop where they store food. Some are even capable of digesting bones; as a rule, however, undigested particles are thrown up as pellets. The 270 species of raptors are divided, on the basis of anatomical structure and other characteristics, into five families: the American or New World vultures (Cathartidae), the Secretary Bird (Sagittariidae), the Old World vultures, hawks, eagles, kites and harriers (Accipitridae), the ospreys (Pandionidae) and falcons (Falconidae).

The largest of the American vultures (family Cathartidae), a group of carrion-eaters, is the **Andean Condor**, *Vultur gryphus* [238, 239], measuring nearly 12 ft across the wings and weighing 25

39

40

241

242

b. It lives in the high Andes up to altitudes of 16,000
t, but in Peru frequently visits the coast to feed on
he dead and dying in the great sea-bird colonies of
he guano islands. The black plumage is relieved by
a ruff of white. Unlike other members of this family,
he male is much larger than the female.

The closely related **American King Vulture**, *Sar-orhamphus papa* [240, 241], ranges from the forests
and savannahs of Mexico to northern Argentina. It
has a yellow fleshy crest on the cere, the bare skin of
he head being yellow and red. The plumage is black
and grey with a rose-yellow tinge. It measures 30 in.

The **Californian Condor**, *Gymnogyps californianus*
242], is the largest bird in North America, equal in
weight and wing span to its Andean cousin. It is now
found only in the coastal ranges of northern and
southern California, where its strength is not much
above 50 individuals, making it one of the rarest
birds in the world. Man is really its only enemy; by
shooting, poisoning and reducing its natural food of
animal carrion, he has driven it to its last stronghold.
It does not begin to breed until six years old and then
only lays one egg; but it may live for half a century.

243

Of all these birds the **Turkey Vulture,** *Cathartes
aura* [243, 244], has the largest range of distribution,
from the extreme south of South America to southern
Canada. The plumage is black, the bare head and
upper neck crimson. The wing span is 70 in. and the
weight 4½ lb.

The **American Black Vulture,** *Coragyps stratu-*
[245, 246], is slightly smaller and is also coloured
black, with a naked lead-coloured head. It range
from the east-central United States to Argentina and
Chile, being very plentiful in some places. In tropical
American towns they are common street scavengers

247

The **Secretary Bird,** *Sagittarius serpentarius* [247], is a distinctive bird and the single representative of the family Sagittariidae. It has a long neck and very long legs—it stands up to 4 ft high—and has the two blunt-ended central feathers of the tail much prolonged. Its plumage is grey and black. An inhabitant of Africa's open plains, it feeds on various small animals, but chiefly snakes; unlike other raptors it hunts on foot.

The family Accipitridae is the largest among the raptorial birds, including a great number of ver-

varied species. Among the most familiar of these is the **Honey Buzzard,** *Pernis apivorus* [248, 249], a common inhabitant of the forests of Eurasia as far east as the Altai Mountains. It shows marked variations in its colouring but can be distinguished from other raptors at close range by the short-

feathered lores. The comparatively long tail has a characteristic pattern [250].

The **Crested** or **Asiatic Honey Buzzard,** *Pernis ptilorhynchus* [251], of south-east Asia, the Celebes, the Philippines and Malaya, is much larger than the Honey Buzzard and is distinguished by a short crest. It is variable in colouration and is divided into a number of races.

The subfamily Milvinae has only two representatives in Europe. One is the **Red Kite,** *Milvus milvus* [252], which occurs in Europe, north-west Africa and Asia Minor. It has a deeply forked tail and is coloured red-brown above and rusty-red below.

The other species is the **Black Kite,** *Milvus migrans* [253], which differs in being dark brown and having a shallow forked tail. It occurs in Europe, southern and temperate Asia, Africa, Malaya and Australia, where it is called the **Fork-tailed Kite.** In both species the sexes are alike in external appearance [254].

xi **Brown-eared Pheasant** *Crossoptilon mantschuricum*

xii **Reeves Pheasant** *Syrmaticus reevesi*

xiii **Common Peafowl** *Pavo cristatus*

Closely related is the **Brahminy Kite,** *Haliastr*
indus [255], which is red-brown with white head, nec
and chest. It measures about 20 in. and is found nea
bodies of water in India, Indochina and Australasia
Common in the forests of Europe is the **Goshawk**
Accipiter gentilis [256, 257, colour plate IX], which
also occurs in Asia, North America, and the palearcti
areas of north-west Africa. It measures about 20 in
in length and has a wing span of about 39 in. The
female is markedly larger than the male. Adult bird
[256] have dark transverse bars on the pale chest an
belly, the young are spotted longitudinally [257] o
their yellowish underparts. The Goshawk is a darin
bird capable of catching a hare or pheasant.
Smaller than the Goshawk, which is larger than
crow, the related **Sparrowhawk,** *Accipiter nisu*
[258, 259], is about the size of a dove, the female bein
somewhat larger. Its colouration resembles that o

255

257

258

he Goshawk. It is mainly a resident in the forests of Europe and Asia, but has become scarce over much f Britain. The nest is built high in the treetops and ntains 4–6 spotted eggs. The Sparrowhawk feeds mainly on small birds. In North America it is replaced by the virtually identical **Sharp-shinned Hawk,** *Accipiter striatus*, which ranges from Alaska and northern Canada to tropical America.

259

261

260

148

Closely allied to the Sparrowhawk is the **Dark Chanting Goshawk,** *Melierax metabates* [260], of Africa south of the Sahara. It feeds on small mammals, birds, reptiles and large insects.

Some of the nine American members of the genus Buteo, though belonging to the group of buzzards, are more like true hawks (Accipiter) in colouration. The **Roadside Hawk,** *Buteo magnirostris* [261], is a common species found from northern Mexico through most of South America.

Found in the steppe regions of eastern Europe, across to eastern Asia, as well as in North Africa, is the **Long-legged Buzzard,** *Buteo rufinus* [262], which has a reddish brown tail. It builds its nest in rocks and banks, rarely on trees.

Somewhat smaller is the **Common Buzzard,** *Buteo buteo* [263], measuring 22 in. and weighing about 2 lb, one of the commonest European raptors. It usually nests in forests or on cliffs, but hunts in open country where it sights its prey from some high vantage-point. The food consists mainly of small rodents. Buzzards show marked variation in colouring [264], albino individuals [267, 268] being not uncommon. It ranges throughout the whole of Europe and a large

264

265

266

267

part of Asia, separated into several geographical races of which the **Steppe Buzzard,** *Buteo buteo vulpinus* [265], makes its home in eastern Europe and western Siberia. The Buzzard is a commanding flier [266] and is frequently seen, especially above its nesting grounds, soaring in graceful curves high up

268

269

in the sky. The nest is built in the treetops (in Britain often on crags) and contains 2–5 blue-white eggs, spotted red-brown. The young on hatching are covered with fine white down feathers [269]. The Buzzard is a beneficial bird and deserves to be protected.

The **Red-tailed Hawk,** *Buteo jamaicensis* [270], is widespread from Alaska to western Panama. The **Jackal** or **Augur Buzzard,** *Buteo rufofuscus* [273], also a red-tailed species, inhabits northeast and southern Africa.

The **Rough-legged Hawk** or **Buzzard,** *Buteo lagopus*

270

271

[271], is a common raptor of the Old and New World tundras. Its legs are feathered down to the toes, and the tail is pale with a black terminal bar. It journeys south in winter, when it may be found in central Europe and across the northern United States. The **White-tailed Hawk** or **White-breasted Buzzard,** *Buteo albicaudatus* [272], is widespread but local from the south-western United States through South America. It is separated into several geographical races. The nest is built in trees and contains 2 or 3 eggs.

272

273

The **Slate-coloured Hawk,**
Leucopternis schistacea [275],
somewhat smaller than the
Common Buzzard, is slate-
grey with a white central band
and a white border on the tail.
It occurs in eastern tropical
South America.

Best known among the eagles
is the **Golden Eagle,** *Aquila
chrysaëtos* [274], a huge bird
30–32 in. in length with a
wing span of about 6½ ft. It is
found in the mountains of
Eurasia, North Africa and
North America. The adult is
dark brown with golden tints
on the head, the young birds a
paler colour with white tail
feathers ending in a black
border.

The **Imperial Eagle,** *Aquila
heliaca* [276], is somewhat
smaller. Unlike the Golden
Eagle, which favours mountain regions, this eagle breeds
in the Mediterranean region,
the warmer parts of Asia and
in north-west India. The
white feathers on the back
contrast sharply with the
black-brown plumage.

275

276

277

278

The **Lesser Spotted Eagle,** *Aquila pomarina,* ne●
in the wooded country of eastern Europe, Asia Min●
and India. It is smaller than the Golden Eagle and
coloured dark brown, the young birds spotted abo●
[277]. Closely resembling it is the **Spotted Eag●**
Aquila clanga [278, 279], which is dark brown, oft●

...th white spots on the tail. Its range includes eastern ...rope and Siberia. It frequents forested plains and ...eppes in the vicinity of bodies of water.

...erreaux's Eagle, *Aquila verreauxi* [280], of north-

east and southern Africa and the **Wedge-tailed Eagle,** *Uroaetus audax* [281], of Australia, Tasmania and New Guinea, are large eagles about the size of the Golden Eagle.

282

283

Ranging from the Ukraine and Morocco to south-east Siberia and Burma is the **Tawny Eagle**, *Aquila rapax* [282], which closely resembles the Lesser Spotted Eagle. This common species feeds primarily on ground squirrels.

The **Crowned Eagle**, *Stephanaetus coronatus* [283] is a large bird 3 ft long and up to 6½ ft across the wings, with a short crest on its nape. It inhabits Africa south of the Sahara, feeding mainly on small antelopes and monkeys.

The **Monkey-eating Eagle**, *Pithecophaga jefferyi* [284], a fine forest eagle of the Philippines, has remarkably strong legs and an extremely deep and compressed bill. When it is excited, its short crest is held erect. The **Harpy Eagle**, *Harpia harpyja*, of tropical America has a similar crest [285, 286]. Measuring more than 39 in. in length, this bird has perhaps the strongest legs of all raptors. It builds its nest in high trees, generally near rivers. Monkeys are a favourite food of both these species.

288

The **Chilean Eagle,** *Geranoaetus melanoleucus* [287
288], is closely related to the buzzards and is placed
by some in the same genus (Buteo). It is common from
Colombia and western Venezuela to Patagonia. The
upper parts, head, neck and chest are slate-grey, the
underparts white and vermiculated in some of its
geographical races. It feeds on carrion but also hunts
live animals.

The **Booted Eagle,** *Hieraëtus pennatus* [289], is so called because of its feathered legs. Though fairly small as raptors go, measuring only about 20 in., it nevertheless belongs among the eagles. It occurs in two colour variations, both dark grey-brown above, the underparts in the lighter form yellow-white with dark longitudinal streaks, those of the dark form coloured dark grey-brown. It frequently appropriates the nests of other birds in broad-leaved or mixed forests. The clutch generally consists of two greenish white eggs [290]. The young hatch after about one month, remaining in the nest for a further nine weeks, the adults feeding them with small mammals and birds. The pictures [291, 292] show a fledged juvenile. This eagle inhabits parts of the western Mediterranean, Asia Minor and southern Russia, extending into central Asia.

293

The **White-tailed Eagle** or **Sea Eagle,** *Haliaeëtus albicilla* [293], like the others of this genus, has bare unfeathered legs. It is the largest of the European eagles, the female measuring up to 3 ft in length and over 8 ft across the wings. The plumage is brown, the head a somewhat lighter shade, the wedge-shaped tail white in adult birds. It breeds in eastern and northern Europe, also in Siberia. Clearly visible in flight is the bird's characteristic wedge-shaped tail. [295].

Bonelli's Eagle, *Hieraëtus fasciatus* [294], is smaller (28 in.) than the White-tailed Eagle. It is dark brown above, pale on the nape, with a fairly long, dark-barred tail. The whitish or yellowish underparts are streaked longitudinally. Its range includes southern Europe, Asia and Africa.

Steller's Sea Eagle, *Haliaeëtus pelagicus* [296, 297], closely related to the White-tailed Eagle, is distinguished by a high, yellow bill. It breeds on the narrow coastal area of the Bering and Okhotsk Seas and in Kamchatka in Siberia.

The **River Eagle** or **African Fish Eagle,** *Cuncuma vocifer* [298], found from Senegal to South Africa, is smaller than the White-tailed Eagle; it has a white head, neck, chest, forward part of back, and tail. It has a loud clear call on the wing.

The **Bald Eagle,** *Haliaeëtus leucocephalus* [299], has only the head, part of the neck and the tail white. It occurs in two forms throughout the whole of North America, generally near lakes and rivers; it is the national bird of the USA, where it is now becoming scarce through hunting, poisoning and disturbance of its nesting grounds.

The **Short-toed Eagle,** *Circaëtus gallicus* [300], belongs to the subfamily Circaetinae, often called serpent eagles because they are particularly fond of snakes. It has a fairly large head, white underparts and whitish or bluish unfeathered legs, measures about 26 in. and weighs 4½ lb. It breeds in Europe, North Africa and the warmer parts of Asia.

Closely resembling it is the **Crested Serpent Eagle,** *Spilornis cheela* [302], of India, Burma, south-east China, Indonesia and the Philippines. It has brown plumage, light spots on the wings and underparts and a broad light brown band across the tail.

Perhaps the best known of the African raptorial birds is the **Bateleur Eagle,** *Terathopius ecaudatus* [301], a champion at aerobatics. Its courtship display includes daring turns and somersaults in the air. The tail is extremely short and the wings long and pointed. The food consists of carrion and live animals up to the size of small antelopes. It occupies Africa south of the Sahara, ex-

299

300

cept for forested West Africa. The nest is built in high trees, the clutch consisting of only one egg. The head, neck, underparts and wings are black, the back red-brown.

The **Long-crested Hawk-Eagle,** *Lophoaëtus occipitalis* [303], plentiful in Africa south of the Sahara, is a smaller species of eagle measuring about 22 in. in length. It is brown with white-barred tail and long crest. It feeds on small vertebrates and insects.

304

305

The subfamily of Old World vultures (Aegypiinae) comprising 14 species, bear a strong superficial resemblance to the American vultures, but differ from them in a number of ways.

The **Eurasian Black Vulture,** *Aegypius monachus* [304, 305], has brown plumage, a bare blue-tinged flesh-coloured neck and a fairly small head above a ruff of fine brown feathers. It weighs 15–26 lb and measures up to 8 ft across the wings. In Europe it breeds only on the Iberian Peninsula, in the Balkans and in the Crimea. Farther east it nests in Asia Minor and the mountains of central Asia. The diet consists primarily of carrion but it also hunts live animals. The nest is usually built in trees, and contains one egg.

The allied **Griffon Vulture,** *Gyps fulvus* [306, 307], is a smaller bird of lighter colour, the head and neck covered with white down; the ruff is white in the adult birds while the young have a brown collar. It breeds in southern Europe, south and north Africa and south-west Asia.

306

307

The **White-headed Vulture,** *Trigonoceps occipitalis* [308], which lives in open country in central Africa, has the head, neck and breast covered with thick white down.

The **White-backed Vulture,** *Pseudogyps bengalensis* [309], of India and the Malay Peninsula, has black plumage and bill. The lower part of the adult's back is white, which distinguishes it from the other south Asian vultures. The White-backed Vulture lives unmolested in its native habitat and is not hunted by the natives. It is not surprising, therefore, that large colonies are to be seen on trees, often on human habitations, and on the outskirts of cities. Both are large birds with wing spans of 7–9 ft.

310

311

The **Pondicherry Vulture** or **Eurasian Kin**
Vulture, *Sarcogyps calvus* [310, 311], of India, Burm
and Siam, has a flesh-coloured head and neck, flesh
lappets on the sides of the naked head, and the cro
and thighs covered with white down, the remainin
plumage being black. It measures about 32 in.

The **Egyptian Vulture,** *Neophron percnopterus* [31
313], differs somewhat from the other vultures in th
shape of the bill, which is long and not as robus

It may still be seen frequently in southern Europe, Africa and south-west Asia all the way to west India and Turkestan. It measures only 23–26 in. and is predominantly white with black primaries. Only the naked face and throat are yellow. The feathers on the nape form a thick crest. It is easily recognized in flight by its long, pointed wings and the long, wedge-shaped tail. In India and Africa it is a common scavenger inhabiting the outskirts of towns.

314

Central, west and east Africa is also the home of the **Hooded Vulture**, *Necrosyrtes monachus* [314], only slightly smaller than the preceding species. The plumage is dark brown, the wings and tail black, the nape covered with brown-white down; the naked areas on the head and throat are a purplish red.

The **Palmnut Vulture**, *Gypohierax angolensis* [315, 316], of west and central Africa, measures 23 in., has

black and white plumage; the bare skin round the eye is grey-blue. It differs from its relatives in preferring the fruit of the oil palm to carrion. It also eats fish, crabs, snails and garbage.

The **Lammergeyer** or **Bearded Vulture,** *Gypaëtus barbatus* [317], was quite common in the mountains of Europe at one time, but is now very rarely seen. It inhabits the mountains of western and central Asia and north and east Africa. It is red-brown above, the wings and tail almost black, the underparts rusty yellow or white. The creamy yellow head has a black band across the eyes and a long black "beard" below the mandible. The bird measures 41–46 in. and has a wing span of over 8 ft. It is also a carrion feeder, carrying large bones and turtles in its talons high up in the air and shattering them by dropping them on rocks.

318

319

The subfamily Circinae, the harriers or marsh hawks, comprises 17 species of slender birds with long tails and long wings. They all possess facial disks resembling those of the owls. They show marked plumage differences between the sexes. The female of the **Pallid Harrier**, *Circus macrourus* [318], is brown above and yellowish below, the male being grey above with white head and underparts. It breeds in the steppes of eastern Europe and west Siberia.

A species with a fairly similar distribution, **Montagu's Harrier**, *Circus pygargus*, has similar plumage except that the male has black bars across the wing. The wing span measures approximately 3 ft. Harriers nest on the ground, the clutch being of 3–5 or more eggs [319]. The female of the **Pied Harrier**, *Circus melanoleucus*, which breeds in north-east Asia, is shown on the nest with her young [320]; the male has striking black and white plumage, which is particularly evident in flight [321]. This species is

320

widely distributed throughout south-east Siberia and northern China, wintering in east India and on the Philippines. The nest, a simple structure of dry grass blades and stems [322], is generally built in grass or among rushes. The male **Hen Harrier** or **Marsh Hawk,** *Circus cyaneus,* is also coloured grey and white; the female is dark brown above and rusty-grey with longitudinal streaks below [323]. This species ranges throughout the Northern Hemisphere, south to the Mediterranean, Iran, India and Indochina, in the Americas to northern South America.

324

The **Marsh Harrier,** *Circus aeruginosus* [324], un-like its relatives, is more frequently found in the neighbourhood of lakes, ponds and marshes, where it nests in reeds or other tall vegetation. It is about the same size as the Common Buzzard, measuring about 20 in., but more slender. The female is dar brown, the head and throat whitish; in the male th tail and a large part of the wings are silvery grey, th head and nape rusty yellow with dark longitudina streaks, the remaining plumage rusty [325]. I

325

326

range of distribution includes the whole of the Old World except for northern Europe, Asia and the deserts and forested regions of Africa.

As a rule the nest [327] is situated among reeds—a pile of dried water vegetation and twigs surrounded by water. The female lays 3–6 eggs. When hatched the young are covered with white down; the feather quills soon begin to show but they are not fully fledged for about eight weeks. At the approach of an intruder the young scatter to hide in the reeds [326].

Of subfamily Polyboroidinae, the **Harrier-hawk**, *Polyboroides typicus* [328], occurs in Africa south of the Sahara. It is 24–26 in. long, with grey plumage barred with black below. The cere, the naked areas around the eyes and the feet are yellow, the wing tips and tail black, the latter crossed by a white band.

327

328

181

329

The **Osprey** or **Fish-hawk,** *Pandion haliaëtus* [331, 332], is the only member of the family Pandionidae. Unlike those of the other raptors, the anterior and hind toes are the same length, the outer toe being reversible like that of an owl, which is of great advantage in grasping prey.

In flight the Osprey is easily recognized by its angled, somewhat pointed wings [329]. It seeks its prey by circling above the water and on sighting it hovers a moment before plunging down after it. The mainstay of its diet is fish, though it also eats other food. It breeds throughout most of the world in the vicinity of water. It is 20–23 in. long. The plumage is dark brown above and white below, and the longer feathers on the nape may be erected to form a crest.

The family Falconidae comprises 58 species, of which the true falcons are especially fast, strong fliers. The upper bill has one or more horny "teeth" which facilitate the tearing of flesh.

A group of fourteen South American species, collectively known as caracaras, differ somewhat from the other members of the family but have the same anatomical structure. One of these is the **Chimango Caracara,** *Milvago chimango* [330], which ranges from southern Brazil to Chile. It is 24 in. long, the plumage brown, the underparts with paler streaks, the rump white.

330

331

183

3

333

334

The caracaras show little affinity to the falcons in their way of procuring food, for they spend much time on the ground feeding on carrion. They are mostly confined to South America, but one, the **Crested Caracara**, *Caracara cheriway*, occurs from northern South America to Texas, the West Indies and Florida. It is virtually identical to the **Southern Caracara**, *Caracara plancus* [333, 335], and may in fact be only a race of this species according to some authorities.

The Southern Caracara feeds on carrion washed up on the shore, consorts with vultures as they feast on a carcass and harasses pelicans until they regurgitate the fish they have caught, which it then eats.

The **Peregrine Falcon**, *Falco peregrinus* [334, 336],

335

336

33

340

341

342

is a fast, strong bird. The adult has a striking moustachial streak and dark eye; it is slate-grey above, the underparts yellowish with transverse bands. The food consists chiefly of other birds. The Peregrine is widely distributed on all the continents—a true cosmopolitan—and is separated into several geographical races of which *Falco peregrinus leucogenys* [337], inhabiting the Asian tundras, is one of the most numerous. This falcon frequently nests directly on the ground in the tundra. Also illustrated are a young bird with remnants of its downy coat still visible preparing to leave the nest [338], and a young falcon of the same race after it has left the nest [339].

Belonging to the once highly prized group of hunting falcons is the **Saker Falcon,** *Falco cherrug* [341], measuring about 18 in., which breeds from Slovakia and the Hungarian plains eastwards beyond Lake Baikal through Asia Minor to India. Occurring in India north to Afghanistan and east to Burma is the related **Lagger,** *Falco jugger* [340], which nests, like

187

343

other falcons, in rocks or trees and hunts chiefly medium-sized birds.

Closely related to the Lagger is the **Prairie Falcon,** *Falco mexicanus* [343], of Mexico and the south-western United States. Its habits are the same as those of its Old World cousins. The smallest of this group is the **Lanner Falcon,** *Falco biarmicus* [344], which is about 16 in. long. The upper parts are slate-grey, the underparts creamy yellow, with longi-tudinal spots. The head is red-brown on top, the forehead white; there is a dark band over the eye and

a narrow, dark moustache. This species is found in Italy, Greece and north along the Adriatic coast, as well as in Arabia and much of Africa to South Africa. The largest of the hunting falcons is the **Gyrfalcon** *Falco rusticolus* [345], measuring more than 20 in. It is distributed in the arctic tundras beyond the forested regions of the Old and New Worlds, hunting its prey both in the air and on the ground.

The most highly valued bird in falconry was the white gyrfalcon, a light phase of this species [346]. Among the normally grey-coloured birds such white

specimens are to be found in varying numbers throughout the range of distribution. In northern Siberia, for example, white, dark-spotted falcons comprise about half the whole population of this group; in northern Greenland almost all adult gyrfalcons are white. In Mediaeval times hunting with falcons was a favourite sport. Adult birds were caught and trained for this purpose. A well trained falcon was worth his weight in gold and among the feudal lords and nobility the gift of a falcon was considered a mark of high favour. Before the hunt a hood was placed on the falcon's head, covering its eyes and thus preventing it from being distracted in any way. A well trained falcon often attacked prey that was larger than the bird itself. The hunting of herons with falcons was very popular; this ancient sport is still carried on in some countries today.

The **Hobby,** *Falco subbuteo* [342], is very like the Peregrine in colouration, but measures only a little over 12 in. It seizes the insects and birds which form its diet in flight. It breeds in the forests of Europe and Siberia, taking over old nests of other birds in

347

348

349

high trees [347]. It is a very agile and swift flier which is a thrill to watch as it pursues its prey. The **Merlin,** *Falco columbarius,* is the smallest of the European falcons. The adult male [348] is about 11 in. long, slate-grey above, with red-brown underparts and an almost white throat. The female [349], measuring 13 in., is brownish grey above, creamy below, and has a rusty yellow nape. It inhabits northern Europe, Asia and northern North America. In tundra and moorland it generally nests on the ground or on rocks. It occurs throughout North America on migration, wintering south to South America.

The **Eurasian Kestrel,** *Falco tinnunculus* [350], is still plentiful in the fields and woods of Europe and in the greater part of Asia and Africa. It measures about 14 in., and has long, sickle-shaped wings and a fairly long tail, which in the male is ashy grey with a broad black and a narrow white terminal band [351]. The male's crown, cheeks and rump are bluish grey and the greater wing-coverts are cinammon-brown spotted black; the cere and the naked eye-rim are yellow. The female has a brown head, and a brown

350

ail with dark bars. When hunting its prey—chiefly
ieldmice and voles—it characteristically hovers in
ne spot. The nest site is generally in trees, rocks or
igh buildings. Kestrels often occupy deserted nests
of crows, pigeons or other raptors [353]. The clutch
is of 4–6 eggs. The young are covered with white
down [354]. Picture 352 shows the female feeding
the young.

352

The 15-in. **Grey Kestrel,** *Falco ardosiaceus* [355], is slate-coloured with black shaft-stripes, the tail and inner web of the wing quills being grey-white. It occurs in the central part of Africa where it is a common inhabitant of the savannahs. Its choice of nesting sites is greatly varied; it sometimes nests in hollow trees and is even known to occupy the deserted domed habitations of hammerheads.

Distributed throughout almost the entire American continent, from the forests of Alaska and Newfoundland all the way to Tierra del Fuego, is the small (9½–11 in.) **American Kestrel** or **American Sparrowhawk,** *Falco sparverius* [356]. The plumage resembles that of the Kestrel. Both sexes have a reddish tail, darkly barred in the female and with a dark terminal band in the male.

357

Fowl-like Birds

The fowl-like birds (order Galliformes), which include the gamebirds, are mostly terrestrial and not
given to flight, which easily tires them, but elude
pursuers by running, hiding in thickets or huddling
close to the ground. They also nest on the ground.
The young leave the nest and are able to fend for
themselves immediately on hatching. Though size
varies considerably, they all have a fairly small head
with a short, stout, arched bill, abbreviated wings,

large strong feet and particularly conspicuous rump
and tail feathers. They are widely distributed
throughout the world.

The megapodes (family Megapodiidae) differ from
all other birds in their nesting habits. They lay their
eggs in large mounds built of vegetation, the eggs
being incubated by the heat (up to 35°C or 85°F)
which is generated by the rotting process. Some
species deposit their eggs in the hot sand on the

358

...ashore. Their range of dis-
...ribution includes Australia,
...Celebes, New Guinea, the
...Philippines and Indonesia. A
...typical characteristic of the
...megapodes are the long toes
...with strong claws.

...The **Brush Turkey,** *Alectura*
...thami [357, 359], is found in
...eastern Australia. The female
...chocolate-brown above,
...brown below barred with grey.
...The wattle on the front of the
...neck is yellow, the bill grey,
...the feet brown. The male
...builds a mound of earth and
...decayed leaves up to 5 ft high
...and 13 ft in diameter, in
...which the female lays the 5–8
...eggs successively, one at a
...time. The eggs hatch through
...the heat of fermentation,
...which is controlled by the
...male. The young are very
...precocious; they dig their way
...out of the mound and can fly
...almost immediately. The
...Maleo Fowl, *Megacephalon*
...maleo [358], of Celebes meas-
...ures about 22 in. It is blackish
...brown, with red breast and
...belly, bare black head and a
...black helmet. The eggs are
...usually deposited in the sand
...where they are incubated by
...the heat of the sun's rays.

...The **Crested Curassow,**
...rax alector [361], like all
...members of this genus, has a

360

...crest of recurved, erectile feathers. It has no knob
...on the bill, the base of which is covered with yel-
...low skin. The plumage is mainly black, with a white
...belly. The 2 or 3 eggs are laid in nests in trees and
...are incubated by the female. This bird occurs in
...South America north of the Amazon.

...The guans (genus Penelope) are smaller than the
...curassows and their colouration is duller–brown to
...olive-green with a bronze sheen. The face and neck
...usually have bright-coloured naked areas, sometimes
...also wattles. The **White-browed, Superciliated**
...or Spix's Guan, *Penelope superciliaris* [360], of
...Brazil measures 26–30 in., and is glossy dark olive-
...green with rusty brown wing-coverts and a brownish
...tail. It is a gregarious bird generally found in large
...flocks, except during the breeding season.

361

362

The small family Tetraonidae, comprising 18 species in all, is distributed in Europe, Asia and North America. These game-birds have the tarsus feathered, sometimes also the toes, and in those species where the toes lack feathers they at least have fringe-like processes on the sides which are shed in spring and grow in again in autumn. These greatly facilitate the birds' movement on snow and ice.

The **Ptarmigan** or **Rock Ptarmigan,** *Lagopus mutus*, inhabits the arctic tundra and some mountain ranges of the Old and New Worlds. The winter plum-

age is white with a black tail, with black lores in th male [362]. In spring it turns grey and brown, th breast, belly and wing quills remaining white [363 Similar seasonal variations are found in the **Willo Grouse** or **Willow Ptarmigan,** *Lagopus lagopu* which lacks the black lores in winter. The summe plumage is predominantly brown [366]. This also a circumpolar species. The **Red Grouse,** *Lagop lagopus scoticus* [365], of British moorland was onc considered to be a separate species from the Willo Grouse, and the only one peculiar to Britain an

363

Ireland. It has no white patches in its plumage although it changes colour somewhat between summer and winter. It is one of the most famous sporting birds in the world and attempts have been made to introduce it to other countries which have heather moors.

The largest of the European grouse is the **Capercaillie**, *Tetrao urogallus* [364], the male weighing 8½–13 lb and measuring more than 3 ft in length. The cock is black with a blue-green sheen, the hen, which weighs only 5½–6½ lb, brown with black and white markings. It occurs in the arctic taiga and the thick mountain forests of Europe. In Siberia it extends as far as the Lena River. It feeds chiefly on berries, shoots and buds of conifers, and on insects and their larvae. In spring the cock starts his remarkable courtship display high up in the treetops while it is still dark [367]. The female lays 8-12 eggs in a crude hollow in the ground [368]. The female alone incubates

364

366

365

197

367

368

and rears the young, which accompany her in search of food the first day after hatching. The Capercaillie has been re-introduced to the Scottish Highlands. The **Siberian Capercaillie,** *Tetrao parvirostris* [369], of the east Siberian taiga is larger than the Capercaillie and has much the same habits. The females of both species are practically identical.

Another typical inhabitant of the woods is the **Hazel Hen,** *Tetrastes bonasia* [370]. Smaller than the Partridge, it is brownish above with dark and light

369

370
371

spots. The male, like that of the Capercaillie, has red wattles above the eye. This species lives in Europe and northern Asia.

In the wild the Capercaillie sometimes interbreeds with the Black Grouse, the hybrids resembling the Capercaillie in size and appearance [371].

199

372

During the courting season from March to May and sometimes in autumn, numbers of **Black Grouse,** *Lyrurus tetrix* [372], meet before dawn in open woodlands, the hens keeping apart from the cocks as they perform their antics. The courtship display of the Capercaillie can be divided into four stages, that of the Black Grouse, whose calls carry further, into two. The latter's performance includes dancing, running about with drooping wings and outspread tail, jumping up into the air and fierce combat among the cocks [372–375].

The Black Grouse occurs on the upland meadows and moors of Europe and Siberia where, like the Capercaillie, it feeds mainly on vegetable matter. The nest is a simple hollow scraped in the ground. The hen lays 6–10 eggs and incubates alone for 2 days. The cock, measuring about 22 in. and weighing about 2 lb, is coloured black with a blue sheen, and has white under tail-coverts; the female, 4 in. shorter, is grey-brown with light and dark markings. The males of both species have red wattles above the eye during the breeding season.

374

The **Ruffed Grouse,** *Bonasa umbellus* [376], resembling the European Hazel Hen, is distinguished by the frills of feathers on the sides of its neck; it measures 19 in. Its range extends from the woods of Alaska and northern Canada south to the mountains of Georgia and California. During the courtship display the ruff and tail are spread wide, and the male makes a characteristic drumming sound.

The family Phasianidae comprises about 170 species of quails, partridges, pheasants, peafowl and jungle fowl. The group is a very mixed one, showing marked variation in size and plumage; e.g., the splendour of the peacock and the dull, drab colouration of the partridge, and it is difficult to find a common denominator. One such attempt at classification has been to divide the birds into polygamous and monogamous, the brightly coloured species belonging to the first group, the duller, drab ones to the second. As always, however, there are exceptions to the rule: some quails, even though their plumage is dull, leave the hen immediately after copulation.

Typical of the New World quails is the **California Quail,** *Lophortyx californicu* [377], which inhabits the Pacific coast of North America in woodlands close to water. It nests and forages on the ground but roosts in trees. Ranging throughout the eastern and central United States to south Mexico is the **Bobwhite,** *Colinus virginianu* [378]. This is an extremely variable species. The male bird illustrated is typical of most populations north of the Rio Grande; it has a white throat, a white stripe above the eye and a black band across it. The crown is rusty brown, the forehead black.

The **Common** or **Migratory Quail,** *Coturnix coturnix* [379, 381], is rarely seen, its presence being more frequently heralded by its characteristic call "wet-my-lips". It inhabits north and southern Africa, Europe and a large part of Asia. Northern populations migrate to Africa and southern Asia, many of them

erishing on the way either in he sea or at the hands of portsmen in some countries vhere they are netted and hot in vast numbers.

'he small, colourful male **3lue-breasted Quail,** *Ex- alphatoria chinensis* [380], was ften kept as a cage-bird. 3rown above, reddish below ith black and white markings n the chin and throat (the emale is duller), it is found n grasslands from south-east Asia to northern Australia.

81

382

An interesting inhabitant of the dense forests of the Malay Peninsula, Siam, Borneo, Sumatra, and Java is the shy, quick-moving **Roulroul** or **Crested Green Wood Partridge**, *Rollulus roulroul* [382, 383], a robust, "round" bird measuring about 11 in. The male has an erect, maroon-coloured "hairy" crest on the head, the upper parts are blue-green, the under-parts black, the head and neck blue-black. The naked eye-rims, feet and the base of the bill are scarle The female is green without the crest and spurs of th male.

These birds occur in pairs or family groups, con stantly rummaging about in fallen leaves for seeds berries and insects. The 8–10 whitish eggs are in cubated only by the female, but both parents care fo the young.

383

38

It seems that the **Common** or **Grey Partridge,** *Perdix perdix* [386, colour plate X], is destined to meet the same end as the quail. Although it is not a migrant and therefore not exposed to as many dangers as the quail, its numbers in Europe are decreasing from year to year. The main reason is undoubtedly the increasing areas of cultivated land and the use of insecticides. At one time a favourite game-bird, it is now protected the year round in some countries. The male is distinguished from his mate by more striking markings on head and breast [384]. The chief foods are the seeds of weeds and insects. Picture 385 shows a nest with eggs and freshly hatched nestlings. This species has been introduced to North America and is well established in parts of southern Canada and the northern United States.

Whereas the Common Quail and Common Partridge are inhabitants of lowlands, the **Rock Partridge,** *Alectoris graeca* [387, 388], prefers the rocky shrub-grown slopes of high mountains up to the snow line. In Europe it breeds in Italy, rarely in the Alps, in the Balkans and in the mountains of Asia all the way to Mongolia. The female sometimes lays two clutches, incubating one herself and leaving the other to the male. The nest, which is generally very well concealed, contains 9—15 brownish yellow eggs. The male is monogamous and both sexes look alike, with bright red bill and feet.

Also found in rugged country are birds of the genus Tetraogallus, inhabitants of the central Asian mountains from the Caucasus to Altai. Along with some species of pheasant they occur above the tree line, descending to lower altitudes only in winter. The **Tibetan Snow Pheasant,** *Tetraogallus tibetanus* [389, 390], somewhat larger than the Black Grouse,

387

388

389

is grey and brown with pale and dark markings on the throat.

One of the most gorgeous of birds is the cock **Impeyan Pheasant,** *Lophophorus impejanus* [391]. The plumage is black with a lovely gold, blue and green metallic tinge, the tail reddish. Its beauty is further enhanced by the crest of long feathers, spreading at the tip. The hen, measuring 25 in., is grey-brown with a pale brown patch on the throat. These birds inhabit the high mountain forests of the Himalayas and neighbouring ranges.

390

391

392
393

In all five species of tragopans,
which live in the Himalayas
and mountains father east, the
upper parts are dotted with
small, oval, black-marginal
spots. These birds nest in
higher sites, often also in trees.
When courting, the cock inflates the large, brightly
coloured wattle on his throat
and erects the two long fleshy
horns above the eyes; neither
of these adornments is visible
at other times. The **Horned
Tragopan** or **Horned
Pheasant,** *Tragopan satyra*
[392], has a blue face and
throat and a short black crest.
Blyth's Tragopan, *Tragopan blythi* [393], is rarely seen
in zoos. Related to the preceding species, it differs in
having the throat and the
naked sides of the head

coloured orange, the back and wings being pale grey with large red spots. The area around the eye is surrounded by white, black-dotted spots. It occurs in two geographical races in the high mountains of Assam and south-east Tibet.

In the eared or snow pheasants (genus Crossoptilon), the whole tail is compressed, and the ornamental plumes have divided vanes; elongated white feathers behind the true ear form the "ears". The **White-eared Pheasant,** *Crossoptilon crossoptilon* [394], of east Tibet is grey and white with a black crown. The **Grey-eared Pheasant,** *Crossoptilon auritun* [395, 396], is plentiful in Kansu; its ornamental tail plumes at one time adorned the heads of high-ranking Chinese mandarins. The dark brown plumage of the **Brown-eared Pheasant,** *Crossoptilon mantschuricum* [398, colour plate XI], is almost black on the neck, the tail being coloured white. It is a native of the mountainous regions of northern China. In all species of eared pheasants the sexes look alike.

397

398

In the firebacks (genus Lophura), the males have sickleshaped feathers in the vaulted tail, and round the eye naked wattles which are distended during the courtship display, covering the sides of the head and projecting above it. The **Crested** or **Malaysian Fireback,** Lophura ignita [397] has several races which are widespread in the jungles of the Malay peninsula, Sumatra and Borneo. The head of the cock is crowned with an erect crest of feathers widened at the tips. It is predominantly purplish-blue and brown, the lower back coppery. They are shy birds, moving about in small groups and keeping to the thick forest undergrowth which they rarely leave.

From Nepal to the Hindu Kush, living high in the mountains along with other species of pheasants, is the **Himalayan Fireback** or **Kalij Pheasant,** Lophura leucomelana [399]. It occurs in two races differing chiefly in the colour of the male's crest. It is found either in thickets or in trees. A truly beautiful and elegant bird is the **Siamese Fireback** or **Fireback Pheasant,** Lophura diardi [400], of Siam and Indochina. The cock is black and grey with a bluish gloss, a tall, bare-shafted crest and a steel-blue belly; the naked sides of the head and the legs are red, the lower back golden-yellow. The hen is mostly greybrown. It lives hidden in the dense jungle and is monogamous, at least according to observations in captivity.

399

400

221

The **Silver Pheasant,** *Lophura nycthemera* [401
was embroidered on the robes of the Chinese mar
darins as long as 500 years ago, and is also bred i
Europe as an ornamental bird to this day. It is blac
and white with red naked face and feet [402]. In i
native home, the mountains of south-east Asia fro
the Himalayas to southern China, there are sever
geographical races showing marked variation i
colour. **Swinhoe's Pheasant,** *Lophura swinho*
[403], of Formosa is distinguished by a white cres
back and central tail feathers.

Compared with these pheasants, the four species
jungle fowl (genus Gallus) are neither particular

402

403

404

beautiful nor remarkable in size. They are distinguished from the other gallinaceous birds by their bright-coloured, fleshy combs and wattles, which are especially marked in the cocks. The tail is vaulted, with long, sickle-shaped central feathers. All are typical inhabitants of forest outskirts, and live in pairs or family groups. The hens, duller than the cocks, lay 5–10 brownish eggs in simple nests and care for the young themselves.

As explained below, the most important bird to man is the **Red Jungle Fowl**, *Gallus gallus* [404], of India and Malaya. The cock of this species has a serrate red comb, red wattles and white ear lappets. The long, pointed neck hackles and those of the rump are orange-red. The crow of the cock resembles that of domestic fowl, as does the cluck of the hen, the only difference being that the latter is heard only when it is some distance from the nest, to avoid making its position known to possible enemies; the farmyard hen clucks while still on the nest. The cock of the related **Ceylon Jungle Fowl**, *Gallus lafayetti* [405], differs from the Red Jungle cock by the pale patch on the yellow-red comb, and the red-brown breast. The hens of both species are very similar. [406].

405
406

213

The Red Jungle Fowl was first domesticated around 3000 B.C. in its native India, whence it spread to other countries. By 700 B.C. it was already known in the Mediterranean region, and today it can be seen around human habitations in the most remote parts of the world. The raising and cross-breeding of birds over the years has resulted in a large number of races and forms [407, 408], some of which show a great resemblance to their jungle ancestor while others have practically no characteristics in common with the wild stock.

Some gallinaceous birds are very gregarious, living in groups which are governed by certain rules and in which each bird has a definite place on the "social ladder" acknowledged by itself and the others. A good example is provided by the domestic fowl. Chicks 15–21 days old already look down upon the younger ones, demonstrating their supremacy by pecking and chasing them away. As the birds grow and mature they begin to test their strength, not only the young cocks and hens among themselves but one sex against the other as well. It is not unusual for a spirited young hen to win a higher place on the social ladder than a young, but less fit cock. The results of

410

411

the skirmishes, which may take the form of mere play or real combats, determine the place of each individual in the community. The pecking is generally directed at the comb and wattles and frequent combats may be interrupted by a lengthier "truce". Unlike the hens, who are not so eager for battle and are satisfied with just chasing others away from their food or pushing them aside on the roost, cocks are more quarrelsome and possess a greater fighting spirit. A strong cock is a real tyrant who will not tolerate any other cock near him. If a weaker cock enters his domain the first sign of the ruler's displeasure is usually enough to send the former on his way. If, however, the two are of about equal strength they engage in combat. With neck hackles erect and wings drooping they crouch facing each other, then suddenly leap at one another striking first with the feet and then with the beak, always aiming at the opponent's face. A strong, experienced and victorious cock stands at the very top of the social order, lording it over the hens as if it were a matter of course. A special note and movements are used to call the hens' attention to food, which creates the impression of great chivalry on his part, evident throughout the whole of the breeding season – that is, practically the whole year. He does not make use of his pecking rights. However, during the moult and influenced by the endocrine glands, all signs of chivalrous behaviour disappear for a time when the cock begins to "show who's boss", chasing all the members of the flock, including the hens, away from the food. This lasts until he has regained his manliness when he once again becomes his old, gracious self. The social order, also known as peck order among hens, is disrupted only by exceptional circumstances, e.g. by a lengthy absence on the part of one of the members of the flock.

412

413

414

Best known of the breeds raised for egg production are the **White Leghorns** [409] and the **Italian** [410] which yield about 200 eggs per hen annually. Also good egg layers are the **Minorcas** [413], bred in both the black and white forms. Some breeds, such as the Wyandotte – the **Silver** and **Blue Wyandottes** are shown [411, 412] – are also raised for their meat. White Leghorns, Italians and Minorcas are all of Jungle Fowl stock, which also includes the handsome **Hamburghs** [414, 415], reared for their delicate and

416

417

tasty meat as well as for their eggs (up to 160 a year). The large Cochin China was first introduced into Europe from Shanghai in 1842. The hens were as much as 26 in. high and weighed 13–14 lb. The **White Cochin** [416] has white plumage with a silvery sheen, and yellow bill and feet. The closely related **Brahma** [417], the pale form of which is generally the most common, is even larger than the Cochin – some specimens weighing as much as 16 lb. **Plymouth Rocks** are of American origin and are raised for their meat as well as eggs.

418

419

420

The cock has a simple, shallowly serrate comb and long wattles [418, 419]. The **Poland** [420] is distinguished by a large white crest on the domed head which sometimes hampers the bird's vision. Polands are mainly an ornamental breed, though they also have good egg yields. Signs of the future crest are already evident in the chicks in the form of small, smooth pads on the nape [421]. From the age of six weeks it has to be trimmed so as not to fall over the eyes. In adult birds the crest is simply bound with a narrow band.

421

422

The **Naked-necks** [422], with their bare head and neck sporting only a few feathers on the crown and nape, certainly cannot be called attractive. The origin of this breed still remains a mystery. Probably the bare neck appeared in several individuals as a chance mutation which, developed by man, became a permanent and hereditary trait. These birds occur in several colour variations and are good food producers.

Of the many existing bantams, shown here is the **Golden Sebright** [423] named after its English breeder Sir John Sebright and developed as an ornamental domestic bird. Also belonging to this group is the **Japanese** [424], of Japan, which is a favourite

423

218

rnamental bird. It is raised
a the most varied colour
orms. The smallest bantams
measure about 8 in. but the
ens nevertheless lay com-
aratively large eggs, about
per cent of their body weight,
whereas those of the heavy
Brahmas equal only 2·5 per
ent of the hen's weight, this
disproportion being a fairly
ommon phenomenon among
irds. The **Silky** [425, 426] is
distinguished by its down-
eathers, which have soft,
lender shafts. This breed
originated in eastern Asia and
he common form is white.
The females, which are good
itting hens, are often used to
ncubate pheasants, ornamen-
al ducks or other delicate
poultry.

424

425

426

219

The **Cheer Pheasant,** *Catreus wallichi* [427], shows very little difference between the sexes, both of which have rather drab brown, reddish and grey protective colouring. The cock's crest is longer than that of the hen. The male is monogamous and shares the duties of incubation and caring for the young. This pheasant is found at altitudes of 4,000–10,000 feet from the north-western Himalayas to Nepal.

In long-tailed pheasants the crest and ears are absent, but the cocks have fairly long, flat, barred tails. These handsome birds live in south and south-east Asia. When courting they inflate the neck and spread the neck feathers, the wings quivering and the long tail swaying from side to side. Eastern China south of the Yangtze is the home of **Elliot's Pheasant,** *Syrmaticus ellioti* [428], which is coloured brown and white.

427

428

One of the largest species of pheasant is the magnificent **Reeves Pheasant,** *Syrmaticus reevesi* [429, colour plate XII], found in the wooded hills and mountains of central and northern China. The cock is sometimes more than 6½ ft long, its grey-white dark-barred tail measuring almost 5 ft. The plumage is yellow-brown, the feathers margined with black, and with black and white markings on the head. The hen is reddish brown with dark markings [430]. In the wild these birds occur in small groups which are disbanded during the courting season, the pheasants then living in pairs, or one cock with several hens. This pheasant has been successfully introduced as a game-bird in several parts of Europe.

The **Ring-necked Pheasant,** *Phasianus colchic* is a well-known game-bird in Europe, though original home is temperate Asia from the Caucas eastwards to the Ussuri region of Siberia, Mongo and China, where it occurs in 31 geographical rac varying markedly in colouration at times. Even ancient times a bird lacking this neck ring, *Phasiar colchicus colchicus,* was brought to Greece from River Phasis in Colchis whence, through ma intervention, it spread to many parts of Europ However, the introduction of ring-necked rac chiefly *Phasianus colchicus torquatus* [431], of Chi led to the dilution of the original stock, most of t existing European birds being hybrids, a mixture many wild populations. There are now a number

433

434

colour mutations among pheasants, e.g. the dark-coloured *tenebrosus* mutant [433, 434]. The pheasant courting season begins as soon as the snow thaws. The cock utters his harsh note "korrk-kok", jumps into the air and flutters his wings. Incubation and care of the young is undertaken solely by the hen [432]. Native to Japan is the closely related **Green Pheasant,** *Phasianus versicolor* [435, 436], the cock distinguished by the blue-black and green on breast and mantle. Ring-necked pheasants prefer park-like country near water, with tall grass, shrubs and occasional trees on which to roost.

435

436

437

438

Whereas Phasianus has a flat tail, in the genus Chrysolophus it is vaulted and longer. These birds are breathtakingly beautiful and are often reared in captivity. The males have a fine erectile cape of nape-plumes. The **Golden Pheasant,** *Chrysolophus pictus* [437], has a yellow head, lower back and rump, a golden-yellow collar with blue-black edge, and red underparts. The female is a dull grey-brown with dark bars [438]. This bird lives in thin mountain forests in the interior of China, avoiding denser woods. It has been introduced to parts of Britain. The **Lady Amherst Pheasant,** *Chrysolophus amherstiae* [439], has a range which meets the western boundary of that of the last species. The mantle

underparts and tail are white with black bars and margins, the crown black with a red crest, the lower back yellow, the upper back and wings black. The magnificent beauty of the mantle is particularly marked during the courtship display, when the cock circles round the hen trying to impress her with his colours and feather ornaments.

The **Common Peafowl,** *Pavo cristatus* [440, colour plate XIII], has the most striking ornamental feathers of all gallinaceous birds. They are brought into play chiefly during the courtship performance. The peacock has a handsome green, blue and purple head adorned with a small crown of bare-shafted feathers; the back is green and blue, the underparts black, the wings black and white, the tail and flight feathers brown. The feathers of the elongated train are a

resplendent green dotted with bronze, blue and green eye-spots. These are not in fact tail feathers but greatly elongated upper tail-coverts. In the company of the peahens on the courting ground, the peacock spreads his magnificent train [441] and whirrs the feathers. He always turns so that he faces the hens with the upper, ornamental side, though the view from the back is also magnificent. The drooping wings reveal the reddish brown colour of the quill feathers, and only now is it possible to see the true tail feathers, which are also erect [442]. The Peafowl is a native of India; it is kept as an ornamental bird not only in Asia but also in Europe and America. In Europe it has become the symbol not of beauty but of pride, perhaps because it does not mix well with other domestic animals. A white form of the Com-

non Peafowl frequently occurs among birds bred in captivity [443, 444].

The **Green Peafowl,** *Pavo
muticus* [445], of the forests
of Burma and Indochina and
as far as Java, looks very like
the previous species. It differs,
however, in that the crest
feathers are fully webbed and
the colour is a more metallic
green.

Both these species inhabit
forests with an undergrowth
of shrubs, and generally live
in small groups.

446

In the jungles of the Malay Peninsula, Sumatra and Borneo lives another avian gem, the **Great Argus Pheasant**, *Argusianus argus* [446]; though without the metallic sheen of the other pheasants it is nevertheless a magnificent bird. The general colouring is grey and brown, but the secondaries are enormously long, the broad webs covered with eyespots. The beauty of the cock's plumage is most evident during courting when, in an open spot in the dense jungle growth, he dances before the hen, his long central tail feathers [447] spread into a fan. The cock may measure up to 6½ ft in length, of which these tail feathers are a large part. It is interesting that the hen lays only two eggs, which is unusual among gallinaceous birds, and that it has no oil gland.

448

449

Similar grey plumage is found in the **Malaysian Peacock Pheasant,** *Polyplectron bicalcaratum* [448], whose long tail feathers, wings and shoulders are covered with large green, white-ringed eye-spots. The female is smaller and also has less marked eye-spots. It inhabits the Malay Peninsula and Sumatra, where it occurs in several different racial populations. When courting, this bird also raises and expands its tail and spreads its wings. The handsomest bird of this genus is **Napoleon's Peacock Pheasant,** *Polyplectron emphanum* [449], from the island of Palawan in the

Philippines. It is smaller than the preceding species, predominantly black and green, and possesses a crest. It has no eye-spots.

Their very shape is evidence that guinea-fowls do not belong among pheasants but to a separate family (Numididae), which comprises seven species of birds of the scrub, steppe or woods south of the Sahara and in Madagascar. They are sleekly rounded birds whose short tail, pointing almost vertically downwards, is completely hidden beneath the tail-coverts in most species. The head and part of the neck are bare. The legs are strong, and guinea-fowls are great runners which can cover 20 miles in a day. They are gregarious and flocks numbering several dozen birds are not unusual. Characteristic of this family is the spangled plumage. Best-known is the **Common** or **Tufted Guineafowl,** *Numida meleagris* [450, 451], with its horny helmet and gape-wattles, a typical inhabitant of the African steppes and savannahs.

This guinea-fowl was domesticated by the ancient Egyptians and Carthaginians. Breeding led to the creation of several colour variants, for example the white strain shown in picture 452.

450

451

452

453

Turkeys (family Meleagrididae) are birds which inhabit the woodlands and scrub of North and Central America; they have no connection with the European country whose name they have been given for some mistaken reason. The **Common** or **Wild Turkey,** *Meleagris gallopavo* [454], which occurs in the wild from Colorado and New York south to northern Mexico, was domesticated by the Indians of eastern Mexico and brought to Europe in the 16th century by the Spanish conquistadors. It became so widespread that today it is bred almost world-wide in

454

number of colour variants,
e.g. white [453]. Turkeys
may weigh as much as 40 lb.
The head and upper neck in
both sexes are bare and warty,
and the male has a fleshy process on the head and a bunch
of long black bristles on the
chest. When courting he struts
with outspread tail and drooping wings, ruffling his feathers
and making gobbling noises
[455]. Wild turkeys are more
slender and have longer legs
than domesticated birds.
When danger threatens they
are more prone to running
than to flight, unlike the related **Ocellated Turkey,**
Agriocharis ocellata [456], of
Yucatan, British Honduras
and Guatemala. This species
has a blue head with yellow-
ed warts; the rest of the
plumage is brilliant metallic
copper and green, with large
buff, blue and violet spots.

457

The **Hoatzin**, *Opisthocomus hoazin* [457], has so many unique features that it is classified in a separate family—Opisthocomidae. Its general appearance is not particularly striking. It measures about 2 ft; the body is long and thin, and it has a long, broad tail and a long loose crest of narrow feathers. The strong bill seems especially large compared with the rather small head. The bird is dark brown above, some of the feathers edged with pale yellow, the underparts a pale reddish colour. It ranges throughout the north-eastern part of South America, where it haunts the dense woods by water courses. The voice is a harsh screech. The diet consists mainly of the rubbery leaves of certain trees as well as the fruit and buds. The food is not digested in the stomach but in the large, muscular two-part crop which is so enormous that it has displaced the breast-bone. Though the wings are in no way atrophied, the Hoatzin is a poor flier. It never rests on the ground. Pairs of these birds generally nest in small groups on the branches of trees or bushes close above the water. The 2 or creamy white eggs are darkly spotted. The chicks are covered with a reddish brown down, remaining in the nest and being fed by the parents for some time when disturbed, however, they rapidly abandon it moving not only with the aid of their feet but also using the two claws at the tip of each wing to hook over branches. As they grow older, these claws disappear and no trace of them remains in adult birds. The chicks are also adept at swimming, using feet and wings, should they accidentally fall from a branch into the water.

458

Cranes, Rails and allies

The order Gruiformes comprises eleven very differ-ent families. They are aquatic birds, with some ex-eptions. The three front toes – not all species have he hind toe – are not webbed except in the coots and finfoots, where each individual toe has a membranous flap. The two sexes look much alike. The young are nidifugous, that is, they leave the nest on hatching. Though there is a superficial resemblance between the cranes and the storks and herons, they possess

459

several different traits and anatomical features which do not allow them to be classified in the same order. Storks build their nests aloft whereas cranes build theirs on the ground. The clutch consists of two spotted eggs and the young are nidifugous whereas storks lay 3–6 all-white eggs and the young are nidicolous, that is, they are reared in the nest to the fledgling stage. Storks are mute; cranes have resonant cry.

The cranes (family Gruidae–which gave the order its name) are long-legged, long-necked birds with a fairly long, compressed bill and a far-carrying trumpet-like call, produced by the coiled trachea or windpipe, sometimes also by the cavities of the breastbone. The feet have strong front toes, the hind toe being short and elevated. The preen gland is well developed, the powder-downs are absent. The birds feed chiefly on plants but also on small animals. An unusual feature is the joint calling of pairs of birds and their courtship dance during which the male and female approach one another, bow, leap high in the air and beat their wings. Cranes are gregarious and when migrating large flocks can be seen flying in V-formation. During the breeding season, however, each pair has its own nesting territory, chiefly in swamp or shallow water. The clutch generally comprises two, sometimes one or three large brown, grey-spotted eggs. Both sexes incubate them for 4 to 5 weeks. The brownish plumage of the juvenile is gradually replaced during the first year by the handsome adult plumage.

The **Common Crane,** *Grus grus* [458, 459], stands about 4 ft high and weighs approximately 13 lb. The bird is grey with a red crown and a black and white pattern on the head and neck. It ranges from northern Europe all the way to Siberia, wintering in North Africa and southern Asia, and occurring as a vagrant in the British Isles.

The white nape, hind neck and throat of the **White-naped Crane,** *Grus vipio* [460], contrast sharply with the bird's slate-grey plumage. The whitish secondaries are long and pointed, the wing quills are black. Somewhat smaller than the Common Crane, it nests in east Asia as far as Ussuri in Siberia, wintering in China and Korea.

460

461

The **Sarus Crane,** *Grus anti-gone* [461, 462], stands about 5 ft high and the adult weighs about 17 lb. It is light grey, with a red head and grey fore-head. The strong bill is used for digging in the ground. This species ranges from India to southern China and as far as the Philippines.

462

463

464

The **Demoiselle Crane,** *Anthropoides virgo* [463, 464], is found from the River Dnieper to eastern Asia and north-west Africa. The secondaries are elongated, forming a train. The plumage is grey, the head and neck black. Behind the eye are white ear-tufts, with feathers extending backward and to the sides. One of the smallest cranes, it stands about 3 ft high.

465

466

The **Paradise** or **Stanley Crane,** *Anthropoides paradisea* [465], is another African species, closely related to the Demoiselle and only slightly larger. In this species the ornamental plumes reach to the ground.

The **Crowned Crane,** *Balearica pavonina* [colour plate XIV], of Africa south of the Sahara, is a majestic bird with a yellow topknot on the crown, black plumage, white and yellow wing-coverts and a black forehead. There is a red throat-wattle and bare, white or red-white cheeks. The bill is fairly short.

The only member of the family Aramidae is the curious, grey-brown **Limpkin,** *Aramus guarauna* [466], 25 in. long, found, in five geographical races, from the swamps of the southern USA and the West Indies to Argentina. Anatomically like a crane, its appearance, habits and digestive system resemble those of a rail. It is resident in swamps or damp forests, where it perches in the trees though normally a ground-dweller. Its main food is molluscs: with its long, slightly curved bill it can extract the body from a snail shell. The bulky nest usually contains six eggs; both parents incubate and look after the dark brown young.

xiv **Crowned Crane** *Balearica pavonina*

xv **Little Ringed Plover** *Charadrius dubius*

The largest family of the Gruiformes is the rails, Rallidae, soberly coloured small to medium-sized birds. The flexible spinal column, short tail, broad wings, narrow, compressed, softly feathered bodies and springy step enable them to move with ease through dense vegetation. Even though they are not poor fliers—many migrate long distances over oceans —they usually run when danger threatens. The strong, stout legs have long front toes and a fairly short hind ne. The male is somewhat larger than the female but otherwise there is practically no external difference between the sexes.

The **Water Rail,** *Rallus aquaticus* [467, 468], is an habitant of marshes in temperate Europe and Asia. s note is sharp and strident, sometimes a squeal

469

resembling that of a piglet. The bird measures about
11 in. in length and is coloured dark brown and
blue-grey, the flanks barred with white. It feeds
mainly on vegetable matter and small animals [469]
Members of the genus Porzana have a shorter beak
The **Spotted Crake,** *Porzana porzana* [470], meas

470

ures about 10 in. and is coloured olive-brown and grey, spotted a lighter shade. It ranges from Europe to Mongolia.

The related **Little Crake,** *Porzana parva* [471], with brown and blue-grey plumage, is less densely flecked. It measures only 7½ in. The female is lighter in colour, with more brown. Both sexes are distinguished by green legs and a green and red bill. The nest is generally concealed among water vegetation near water and contains 4–8 yellow-brown, speckled eggs [472]. It breeds from central and southern Europe to Persia.

243

473

The **Moorhen** or **Common Gallinule,** *Gallinula chloropus* [473], is an attractively coloured bird brownish black above with slate-grey head and underparts, and white on flanks and under tail-coverts. The frontal plate and bill are red, the latter tipped with yellow, the legs green. It is widely distributed throughout the whole world except Australia. When running and swimming it continually flips its tail.

Inhabiting the warm regions of the Old World, from southern Europe and Africa to east Asia, is the large purplish blue **Purple Swamphen,** *Porphyrio porphyrio*, which occurs also in about 20 racial populations, one in Madagascar, others in southern Asia, the Malay islands, Australia, New Zealand and the Philippines. Illustrated here is *Porphyrio porphyrio poliocephalus* [474], one of several east Asian sub-

species which differ from the all-purple western birds in having grey heads.

Representative of the South American species of rail is the **Ypecaha Wood Rail,** *Aramides ypecaha* [475], a handsome bird measuring about 18 in. It is olive-green above with grey head and breast and white throat. The familiar **Eurasian Coot,** *Fulica atra* [476], 15 in. long and weighing only about 1¼ lb, is coloured an intense black, with a white bill and frontal plate or shield, and cannot be mistaken for any other bird. The toes have broad lobes of skin which allow easy movement on water. When flushed it runs a considerable distance on the water's surface before taking to the air. It forages for its food chiefly by diving, the diet consisting mainly of vegetable matter, though it may also feed on aquatic animal life. The nest is a comparatively sturdy structure built in or close to aquatic vegetation and containing 7–15 greyish yellow, dark-spotted eggs. The Coot ranges throughout Europe, North Africa, Asia and Australia. The **American Coot,** *Fulica americana*, has the same white bill and frontal plate, but is

grey with only the neck black. It has similar habits to the Eurasian Coot and occurs from Canada to southern South America.

The **Kagu,** *Rhynochetos jubatus* [477, 478], is a unique bird on whose classification ornithologists are not in complete agreement but which is grouped with the cranes and rails. It is the only species of the family Rhynochetidae. The quill feathers are very fine so that the bird is barely able to fly; the whole body of the adults is covered with patches of down. The Kagu has an oil gland and short blind branches off the intestines. The nostrils are overhung by a rolled-up membrane which apparently serves to protect them when foraging for food in soft humus. The plumage is slate-grey with a pronounced erectile, 5-in.-long crest which is used in the courtship display; this display also includes half-opening the wings. It measures 22 in. and weighs about 1 lb. Though there is not much meat on the bird it was at one time hunted with dogs in its native island of New Caledonia, north-east of Australia, and sold in the market. Today the Kagu is limited to the inaccessible forest highlands where, though protected, its existence is threatened by the spread of wild dogs.

479

The seriemas (family Cariamidae) consists of two species ranging from central Brazil to Paraguay and northern Argentina, and are the only descendants of a long-extinct group of large birds dating from the Early Tertiary Period. The **Crested Seriema,** *Cariama cristata* [479], stands 3 ft high and is a good runner. The plumage is pale yellow-brown with fine horizontal stripes visible only at close range, the throat and breast with marked longitudinal stripes. Seriemas inhabit grassland pampas where, either singly or in groups, they forage for grasshoppers and other insects, lizards and snakes, and nest and roost in low trees. The clutch consists of two pinkish, brown-spotted eggs.

480

Among the bustards (family Otididae) are found birds the size of a hen as well as huge species, among the heaviest of all flying birds. Bustards are also excellent runners, their home being the grassy plains and brushlands of the Old World, chiefly Africa. The strong legs have only three toes, the hind toe being absent. When asleep, a bustard does not tuck its head under its wings but lays it back between its shoulders. The diet consists of seeds, leaves and shoots, also worms and snails. The male is a good deal larger than the female, and differs also in colouration. Particularly impressive is the bird's courtship performance. For example, the **Great Bustard,** *Otis tarda,* inflates the throat pouch, which is found

481

482
483

only in adult males, erects the bristly feathers at the base of the bill, tips the head back, extends the wings and turns them inside out, thus encasing the body in a magnificent black white and golden wreath of feathers, and finally it spreads the tail to form a fan, white side out, so that the bird looks like a moving white ball [480]. The female [482] alone looks after the young. The two brown eggs are laid in a simple hollow [481], incubation lasting from 20 to 28 days.

Another of the many species of bustards is the **White-bellied Bustard,** *Eupodotis senegalensis* [483], found frequently in the northern borders of tropical forests as far as the Nile, Kordofan, and Abyssinia. The feathers on the back and wings are a rusty red in both sexes; this colour extends to the neck of the female, whereas the male's neck is blue.

Waders, Gulls and Auks

The order Charadriiformes comprises about 300 species of birds divided into 15 families which are very diverse superficially but which possess a number of common anatomical characteristics. These include the structure of the voice box, the manner of attachment of the tendons in the legs, the structure of the palate bones, the arrangement of the flight feathers, and the long tuft of feathers on the oil gland. The order may be roughly divided into three groups or suborders, the largest including 12 families of waders, the second consisting of the gulls, terns and skuas (jaegers), and the third of the auks—birds highly adapted to life in the water.

The waders (Charadrii) are small to medium-sized birds with fairly long legs and narrow bills. The leg is adapted to wading—the tibia is bare, the hind toe short, if not completely absent, and somewhat higher than the front toes. The wings are long and pointed and the birds are tireless and swift in flight. They are usually found near water, though some species inhabit dry plains and semi-deserts. There is no difference in appearance between the sexes as a

488

ule, and they often form large flocks after breeding. The clutch consists typically of four pear-shaped eggs arranged point to point in a shallow nest. Both adults usually share the parental duties, and the young abandon the nest shortly after hatching.

The seven species of jacana, family Jacanidae, look much more like moorhens than waders with their long toes and claws and their frontal shields. They also have spurs on their wings. The **African Jacana or Lily-trotter**, *Actophilornis africanus* [484, 485], about 10–12 in. long, is the larger of the two species found in Africa. Its body is dark chestnut, the crown and nape are black, the cheeks and neck white shading to a yellow gorget. The frontal shield is pale blue. This jacana is common throughout east and central Africa on open lakes with many floating plants such as water-lilies. The nest also floats with its clutch of four very glossy, dark brown eggs. After breeding jacanas form small flocks like other waders.

The family of oystercatchers (Haematopodidae) occur on the coasts of the whole world except in the arctic regions. Some ornithologists recognize six species, others only four. The **Common Oystercatcher**, *Haematopus ostralegus* [486], of the Old World, frequents the water's edge, where it forages in the mud for crustaceans and worms; with its strong red bill it is able to open mussels. The plumage is black and white, the short legs red. It generally nests on the shore among stones or thin vegetation [487], but in Scotland is found far inland. It is recorded to have attained the age of 34 years. The **American**

Oystercatcher, *Haematopus palliatus*, is found on the coast of eastern North America, the Caribbean, and locally on both coasts of tropical America. It resembles the European bird but has a brown back. An all-black bird with red legs, the **Black Oystercatcher**, *Haematopus bachmani*, inhabits the Pacific coast from Alaska to the southern part of the Californian peninsula. All three birds are alike in habits and are sometimes considered to be races of a single species.

The majority of waders are members of the family Charadriidae–plovers and lapwings. Abundant in Europe and temperate Asia is the bright-coloured **Lapwing**, *Vanellus vanellus* [488], measuring 1 ft in length and weighing 7 ounces. The nuptial plumage of the male is black above with a lovely metallic sheen. The head is adorned with a long crest. The

489

colouration of the younger birds [489] and the wint
dress do not show such marked contrasts.

In spring, returning from their winter quarters, t
males occupy the nesting grounds where they pe
form their characteristic courtship display, which
accompanied by wild calls. The display consists
somersaults and plummeting flight [490]. The fo
olive-brown eggs with dark markings are practical
invisible in their shallow nest in the grass [492].
many places lapwings may be found nesting in d
fields. The young lapwing, when several days o
[491], is provided with protective colouration so th
it easily escapes notice.

The **Téru-téru** or **Neotropic Lapwing**, *Belono,
terus cayennensis* [494], belongs to the group
lapwings which have a large spur on the bend of t
wing; about half the lapwing species have this grow
which may be either blunt or sharp. Its range e:
tends from Colombia to northern Argentina, whe
its loud cry can often be heard near human habit
tions. The plumage is grey-brown above, whi
below, the black forehead and throat edged wi
white, the breast white. The neck crest is not ve,
prominent.

The **Wattled Lapwing**, *Sarciophorus malabaric;
[493], ranging from the Himalayas through India
Ceylon, has no spur but is distinguished by the yello
wattles at the base of its bill. The plumage is coffe
coloured, with white underparts, and the black crow
is separated from the rest of the head by a white ban

490
491

49

It breeds in dry, open regions, laying four pale eggs into a shallow unlined hollow in the soil.

The **Little Ringed Plover,** *Charadrius dubius* [495, colour plate XV], measuring about 6 in., is coloured black, brown and white. It breeds in northern Europe and Asia, wintering to the Mediterranean and southern Asia. It can often be seen running rapidly along the stony and sandy shores of lakes, flooded gravel-pits and rivers. Every now and then it stops to bow several times, then it flies off a short distance or

patters away on its long legs. The female generally lays four eggs in the nest, a shallow depression frequently scraped in gravel; the eggs are difficult to distinguish from round pebbles.

The **Ringed Plover**, *Charadrius hiaticula* [496], is about 1½ in. larger, with a white wing bar and black bars on the throat and forehead; the base of the bill is orange-yellow, but unlike the preceding species it is without the yellow circle round the eye. The Ringed Plover breeds mainly on the coasts but also on the inland waters of Europe, northern Asia and northern North America, ranging south to Africa, southern Asia and South America. American birds are some-

times treated as a separate species, called the **Semipalmated Plover**, *Charadrius semipalmatus.* The nest is a shallow scrape lined with small stones or shells [498]. The **European Golden Plover**, *Pluvialis apricaria* [497], measures almost 1 ft. The back in all seasons is dappled with golden-yellow spots, which give the bird its name. The breeding plumage is black below, separated from the upper parts by a white band. It breeds in northern Europe and across southern Asia to Taimyr in Siberia, preferring open moorland and peat bogs. The **Lesser** or **American Golden Plover**, *Pluvialis dominica,* is virtually identical in appearance but has dusky buff,

497

498

not white underwings. It nests from north-east Siberia across arctic America and winters in southern South America; in autumn it migrates off the Atlantic coast, in spring, up the Mississippi valley. It is a vagrant to Britain and western Europe.

The curlews, of the genus Numenius, are distinguished by a long, downcurved bill. The eight species of these fairly large shore-birds inhabit Europe, Asia and North America. The **Curlew** or **Whaup**, *Numenius arquata*, is a typical representative of this distinctive genus and the largest of European curlews, measuring 21 to 23 in. and weighing about 2¼ lb. The plumage is grey-brown with darker streaks [499, 500]. During the breeding season its slow rippling note is well known. It nests from Ireland to beyond Lake Baikal in south-east Siberia, wintering in South Africa and southern Asia. Its favourite breeding haunts are moorland and damp meadows. Newly hatched chicks have extremely short bills but these grow rapidly and by the time the birds are 20 days old there is already a distinct downward curve [501].

501

502

The **Whimbrel,** *Numenius phaeopus,* is smaller than the Curlew—it weighs about 1 lb and measures a little over 16 in. The black-brown top of the head is divided down the centre by a pale lengthwise band [502]. It breeds in the tundras and moors of northern Europe, Asia and America, and winters in Africa, southern Asia and South America.

xvi **Black-tailed Godwit** *Limosa limosa*

xvii **Common Sandpiper** *Actitis hypoleucos*

xviii   **Crowned Pigeon** *Goura cristata*

Most members of the family Scolopacidae have a bill which is longer than the head. The colouration is not striking and the hind toe, which is absent in the plovers, is well developed (except in the Sanderling).

The **Black-tailed Godwit,** *Limosa limosa* [503, colour plate XVI], measuring 16 in., is a long-legged, long-billed bird coloured rusty brown, the terminal portion of the white tail being black. In winter the upper parts are greyish brown, the underparts whitish with a rusty tinge. Its plaintive cry can be heard in the vicinity of its nest, which is located in damp meadows near water [505]. It breeds in a narrow strip of territory from Britain to Kamchatka in Siberia. Its American counterpart is the **Hudsonian Godwit,** *Limosa haemastica,* which differs only in the colour of the underwing. It nests in north-west Canada and winters in southern South America, following the same migration routes as the American Golden Plover.

The related **Bar-tailed Godwit,** *Limosa lapponica* [504], is found in the northernmost parts of Eurasia, wintering on the Atlantic coast of Europe

503

504

05

506

from the British Isles to the Iberian peninsula. It has the tail feathers barred horizontally and the bill curved slightly upwards. The underparts, head and neck are reddish brown during the breeding season, the winter plumage is entirely grey.

The **Redshank,** *Tringa totanus* [506], somewhat larger than a thrush, has long red legs and a red, black-tipped bill. The plumage is greyish brown with darker bars and streaks. It breeds throughout most of Europe and temperate Asia. The white bar along the wing is visible only in flight. This characteristic is absent in its relative the **Spotted Redshank,** *Tringa erythropus* [507], which also has red legs but in summer is distinguished by its black plumage. It is an arctic species breeding in Lapland and northern Asia to the River Anadyr in Siberia

507

wintering from the Mediterranean southwards. It forages for food on sandy shores at the water's edge [508].

The grey and white **Greenshank,** *Tringa nebularia* [509], the same size as the preceding species, is distinguished by its green legs and slightly upturned bill. It breeds from Scotland to Kamchatka, migrating in winter to South Africa, southern Asia and Australia. Breeding in similar habitats in the New World, from Alaska across northern Canada, is the **Greater Yellowlegs,** *Totanus melanoleucus,* which winters on the coasts from mid USA to South America and is everywhere an abundant migrant. It is very similar in form and pattern to the Greenshank but differs in having bright yellow legs. It occurs as a vagrant in the British Isles.

The **Wood Sandpiper,**
Tringa glareola [510], about
the size of a thrush, is brown
above, the feathers edged a
lighter shade, the underparts
white, the end of the tail
thickly barred with brown. It
nests in the northern half of
Europe and Asia near water,
on wet meadows, in tundras
and forest swamps. It is shown
in the company of the **Little
Stint,** *Calidris minuta* [511].
These two species are represented in North America by,
respectively, the **Solitary
Sandpiper,** *Tringa solitaria,*
and the **Least Sandpiper,**
Erolia (Calidris) minutilla.
Each is very similar in appearance and habits to its Old
World counterpart. Both nest
in northern Canada and
Alaska and winter to tropical
America, occurring all over
North America on migration.
The **Terek Sandpiper,**
Xenus cinereus [512], looks
rather like the Common Sandpiper but has a longer and
more upcurved beak, and
comparatively short yellow
legs. The upper parts are
grey-brown, reddish brown in
the young. It measures 9 in.
This species breeds from Finland throughout the central
part of Siberia to the Chukot
peninsula, preferring water
courses in forested areas but
also nesting in tundras by
rivers and lakes. The picture
shows how the small, leggy
young hide under the mother's
wing in bad weather. The male
remains close to his family,
flying noisily at intruders.
The ashy-grey plumage and
general appearance of the
Polynesian Tattler,
Heteroscelus brevipes [513], resemble the Spotted Redshank.
The note, however, is more
like that of the Common

510

511

Sandpiper. It is believed that this species breeds discontinuously in eastern Asia in the alpine zones of mountain ranges; it winters in south-west Pacific. The related **Wandering Tattler**, *Heteroscelus incana,* breeds in the easternmost tip of Asia and in Alaska, migrating down the Pacific coast of North America to southern South America and Hawaii in winter. The **Common Sandpiper,** *Actitis hypoleucos* [colour plate XVII], about the size of a lark, is olive-brown with black markings, the head, throat and breast grey-white

512
513

with faint black streaks. The nest is generally located on the river banks and lake shores of Europe and northern Asia. It flies jerkily close above the water and on land it continually pumps its tail up and down like a wagtail. The **Spotted Sandpiper,** *Actitis macularia,* is identical in habits and actions, and in winter resembles the Common Sandpiper; in summer it is heavily spotted below. It nests throughout North America and winters in the American tropics.

The snipe differ from the preceding members of this family in having comparatively short legs and very long bills; also in having the eye set far back on the head, which is doubtless connected with their method of probing for food in mud, peat, etc. [515]. The **Common Snipe,** *Capella gallinago* [514], measures 11 in., of which the bill takes up one-third. The male performs his courtship display high up in the air. As he

swoops down every now and then the vibration of the outermost tail feathers causes a peculiar loud drumming sound. The snipe nests on wet meadows and swamps from North America to Iceland and through Europe to southern Asia as far as Japan and the Himalayas. In winter it is found south to Africa, South America and southern Asia. The eggs are pear-shaped, greenish yellow, spotted with grey. The young, which hatch after 20 days, have excellent protective colouration [516]. The smallest of this group is the **Jack Snipe,** *Lymnocryptes minimus* [517]. The flight of this bird, unlike that of the Common Snipe which rises rapidly and flies a zig-zag course, is slower and more direct. The plumage is black above with a green gloss and marked pale streaks, otherwise it looks very like the preceding species. It breeds in northern Eurasia, wintering to Africa and southern Asia.

The **Woodcock,** *Scolopax rusticola* [518], of Eurasia is a larger bird about the size of a pigeon. When it crouches on the ground among fallen leaves its rust-brown, darkly patterned plumage makes it practically invisible. A bird of the woods, it feeds in damp locations where it can probe in the soil with its beak. In appearance, there is practically no difference between the sexes. The female tends the young by herself. The **American Woodcock,** *Philohela minor*, is somewhat smaller but essentially similar in appearance and habits. It nests in eastern temperate North America, wintering in the southern part of its breeding range.

The 23 species of the genus Calidris are mostly small, brownish birds breeding on the arctic coasts an tundras of the Old and New Worlds. They are s much alike that it is difficult to tell them apart. Mos of them have a white lengthwise stripe on the win which is visible only in flight. When migrating t South Africa, Australia and South America the often gather in large flocks [520]. The **Dunli** *Calidris alpina* [519], is about the size of a small thrus In spring and summer it is rusty brown above an white below with a black patch on the belly. In winte the plumage is predominantly grey and the blac patch is absent. It breeds in the northern parts c both worlds, wintering from the mid northern tem perate zone to North Africa, Mexico and India.

520

521

The **Little Stint,** *Calidris minuta* [521, 522], measures only 5 in., its colouration resembling that of the
Dunlin except that it has no black on the belly. It
breeds in the northernmost tundras of Europe and
Asia eastwards to the mouth of the Indigirka on the
Siberian Sea. The fairly large, 10-in.-long **Knot,**
Calidris canutus [523], is rusty below and brown
above, the feathers bordered with rust; in winter,
however, the upper parts are grey and the underparts
white. It breeds on the shores of the Arctic Ocean
where it is quite plentiful; large flocks numbering
hundreds or thousands of birds are frequently seen
during the migrating season on the coasts of Europe,
Asia and the Americas.

522

523

524

525

266

The **Curlew Sandpiper,** *Calidris ferruginea* [524], in its winter plumage looks like the Dunlin but is somewhat larger with a white rump and a slightly longer, downcurved bill. The nuptial plumage is reddish above, the feathers flecked with black, the underparts a glowing rusty red. It inhabits the moss-grown tundras of Taimir and the New Siberian Islands. In South Africa, where it spends the winter, it is one of the most abundant of the northern species of waders. Though an Old World species it occasionally strays to the east coast of North America on migration. The **Purple Sandpiper,** *Calidris maritima* [525], measures 8 in. In winter the upper parts are dark greyish brown, in summer lighter with a purple gloss. It breeds on the rocky shores and moss-grown mountain slopes of the arctic coasts and when migrating can be seen on rocks jutting out into the sea or on piers. Unlike the other members of its genus, it does not winter to the tropics but only as far south as the rocky coasts of northern Europe and the north-eastern United States. A bird of barren lands, it nevertheless does not appear to fear man.

The **Great Knot,** *Calidris tenuirostris* [526], is little known to date and it is quite possible that it may be a geographical variant of the Knot, though its breeding plumage is not rusty below. As far as we know this species nests above the timber line in the mountains of the Chukotski Peninsula and occurs on the sea

526

coast during migration, when it makes its way as far as northern Australia. The eggs are laid in a scrape in the ground among the sparse vegetation which consists chiefly of lichen. The young birds resemble lichen-covered stones [527], the colour of their down blending perfectly with their environment.

527

267

528

529

Also found on the Chukotski Peninsula is the **Spoon-billed Sandpiper,** *Eurynorhynchus pygmaeus* [528], about 6 in. long, distinguished by its shovel-shaped bill. It feeds on small animal life which it finds on shores or on dry land. The breeding plumage is rusty brown above, on the head and neck, spotted with black, and white below. The winter dress has grey in place of the rusty hues. The bird winters in south China west to Burma.

The **Ruff,** *Philomachus pugnax* [529], with its long legs and bill resembles a large Knot. There is a marked difference between the sexes — the female is much smaller than the male and there is also a great difference in the breeding plumage. The male is about 10 in. long with, in the breeding season, a ruff of long feathers round the neck and a large crest. The ruff is expanded only during the courting display, otherwise it lies flat [530]. The feathers of the ruff, as well as of the back and breast, show great variation in colour. They may be white, yellow, brown, glossy black, speckled, dappled, or a combination of several colours. The female is grey-brown above, the edges of the feathers paler [531], the male sporting the same plain colours in winter. The feathered ornaments of the male come into their own during courting when the cocks gather on the leks (dancing grounds), where

hey stand with expanded ruffs
acing one another, spread
heir tails, hop towards each
ther, dance with legs bent,
eign combat and sometimes
ven attack their rivals. The
Ruff breeds from northern
France, Norway, Hungary,
hrough Siberia to the Indigirka where it inhabits moss-
grown land in mountains and
owlands as well as wet meadows. Like the Curlew Sandpiper it occasionally strays to
North America on migration.
t winters in Africa and southern Asia.

530

531

532

In the three members of the family Phalaropodidae the female is slightly the larger of the two sexes, the more colourful and also the more active partner in courtship and selection of the nesting site, whereas the male incubates and tends the young. Unlike the other waders the phalaropes are excellent swimmers, for they have lobed webs on each toe, a short hind toe, legs flattened on the sides, thickly feathered underparts and fairly long necks and bills. They breed in open, moss-grown areas dotted with small fresh-water pools in the northern regions of the Old and New Worlds and feed on insects and their larvae. During the breeding season the female of the species illustrated, the **Northern** or **Red-necked Phala-rope,** *Phalaropus lobatus* [532], is grey above with yellow-white markings, white throat and belly and rusty brown neck. The male is duller. The non-breeding plumage is mainly grey and white. The Red-necked Phalarope migrates chiefly at sea off all the coasts of the world, but also occurs inland in some places. It winters on the oceans of the south temperate zone. The female helps to build the nest but that is the only maternal duty she performs.

The seven species of stilts and avocets (family Recurvirostridae) are slender, black and white birds

533
534

the size of a lapwing. They are very good fliers,
although one would not guess it from the long legs
and webbed toes. With their narrow, slightly upcurved bills, they probe for food – larvae, insects and
crustaceans – in the soft mud at the bottom of
shallows. The **Eurasian Avocet,** *Recurvirostra*
avosetta [533], 17 in. in length, has a black crown,
wing-bar and bill. It breeds on the sea coasts of
Europe and western Asia, but is also found on inland
lakes, especially in brackish waters, from the Neu-
siedler Lake in eastern Europe through western
Siberia to Mongolia. The nest is built in low sand or
mud banks [534]. The slight upward curve of the bill

is already evident in newly hatched birds [535]. The **Black-winged Stilt,** *Himantopus himantopus* [536], measuring 15 in., has even longer legs than the Avocet. The male has a dark crown, while the head of the female is entirely white. In flight the long red legs extend over 5 in. beyond the end of the tail [538]. This bird is widespread throughout temperate Europe, Asia, the southern half of Africa and Australia. The **Black-necked Stilt,** *Himantopus mexicanus* [537], breeds from the southern and western United States to Peru and Brazil. It is black above with a white forehead. It may be a race of the Black-winged Stilt.

535

536

537

The **Egyptian Plover,** sometimes called the **Crocodile Bird,** *Pluvianus aegyptiacus* [539], belongs to the family Glareolidae—coursers and pratincoles—and occurs on the banks of large waterways in Africa from Senegal to the Nile. The clutch of 1–4 eggs is hidden in the sand and for a long time the eggs of this species remained unknown. The crown, cheeks, back and breast-stripe are black, the wings and shoulders grey, the throat white, and there is a line of white extending from above the eye to the back of the head. The Egyptian Plover measures 9 in.

The gregarious **Common** or **Collared Pratincole**, *Glareola pratincola* [541], is slightly larger and is distinguished by a sharply forked tail. The outer feathers are about 2 in. longer than the inner ones, this being particularly evident in flight. The upper parts are olive-brown, the underparts yellow-brown. The buff throat is surrounded by a black line. The Pratincole generally nests in small colonies near water, mainly on dried mud. It inhabits sparsely vegetated areas in south-east Europe, south-west Asia, India and Africa.

It has already been stated that not all shore-birds live near water. The **Stone Curlew**, *Burhinus oedicnemus* [540], of the family Burhinidae, for example, prefers dry situations and semi-deserts with sparse vegetation. The yellow-brown colouring indicates that these are inhabitants of areas where sand, stones and mud predominate. The Burhinidae form an independent family whose members are marked by a fairly large head, large yellow owl-like eyes and long legs with big "knee" joints. The strong legs lacking the hind toe also indicate that the stone curlews are good runners. They are nocturnal birds. The Stone Curlew occurs in southern and central Europe, North Africa, and south and central Asia. Other species inhabit east Asia, Australia and tropical America.

The small, compact, snow-white, thickly feathered sheathbills (family Chionididae) are birds the size of a dove. The two known species resemble gallinaceous birds rather than waders. Despite the fairly short wings, they are excellent fliers which make their home on the islands off the Antarctic continent. Both have

a saddle-like horny sheath at the base of the bill which covers the nostrils. The front toes are joined by rudimentary webs and the hind toe is well developed. The naked lores are covered with pimples which are especially pronounced in the male, and there is a blunt spur at the bend of the wing. Sheathbills eat everything they can get hold of—sea-life of all kinds, eggs and chicks filched from the colonies of other birds, carrion and vegetable food. The **American Sheathbill**, *Chionis alba* [542], frequently visits the Falklands and the coasts of southern South America, though it is not known to nest in either locality.

At this point we come to a group of birds reminiscent of the tube-noses. Distinguished by slender bodies, long, narrow, pointed wings and soaring flight, they,

too, are birds of the sea. The gulls form one group of this type. Like all marine birds they are coloured grey, white, black and white, or brown. The underparts are white, and it may be that this serves to camouflage the bird, so that fish, which form the mainstay of its diet, do not see it until too late. The gulls (Lari) are medium-sized birds whose flight feathers are elongated, thus increasing the span of the wings; the feet, with webbed toes, are adapted for swimming. Gulls moult twice a year, the summer and winter plumages being somewhat different. They usually nest in groups, sometimes in very large colonies. The young are able to leave the nest shortly after hatching, but are fed by the adults, bill to bill, for some time. In all, there are about 85 species in the group, including the terns and skuas. Also related are the three species of skimmers.

There are only four species of the family Stercor-ariidae. They are called skuas in Britain, but in North America this name is reserved for *Stercorarius skua*, the other species being known as jaegers. Three species breed throughout the high arctic regions of the world and winter on the oceans of the south temperate zone. The breeding range of the Great Skua is unique among birds: one population occurs around the world in the subarctic belt of the

547

Northern Hemisphere, the other throughout Antarctica and up the west coast of South America to Peru; at all times the populations are separated by several thousand miles. All four may be seen along the coasts of Europe. Characteristic features of the family are the hooked bill consisting of four horny layers, the generally dark plumage, two long central tail feathers, and sharply angled wings. Skuas seldom catch fish themselves, preferring to obtain their food from other birds. Being excellent fliers, they harass gulls, cormorants and other sea-birds until they give up their catch. They also feed on carrion and, during the nesting season, on the eggs and young of other birds. Their two eggs take 3–4 weeks to hatch, both parents sharing the duties of incubation.

The **Skua** or **Great Skua,** *Stercorarius skua* [543], is a robust brown bird, about 23 in. long, with a white spot visible on the wing when folded, and a white

548

549

speculum when outspread. The **Long-tailed Skua** or **Jaeger,** *Stercorarius longicaudus* [544], is the smallest of the four species, measuring only 21 in. including the two long central tail feathers, which may project as much as 8 in. beyond the others. Like the two other smaller skuas it has two colour phases – light and dark, which is rare. The pale breast and extremely long central tail feathers, which are absent in the young, make it easy to identify this bird even in flight [545]. The somewhat larger **Arctic Skua** or **Parasitic Jaeger,** *Stercorarius parasiticus* [546], has pointed tail feathers projecting only about 3 in.

550

The gulls and terns (family Laridae) are birds whose bill has an undivided horny sheath. In the gulls it is downcurved at the tip, and in the terns it is slender and pointed. Gulls cannot dive deep but float buoyantly on the water like corks; they fly and soar excellently. The variety of food taken includes fish, garbage, carrion, crustaceans, snails, shell-fish, worms and insects, and most species are not averse to filching the eggs of other birds. Best known of the European gulls is the **Black-headed Gull,** *Larus ridibundus,* with red bill and feet and black-tipped wings. In the nuptial plumage [547, 549], the head is chocolate-brown, in winter it is white with a dark spot. The juveniles are brownish above with a black terminal band [551] on the tail. Black-headed Gulls breed in large colonies where the nests, built from the stems of aquatic vegetation, are placed close to one another. The clutch consists of 2 or 3 dirty green, spotted eggs [548]. These gulls inhabit Europe and temperate Asia, migrating in winter to southern Europe, north Africa and southern Asia. In winter, this species strays with some regularity to the east coast of North America, where it mingles with flocks of **Bonaparte's Gull,** *Larus philadelphicus,* a smaller

551
552

but essentially similar-looking species which nests in northern North America and winters along both coasts to Mexico. The Black-headed Gull feeds on a variety of aquatic life and small fish, as well as vegetable food. This species is beneficial to agriculture, for it destroys insect pests, grubs and worms in the fields [550] and often picks caterpillars from trees.

The **Mediterranean Gull,** *Larus melanocephalus* [552, 553], about the same size as the Black-headed Gull, has a jet-black head in summer. Unlike the preceding species, in flight the tips of the wings show pure white without any black. The breeding range is very limited, being almost restricted to south-east Europe on the Black Sea, where these gulls nest in very large colonies. Isolated nesting grounds are also to be found in Hungary and in the Gobi Desert—a remarkable distribution.

281

554

556

555

Widespread from Ireland through Scandinavia, in northern Asia and in north-western North America, is the **Common** or **Mew Gull,** *Larus canus* [554]. Somewhat larger than the Black-headed Gull, it is pale grey above; the rest of the plumage is white, the bill and feet greenish yellow. The young have a narrow border on the tail and are mostly greyish brown [556]. As soon as these gulls appear on their breeding grounds in spring they begin their complicated courtship display, which sometimes involves many birds at once. The mating itself is also preceded by an interesting display in which the partners stand side by side lifting pebbles or grass with their bills and tossing them abruptly over their backs. As a rule the Common Gulls lay three eggs [555], which take 26 days to hatch. The young fledge at 8 weeks.

Another abundant species is the **Herring Gull,** *Larus argentatus* [558, 559], a faithful follower of

557

558

559

560

ships. It is coloured much like the preceding species, but most races, including North American forms, have pink legs. It is about the size of a buzzard. The large yellow bill has a red spot at the tip of the lower jaw. It is difficult to distinguish the brownish young birds [560] from those of other large gulls. The

Herring Gull usually nests colonially in various situations—on coastal beaches, cliffs and sand dunes, as well as on the roofs of houses and other buildings. It nests in various locations in the colder parts of the Northern Hemisphere, wintering south to Africa, southern Asia and central America. Even though the

561

pairs do not remain together throughout the year, they meet again at the breeding grounds, to which they may pay a short visit in February, arriving to nest in Europe in March and April. The clutch [557] consists of 2 or 3 eggs which both sexes incubate. The young abandon the nest soon after they hatch, and are recalled by the shrill cry of the parents, to which sometimes the young of other birds [561] also respond. The Herring Gull feeds on carrion, worms, crustaceans and snails, and sometimes on eggs from neighbouring nests. The **Lesser Black-backed Gull,** *Larus fuscus* [562, 564], is the same size and

565

566

567

286

has a slaty grey or black mantle and wings and yellow legs. Unlike most marine birds its breeding range is rather limited—from Iceland to the White Sea, including the British Isles, north-west France and Scandinavia. During migration and in winter it is widespread on coastal and inland waters throughout Europe, and even strays occasionally to the northern Atlantic coast of the United States. Like the Herring Gull it nests on the coast among vegetation and boulders [563], also inland on moors, and the young are covered with grey-brown down [565]. Similar in colouring though much larger is the **Great Black-backed Gull**, *Larus marinus* [566], which can also be identified by its pale flesh-coloured legs. It inhabits the coasts of northern Europe and north-eastern North America. The picture shows a pair of courting gulls.

The **Black-legged Kittiwake**, *Rissa tridactyla* [567], has no hind toe, as its scientific name indicates. The adult bird is white with a grey mantle and black wing tips. The plumage of the juveniles is similar except that they have a black neck-stripe and in flight a black band is visible lengthwise on the wing. A bird of the open seas, it nests on the rocky coasts of the North Pacific and North Atlantic, usually in the company of other marine birds. In winter it occurs south to the Mediterranean, Japan, California and the middle Atlantic states of the USA.

Terns are slenderer than gulls, with short legs, comparatively long, forked tails, narrow bills, narrow wings and light and graceful flight. The **Common Tern,** *Sterna hirundo* [568, colour plate XIX], measuring 14 in., has a black-capped head, pale grey upper parts and red feet; the coral-red bill is tipped with black. A tern's nest is a simple affair, sometimes merely a depression in the sand, sometimes made of grass stems or of reeds washed up by the tide [569]. Courting takes place in spring both on the ground and in flight, when the male, carrying a small fish in his bill, is followed high in the air by the female,

570

uttering loud, harsh cries [570]. When feeding, the tern flies close above the water's surface, rising now and then and hovering in one spot with rapidly beating wings and hanging tail [571] to sight its prey. When it does so it plunges into the water with a splash. The Common Tern occurs in Europe, Asia and North America, flying long distances to its winter quarters in Africa, southern Asia and South America. Young birds already capable of flight may still have bits of down on their heads [572]. The **Arctic Tern,** *Sterna macrura* [573], has a blood-red bill without a black tip and a longer tail. It breeds on the coasts of northern Europe, Asia and America, and migrates long distances, mostly at sea, sometimes as far as the Antarctic. Some birds may travel 22,000 miles in one year. The 1–3 eggs are laid directly on the ground [574], or in a rudimentary nest.

571

574

575
576

The **Sandwich Tern** or **Cabot's Tern,** *Sterna sandvicensis,* is about as large as the Black-headed Gull. It has a short forked tail and a long black bill with a yellow tip. It breeds only on certain stretches of Europe's coasts and on those of south-eastern North America, the Gulf coast and eastern Mexico. In Europe it is sometimes found in colonies together with the Black-headed Gull [575].

The 9-in.-long **Little** or **Least Tern,** *Sterna albi-frons,* has a black crown and a white patch on the forehead [576]. It nests in scattered localities both on the coast and far inland on all continents except South America. In winter it retreats to tropical waters of Africa, Asia and America.

Terns of the genus Chlidonias are darker and smaller than the Common Tern and their tails are less forked. Their favourite haunts are shallow, muddy inland waters where they nest in small colonies and fly close above the surface hunting their prey—chiefly insects and their larvae. The **Black Tern,** *Chlidonias niger* [577], makes its nest on floating, rotting masses of vegetation in swamps and pools, usually among reed-beds [578].

The breeding plumage is almost entirely black and

579

grey-black. Note the slightly forked tail of the Black Tern in flight [579]. In the non-breeding plumage both young and old birds have white forehead, neck and underparts and there is a dark patch on either side of the breast [580]. Picture 581 shows two birds in the first year (on the left) and an adult bird in the intermediate plumage (on the right). The Black Tern is about the size of a blackbird but with longer wings. It breeds in Europe and Asia Minor eastwards to central Asia, and also inhabits a large part of North America. It winters on semitropical and tropical waters throughout the world.

582

White cheeks, black crown and dark grey underparts are characteristic features of the **Whiskered Tern**, *Chlidonias hybrida* [582, 583], which is the same size as the Black Tern. The underside of the wing, visible only in flight, is coloured white. The nesting habits are similar to those of the preceding species and both may be frequently found in the same colony. The Whiskered Tern occurs in the warm regions of Europe and Asia, South Africa and Australia.

Related to the terns but with unique characteristi are the skimmers (Rynchopidae), all of which ha black and white plumage. At hatching the mandibl of the chick are of equal length but by the time is nearly full-grown the lower is longer than t upper, which fits tightly into it. Both are very narr towards their tips. The use of this remarkab adaptation is seen when the skimmer fishes: it fli close to the water, its wing-beats keeping above bod

583

evel, and shears the surface with the lower bill.
When this makes contact with a small fish or other
prey, the upper bill closes smartly on it, and it is
thrown into the air and swallowed in one continuous
movement as the bird flies on. To give the necessary
strength forward, the neck muscles are particularly
powerful and special projections of the skull reinforce
its junction with the spine. As skimmers hunt mainly
at dusk or at night, they have vertical slit pupils to
protect their eyes by day.

There are only three species: in Asia, Africa and
America. The last, the **Black Skimmer**, *Rynchops
nigra* [584], is the biggest, about 20 in. long, and
is found all down the Atlantic coast from near New
York to Argentina and along the Pacific coast of
South America. It nests in colonies on beaches, the
female laying 2–5 eggs in the sand and doing most of
the incubation. The young leave the nest scrape soon
after hatching.

585

The auks (family Alcidae), which are remarkably similar to the penguins in many ways, are sometimes considered to be an independent order or suborder. They inhabit the cold seas of the northern hemisphere and, unlike the penguins, are good fliers, the action being strong, rapid and straight. Except for the Puffin, which is able to take to the air from level ground, all other auks take off from high rocks or cliffs. On the water they run along the surface flapping their wings for about 12 yards before becoming airborne. Water is their natural element and they are fine swimmers and divers; the legs, equipped with webbed toes, serve as a rudder, the body being propelled forward by the movement of the short wings.

They remain underwater for as long as two minut and can dive to depths of 30 ft or more. The sea the source of their food supply, which is chiefly fis and floating plankton. Auks come to land only breed, most species laying a single egg on the ste cliffs where they nest in colonies. They make no ne but deposit the egg on the bare rock, usually in crevice. Both sexes share the duties of incubatio which takes from 24 to 36 days, and care for t young. Fledglings are fed by the parents for 18 da after which, though not able to fly properly, the flutter down from the cliff. Even if they fall on th rocky shore instead of in the sea they remain u harmed, thanks to their thick coat of feathers and t wings, which break their fall. Once they are mature, probably at two years, the adults remain faithful to the same breeding site.

The **Great Auk,** *Alca impennis* [585], an extinct species since 1844, was once widespread in the North Atlantic; it stood about 30 in. tall. It had degenerate wings and was incapable of flight, which contributed towards its extermination. There are about 80 specimens of this bird in museum collections, two of which are shown in the picture; on the left is a mature bird, on the right a young bird with the plumage as yet incompletely coloured.

The **Razorbill,** *Alca torda* [586], measures about 18 in.; the head, neck and back are almost black, the throat, breast and belly white. A white line extends from the eye to the top of the high, compressed black bill, which is marked by transverse grooves, one of them coloured white. The Razorbill is found in abundance among the bird colonies of the North Atlantic coasts. The Channel Islands and Brittany are its southernmost European nesting grounds, Labrador the southernmost in the New World.

The commonest auks of the northern shores of the Atlantic and Pacific are **Brünnich's Guillemot** or **Murre,** *Uria lomvia* [587], and the **Common Guillemot** or **Murre,** *Uria aalge* [588–590]; murre

586

587

588

589

is the North American name. The first, measuring
16 in., differs from the second (about 18 in. long) in
having a shorter, stouter bill with a pale edge to the
maxilla. Both species are dark brown with white
breast, belly and tips of the secondaries. The
Common Guillemot breeds as far south as Portugal
and in North America all the way to California, but
Brünnich's Guillemot is limited to the far north,
though it occurs further south in winter. In many
nesting grounds, for example in Iceland, the two
species may be found together.

Frequent among colonies of Common Guillemot is
the **Ringed** or **Bridled Guillemot** or **Murre,** an

interesting variety with a narrow white ring round the eye and a narrow white streak behind it [589]. This variety increases in number towards the north and on Bear Island, for example, it comprises half the guillemot population.

In April or early May, both species return to the nesting grounds where they perform their courting display both on the cliffs and on the open sea. Here whole flocks fly in circles and dive beneath the waves to the accompaniment of loud cries. At the breeding cliffs they engage in fierce combat for the choicest situations, a third bird often occupying the site as two fight. The single egg laid by guillemots varies greatly in colour from white to dark green with dark spots. Adult birds greet each other with a laughing cry "gaa-gahaha" when changing places on the nest. The egg has a thick shell and is pear-shaped, so that it rolls in a small circle if set in motion and rarely falls off the narrow ledge. Although vast numbers of both young and old are packed close together on the cliff ledges the adults always identify their own offspring and will drive away those of other birds.

All inhabitants of the rocky shores of the far north [591] feed in the sea. Sometimes their numbers run into thousands, and nesting side by side are various species of auks and gulls, as well as ducks, with the

591

Gyrfalcon a frequent visitor, for the cliffs provide it with a rich store of food.

The **Black Guillemot**, *Cepphus grylle* [592], is another circumpolar species. Measuring almost 14 in., it is about the size of a pigeon. It is distinguished by its dark nuptial dress, which is uniformly very dark brown except for a white wing patch and red feet. In winter it is white below with white-spotted upper parts. It does not stay as close to the sea as other auks, smaller colonies being reported at altitudes of nearly 2,000 ft, or among rocks some distance inland. The Black Guillemot lays two eggs in cliff crevices or crannies, beneath rocks or between boulders. On the Pacific coasts from the Bering Sea to Japan and California it is replaced by the **Pigeon Guillemot**, *Cepphus columba*, a species practically identical in appearance.

The **Least** or **Knob-billed Auklet**, *Aethia pusilla* [593], smallest of the auks, inhabits the coasts of the Bering Sea and the Aleutians. It is black above,

592

593

301

594

white below; the forehead carries elongated, pointed feathers and there is a small tubercle at the base of the bill. Both these adornments are absent in the non-breeding plumage.

The **Parakeet Auklet,** *Cyclorrhynchus psittaculus* [594], also inhabits the coasts of the Bering Sea, but in winter ranges south to Japan and Oregon. It, too, is black above and white below and is distinguished by an orange-yellow upcurved bill. Another auk of these parts is the **Horned Puffin,** *Fratercula corniculata* [595], North Pacific counterpart of the Atlantic Puffin, distinguished chiefly by its bill, which is high, greatly compressed and gaudily coloured, especially during the breeding season. It nests on grassy slopes

595

302

where, with its beak and feet, it digs a burrow up to 6 ft deep in which the female lays its single egg. The adult bird measures 14 in.

The same compressed bill distinguishes the 16-in.-long **Tufted Puffin,** *Lunda cirrhata* [596], which occurs on both the Asian and American coasts of the North Pacific, southwards to California. It is uniformly brown with white bands on the head and a tuft of long white feathers hanging from above each eye. Unlike most auks, but like most other birds, the Tufted Puffin does not stand or walk on the foot and tarsus but on the toes. It is also a very good flier, capable of ascending to considerable heights. In some places it is very abundant; for example, 100,000 pairs were counted on an area of $7\frac{1}{2}$ square miles on one of the islands in the Bering Sea.

597

Pigeons and allies

The pigeons and their allies form a distinctive group (order Columbiformes) comprising two families: the sandgrouse (Pteroclidae) and pigeons (Columbidae). They are medium-sized birds differing from all others in certain features. The bill is short, with a swollen cere at the base which covers the nostrils. The feathers are loosely attached in the skin and are downy at the base. These birds are able to suck up water and therefore need not raise their heads for it to run down into the throat. When resting they do not tuck the head under the wing but pull it down between the shoulders. Most pigeons live in woods, are good fliers and feed chiefly on vegetable matter such as fruits, seeds and young shoots. The nest is a flimsy structure; they lay usually two white eggs.

Sandgrouse resemble pigeons anatomically, though they lack the cere at the base of the bill and have feathered legs. Superficially, with their soft grey and brown plumage, they look much more like long-tailed partridges and approach them in habits also, living often in flocks on the open desert or steppe country of Asia, Africa and southern Europe, where they are prized as game-birds. Their 2 or 3 eggs, laid in an open scrape, are protectively coloured. The male sits by day and the female by night. The young leave the nest soon after hatching and, pigeon-like, are fed by both parents with regurgitated food. There are 16 species, of which the **Black-faced Sandgrouse,** *Eremialector decoratus* [598], is one of the smallest, (10 in. long). It is resident in thorn-bush and scrub areas of east Africa. The central tail-feathers are not long and pointed as in most other species, nor is it so gregarious; but flocks form early in the morning when the birds fly to drinking places, where they share the pigeons' ability, unique among birds, to suck up water.

Nearly 300 species of pigeons are distributed throughout the whole world with the exception of the polar regions; the majority occur in the tropical regions of Asia. The extinct family of dodos (Raphidae) can be reconstructed from old drawings. Thus

598

the **Dodo,** *Raphus cucullatus* [597], of Mauritius in the Indian Ocean, which disappeared from that island around 1681–92, was a large flightless bird measuring about 4 ft, with a heavy, fat body.

Most pigeons live in trees, alighting on the ground only to feed and drink. Some species, however, favour the ground, where they spend most of the day running about among the shrubs, taking to the branches of trees only to roost or when nesting. Perhaps the best known of this group is the **Bleeding Heart Pigeon,** *Gallicolumba luzonica* [599], of the Philippines. Measuring about 1 ft, it is blue-grey above with black bars across the wings, white below with a striking red patch on the breast resembling a bleeding wound.

Belonging to the group of fruit pigeons is the **Red-knobbed Imperial Pigeon** or **Nutmeg Pigeon,** *Ducula rubricera* [600], which has a red knob at the base of the bill, a pink throat and head and greenish back, wings and tail. It lives on the Bismarck Archipelago and the Solomon Islands. Another fruit pigeon is the **Two-coloured Imperial** or **Nutmeg Pigeon,** *Ducula bicolor* [601], which is mainly milky white with black flight feathers and a black-tipped tail. Sometimes these birds form huge flocks which settle in the trees and shrubs on the shores of islands stretching from the Bay of Bengal to New Guinea. They live chiefly on the fruits of various trees. Fruit pigeons are tree-living birds which seldom come to the ground; there is a wide variety of species ranging

599

600

305

throughout the Indo-Malayan and Australian region. Their diet consists of fruits, chiefly nutmegs, which the pigeons swallow whole, leaving it to the stomach to separate the flesh from the kernel, measuring $1\frac{1}{2}$–2 in., which then passes on to the intestine intact. Of all the pigeons, the one which merits particular notice is the **Rock Dove,** *Columba livia* [602], from which all the many varieties of domestic pigeons have sprung. Its plumage is grey-blue, the rump white, and there are two black wing-bars and a black terminal band on the tail. The neck feathers have a green and purple sheen which turns to red on the throat. The Rock Dove is native to southern Europe, North Africa and central and southern Asia. Although it is also found inland it is most plentiful in the wild state on the coast, where it nests on high cliffs, preferably in caves. Pigeons have served to carry messages for thousands of years. The first records date from ancient Egypt in about 3000 B.C. In central Asia the raising of pigeons goes even further back. Since then, artificial selection has

601

602

given rise to many varieties differing not only in colour but also in shape, plumage and voice. Domestic pigeons are generally hybrids of several pure strains. The flocks of pigeons encountered in many towns and cities throughout most of the temperate parts of the world are domestic birds turned wild. With each succeeding generation even the most diversely patterned show an increasing resemblance to the Rock Dove [603]. They nest under the eaves of old buildings and often on the bare ground [604].

605

606

Colonies of domestic pigeon
are governed by certain rule
like colonies of wild Roc
Doves. But the social order
not as developed as amon
domestic fowls since eac
pair, provided with the priv
acy of its nest, is fairly inde
pendent. The birds zealousl
guard their small territory
which is respected even b
stronger individuals of highe
social rank. Whenever
strange bird approaches, th
pigeon to whom the nest be
longs shows its displeasur
visually and with its voice. I
the intruder is too bold,
fight ensues. Where priva
ownership of the nest and a
area around it is not respected
the result is often permanen
hostility. The size and boun
daries of this area vary, de
pending on the mood of th
owners, external factors an
changes in the fitness of th
respective birds.

The **Racing Pigeon**, greatl
resembling its progenitor th
wild Rock Dove, was bred fo

607
608

its powers of orientation. Even when far from home a well-trained bird will usually find its way back. Some are known to have returned from distances of more than 600 miles, their rate of travel being about 50–55 miles per hour. Racing pigeons occur in many colour and pattern variations [605, 606].

Very popular in some European countries are the Strassers, belonging to the group of coloured pigeons which occurs in many plumage variations and became widespread because it produces frequent broods and requires little care, procuring most of its food by itself in the fields. The picture shows the **Strasser Black** [607].

The **German Beauty Homer** [608], one of the three varieties of beauty homers, is a fairly recent variety which was developed from the Racing Pigeon, the chief emphasis being placed on the shape of the head.

609

In the trumpeters the most important trait is the remarkable voice, resembling the sound of a distant drum. The **German Trumpeter** [609] has a crest at its nape and feather ornament above the bill. The legs are thickly feathered or muffed. The Czech swallow muffed birds are distinguished by a lovely body structure and long, thick leg feathers. They have a shell-shaped crest on the head and a coloured spot on the forehead. A particularly striking variety is the **Czech Swallow Tiger,** raised chiefly in Bohemia [610].

A large group of selectively bred pigeon varieties are

610

the tumblers, in which special emphasis is placed on the powers of flight. Good tumblers should form a compact flock the moment they are released and rise rapidly in spirals to great heights. Some varieties make solo flights, others are distinguished by their sharp loops and turns at full speed. As a group, however, these pigeons are not of uniform shape and colour. Pictured here is one of the short-billed varieties–the **Prague Tumbler** [611].

When cooing, every pigeon slightly inflates the throat; but the pouters, in which this characteristic is purposely developed and perfected by breeders, achieve the greatest dilation. The **English Pouter,** bred in England more than 250 years ago, is distinguished by its erect carriage and white "heart" on the crop [612]. Another

variety is the **Brünner Pouter,** smaller and more slender than the others and occurring in several colour forms [613].

The **Carrier** [614] belongs to the group of wattled pigeons, distinguished by the peculiar swellings at the base of the bill which gave them their name. Besides these it has a ring of wattles round the neck. The Carrier is a tall, robust bird, originally from Egypt and the Orient, reared in England for more than 300 years and today a popular bird in many countries.

Besides pigeon varieties bred for their shape, voice or mode of flight, there are those where

the primary factor is the feathering. The chief ones are the **Fantail,** one of the oldest varieties, with its magnificent fan-shaped tail [615] and the **Jacobin** [616, 617], in which the head is adorned with three striking feather ornaments.

617

The **Stock Dove,** *Columba oenas* [618], the same size as the Rock Dove (13 in.), is dove-grey with two metallic green patches on the sides of the neck and two black wing-bars. It nests in holes in trees, sometimes those abandoned by woodpeckers, in some regions in rabbit-holes in mud or sand banks. Where there are few hollow trees it will also lay its eggs in buildings and in man-made nest boxes [620]. The young, like those of all pigeons, have soft bills which they poke inside those of the adult birds to feed on "pigeon's milk" regurgitated from the crop. Later they are fed with half-digested grain [619]. The Stock Dove, like most pigeons, has several broods a year. The first eggs are usually laid in April, incubation taking 15 to 17 days. While the male is still caring for the young (it takes over 3 weeks for them to mature) the female is already incubating a

618

619

620

621

new clutch, laid in a new, hurriedly built nest. A closely related bird (short wings and long tail are characteristic features of these tree-living species) is the **Wood Pigeon** or **Ring Dove,** *Columba palumbus* [621, 623], somewhat larger than the Stock Dove. It has a white bar on the wing and white patches on either side of the metallic green neck. The male's deep, cooing note can be heard in the vicinity of the nest, a flimsy structure of twigs in which the female lays her two white eggs [622]. Both Stock Dove and Wood Pigeon are found in Europe, north Africa, western Siberia and central Asia.

622

623

624

The genus Columba also occurs in the Americas–
about 20 species in all. The **Scaled Pigeon,** *Columba
speciosa* [624], has neck feathers edged with black,
those on the breast and belly wine-coloured with
dark borders, the head and back red-brown. It is a
fairly small, 12-in.-long pigeon inhabiting Central
America and northern South America. The some
what larger **Picazuro Pigeon,** *Columba picazur*
[625], has a neck ring of black-edged feathers, the
head and underparts are crimson, the back grey. I
inhabits much of Argentina and the southern part o
Brazil.

625

626

The slender **Mourning Dove,** *Zenaidura macroura* [626], measuring about 12 in., has long, pointed tail feathers, grey and brown plumage with wine-coloured underparts, black patches on the shoulder feathers and a patch on either side of the head. It is a common species occurring from southern Canada to western Panama, and also on some of the islands of the Caribbean.

A now extinct species is the **Passenger Pigeon,** *Ectopistes migratorius* [627], a slender bird with a long, wedge-shaped tail, grey-brown above and red-brown below. The female was less brightly coloured. The Passenger Pigeon inhabited the United States and Canada east of the Rocky Mountains. It is a classic example of a species which rapidly disappeared, after being abundant only a short time previously. Flocks of these pigeons measured over half a mile across and many miles in length. They were slaughtered in millions, yet it is hard to believe that man was the cause of their passing. The last wild specimen was recorded in 1899 and the last one in captivity died in 1914 in Cincinnati Zoological Gardens.

627

628

A common inhabitant of wooded country in Europe is the **Turtle Dove,** *Streptopelia turtur* [628, 629], a predomi-

nantly brown and grey bird with a black and white oblique striped patch on either side of the neck. In spring its purring call can be heard from bushes and treetops, often in the vicinity of water. In autumn, before leaving for the south, Turtle Doves gather in small groups in the fields. The species ranges throughout Europe, a large part of western Asia and north Africa.

More widespread is the **Laughing Dove,** *Streptopelia senegalensis* [630], which extends through the whole of Africa, south and central Asia and India, where it occurs in several varieties. It has a black band across the throat spotted red and brown, the remaining plumage being grey and brown. In central Asia it frequently nests on human habitations.

631

632

The **Collared Turtle Dove,** *Streptopelia decaocto* [631], is a good example of how certain bird species greatly extend their range of distribution within a very short time. In Europe it originally inhabited only the Balkan Peninsula, but during the past thirty years it has spread throughout all central and part of western Europe to inhabit an area covering three-quarters of a million square miles, its boundaries having moved some 1,250 miles. It is interesting to note that where it has spread to northern Europe it does not migrate south but remains there throughout

the winter months, sometimes even nesting at that time. The Collared Turtle Dove is found only in the close vicinity of human habitations in gardens and parks; it is not seen in woods. The plumage is grey-brown above, the underparts somewhat lighter, with a narrow black neck-band. It resembles *Streptopelia roseogrisea* (next page) but has an entirely different note which sounds like "coo-cooo-coo". Picture 632 shows one-week-old nestlings. The droppings are piled around the edges of the simple nest, which is usually built in a tree. Picture 633 shows 12-day birds.

634

635

The pigeon shown on a man-made nest with its mature offspring [634, 635], is the **Pink-headed Dove**, *Streptopelia roseogrisea*, of central Africa, which may be a geographical race of the preceding species. It is often reared in captivity as a song-bird. It, too, has a black neck-band, but unlike *Streptopelia decaocto* its plumage is creamy-brown.

The **Talpacoti Dove** or **Ruddy Ground Dove**, *Columbigallina talpacoti* [636], 7 in. long, with rusty plumage and grey head, makes its home from northern Mexico to northern Argentina and Paraguay. The **Diamond Dove**, *Geopelia cuneata* [637], of Australia is the same size, and has small white spots on the wings. Both these pigeons are often raised in captivity.

636

637

323

One of the handsomest wild
pigeons is the **Crested
Bronzewing,** *Ocyphaps lop-
hotes* [638], 13 in. long, with a
pointed crest. It is the commonest species in north-west
Australia.

The **Nicobar Pigeon,** *Caloe-
nas nicobarica* [639], has
several remarkable features,
including long, sickle-shaped
neck hackles, which form a
sort of mane, and a small knob
at the base of the bill. The
plumage is black with a green,
blue and copper sheen, the
tail is white. It occurs in pairs
or small flocks from the
Andamam Islands through
New Guinea to the Solomon
Islands.

The largest pigeons, measuring about 30 in. and weighing
approximately 4½ lb, are the
members of the genus Goura.
They are distinguished by
handsome erect crest feathers.
The three species are natives
of New Guinea, where they
are common inhabitants of
the coastal forests. They forage for food on the ground,
perching on the low branches
of trees only when disturbed or
to roost. The **Crowned
Pigeon,** *Goura cristata* [640,
colour plate XVIII], has a
plumage in shades of blue.
The feathers of its fan-like
crest have divided webs.

639
640

641

642

Parrots and allies

Parrots (order Psittaciformes), are probably the most intelligent group of birds after the crows. Their fleshy tongues enable them to repeat words and use them in certain specific situations; their powers of memory and mimicry are well developed, but parrots do not possess the ability to reason. The structure of the syrinx allows certain modulations of the voice. Parrots have short, strong legs with two toes in front and two behind (the first and fourth), giving them a firm hold. The feet are used to manipulate food and carry it to the beak, which is short and stout and is used also when climbing. The strong upper mandible is hinged to the skull and is therefore moveable; in seed-eaters it is down-curved at the tip to hold the food while it is being crushed by the lower mandible. At the base of the bill there is a broad cere which covers the nostrils. Though the body is short the long tail makes the bird appear slender. The two sexes may be alike or may exhibit marked differences in colouring. These gregarious birds are inhabitants of forests in tropical regions. The males are monogamous and pairs are very devoted, some remaining together for their whole lifetime. Parrots rarely build their own nest, preferring to lay the eggs in holes in trees or, though less frequently, in cavities under stones or in cliffs. The young are nidicolous, being fed by the adults from bill to bill with food regurgitated from the crop.

Of the three New Zealand parrots of the genus Nestor one is now extinct. The olive-brown **Kea,** *Nestor notabilis* [641], measuring 18 in., is distinguished by its long, downcurved, hooked bill. It feeds on vegetable matter, insects and worms, sometimes also carrion. It is chiefly a ground bird and nests in the crannies and fissures of rocks. The cockatoos (Cacatua), natives of Australia and the East Indies, are distinguished by a bill in which the upper jaw overlaps the narrow lower jaw, and by an erectile crest. The **White-crested Cockatoo,** *Cacatua alba,* measures 18 in. and is entirely white, with a crest of feathers broadened at the tip [642]. It inhabits the northern and central Moluccas. The **Salmon-crested** or **Pink-crested Cockatoo,** *Cacatua moluccensis* [643], of the southern Moluccas, is 20 in. long, with white, salmon-tinged plumage. It too has a broad crest, but its longest feathers are red.

643

The **Lesser Sulphur-crested Cockatoo,** *Cacatua sulphurea* [644], has a yellow crest of narrow recurved feathers, and yellow cheeks. Otherwise it is entirely white. Being relatively small (14 in.) it is a popular cage-bird. Delicate colouration marks the **Galah** or **Roseate Cockatoo,** *Cacatua roseica-pilla* [646], which is ashy grey above and pink on the head and chest. The crest is composed of broad, flat feathers and is not as long as in the preceding species [645]. It occurs in western and northern Australia.

645

646

A remarkably beautiful bird is **Leadbeater's Cockatoo,** *Cacatua leadbeateri* [647], also of Australia, in which the crest is a combination of red, white and yellow. The upper parts are white, the underparts pink. When at rest it folds its crest on the nape [648]. The **Little Corella** or **Bare-eyed Cockatoo,** *Cacatua sanguinea* [649], has a small, broad crest and a bare eye-ring. All these species are considered as pests in Australia because they damage crops.

647

648

650

The subfamily of lories comprises 62 species whose range extends from New Guinea to Australia and Polynesia. They have slender bills and fringed tongues with which they suck the pollen and nectar from flowers.

Typical of these species is the **Rainbow Lorikeet,** *Trichoglossus haematodus,* measuring 15 in. and weighing 6 ounces. It is a native of Australia and the East Indies where it occurs in a large number of colour forms. One subspecies, *Trichoglossus haematodus moluccanus* [650], has a lilac-blue head and belly, a red breast and orange-yellow sides.

651

The **Black-capped Lory,** *Domicella lory* [651], is scarlet with a black crown and bright green wings. It is a favourite pet with a good talent for repeating words. It occurs in several races on New Guinea and on several of the islands adjoining this territory. The **Kakapo** or **Owl Parrot,** *Strigops habroptilus* [652], of New Zealand, with its soft plumage, the disc of feathers round the eye and its nocturnal habits, is

652

ery much like an owl. This
-ft-long grey-green parrot is
ightless and spends almost
ll its time on the ground.
During the day it hides in
oles in rocks and under tree
oots in which it nests, coming
ut to feed towards evening.
t makes use of its short wings
nly when descending to the
round from higher eleva-
ions.

The most favoured pet of all
s the **Budgerigar,** *Melopsit-*
acus undullatus [654, colour
late XX], a small bird measuring about 7 in., with a long
ointed tail and swollen cere
653]. The wild form, found
n Australia, is coloured green,
he forehead and cheeks
ellow with three black spots
n the latter; the upper parts
re black with yellow trans-
erse bands. Man has bred a
vide range of lovely colour
ariations. Some birds are
ood at imitating human
peech.

53

654

655

Bourke's Parakeet, *Neophema bourkii* [655], closely resembles the previous species and has the same range of distribution. It is only about 1½ in. longer. The upper parts are olive-brown, the underparts rose-pink spotted with brown. The male is distinguished by a blue frontal band. These birds are most active towards evening.

Like other parakeets, the **Red-rumped Parakeet** *Psephotus haematonotus* [656], measuring 11 in. and coloured blue-green with a yellow belly and red rump, nests in hollow trees. The young hatch after 18 to 20 days and leave the nest after 30 to 35 days. During the nesting season they form large flocks which wander over the Australian grasslands.

656

657

The **Rosella Parakeet,** *Platycercus eximius* [657], another Australian species, is a favourite with breeders because of its bright colouring and pleasant demeanour. The head and breast are red, the cheeks white, the underparts green, the back black with yellow borders. The tail is green and white, the wings blue. The diet of this species consists chiefly of grass seeds.

The 13-in.-long crested **Australian Cockatiel**, *Nymphicus hollandicus* [658], is grey with white patches on the wings, a yellow head and crest and a yellow-red ear patch. These birds roam together in large flocks over the grasslands of inland Australia. Its habits are similar to those of the budgerigar; it also does not use its foot to hold food, and it too is able to learn several words and whistle melodies. Pairs are very affectionate [659] and it is difficult to separate them.

658
659

xix **Common Tern**
     Sterna hirundo

xx **Budgerigar**
    Melopsittacus undullatus

xxi **Rosy-faced Lovebird** *Agapornis roseicollis*

660

The area from the Solomons to Indonesia is the home of the 16-in. **Red-sided Eclectas** or **King Parrot,** *Lorius roratus* [660], remarkable in that the two sexes are utterly unlike in colouration. The female is red with blue or purple markings, the male is green with red flanks and under wing-coverts. The tail is comparatively short.

The parakeets are distinguished by a long, graduated tail, green plumage and elegant carriage. Twelve species of these parrots are found in tropical Africa and Asia. All are rapid fliers. The **Green Parakeet,** *Psittacula krameri* [661], inhabits the woods and gardens of lowland districts from southern China through India and east Africa to Lake Chad. The distribution is discontinuouş.

The related **Large Indian Parakeet,** *Psittacula eupatria* [662], measuring 18 in., is coloured blue-grey on the nape and cheeks and has a rust-brown spot on the shoulder. Its range extends from India to Indochina.

663

664

The next two species of parakeets are distinguished by a black "beard" extending from the base of the lower bill to the lower edge of the cheek and by the narrow black band on the forehead. The first of these is a green bird with blue-tinged head, the **Bearded** or **Red-breasted Parakeet,** *Psittacula alexandri,* which occurs in the East Indies and southern Asia in several races. The form *Psittacula alexandri fasciata* [663] inhabits the foothills of the Himalayas, Malaysia and southern China. The **Upper Yangtse** or **Chinese Parakeet,** *Psittacula derbyana* [664, colour plate XXII] is delicately coloured with a grey-blue head, the grey-blue underparts ringed with a wine colour. It occurs in the forests of south-east Tibet and south-west China.

One of the loveliest parakeets is the 14-in. **Blossom-headed Parakeet,** *Psittacula cyanocephala* [666], of

665

666

667

India and southern China. The male has a wine-coloured head, grey at the edges and bordered with black, and there is a brown-red patch on the shoulder. The head of the female is blue-grey edged with yellow. The **Slatey-headed Parakeet**, *Psittacula himalayana* [665], is found at altitudes up to 8,500 ft in its range of distribution in north India and north-western China. It measures 16 in. and is coloured green with a black-grey head and red patches on the shoulders.

Favourites among the exotic species are the 9 members of the genus Agapornis. They are small robust parrots with comparatively large heads and strong bills. Heads and tails are brightly coloured; the remaining plumage is green. These birds are at home in tropical Africa where they nest in cavities in trees, sometimes occupying termites' nests or those of seed-eaters. They line the cavity with bits of twigs, bark, grass blades and leaves to form a spherical hollow in which the 3–5 eggs are laid. Some species carry the building material in their bills, others insert it in the tail, back or neck feathers, shaking it loose inside the cavity. The young hatch in about 20 days, remaining in the nest for about a month, after which the parents drive them off. Members of a flock are very gregarious and when danger threatens they will settle on a branch huddling close to one another.

The pretty 6-in.-long **Masked Lovebird**, *Agapornis personata* [667], has a red bill and naked white eye-rims; it makes its home in the plains of Tanganyika. The form most commonly bred in captivity is *Agapornis personata fischeri* [668], with red forehead, orange-red cheeks and throat, and olive-yellow crown and nape, originally from Lake Victoria. The **Rosy-faced** or **Rose-ringed Lovebird**, *Agapornis roseicollis* [669, colour plate XXI], of Angola has a yellow bill, rose-red forehead and rose-coloured cheeks and throat. It measures 7 in., and commonly breeds in weaver-birds' nests.

The **African Grey Parrot,** *Psittacus erithacus* [670], is a favourite cage-bird not because of its plumage, which is sombre grey with a red tail, but because of its powers of speech. It is the best mimic of all parrots. In the wild it flies with chattering screams in flocks which are a common sight in the rain-forests of western and central Africa. It nests in holes in trees. In captivity it has been reported to reach the age of 70 years.

The 26 species of amazons, found in Central and South America, have the same stout body and short straight tail as the Grey Parrot. They are mainly green birds, with bright colours on the head, wings and tail, measuring 11–19 in. in length. They are rapid, powerful fliers and are also adept at climbing the branches of trees, where they nest in cavities. A common inhabitant of Brazil is *Amazona aestiva* [671, 672], measuring 14–16 inches and coloured green with a yellow face, blue forehead and blue or red at the angle of the wing.

673

674

Cuba and the Bahamas are the home of the **Cuban Parrot**, *Amazona leucocephala* [673, colour plate XXIII], which has a white forehead and red throat.

Less gaudily coloured is the 1-ft-long **Monk** or **Loro**, *Myiopsitta monachus* [674], which differs from the other parrots in its nesting habits, building large communal nests of twigs. The placing of one dwelling next to the other in the branches of a single tree gives rise to a huge mass in which each pair of birds has its own compartment. A related species found in the forests of Brazil is the **White-eared Parakeet**, *Pyrrhura leucotis* [675], a colourful bird, mainly green with a grey-brown head, bluish sides of the neck, red-brown cheeks, a white ear patch and a bib of grey, white-edged feathers. The lower back, a patch on the belly and the tail are dark red.

676

Of the numerous species of American parakeets or conures of the genus Aratinga, distinguished by wedge-shaped tails and pointed wings, the ones illustrated are the **Cuban Conure,** *Aratinga euops* [676], a green bird with red feathers on the head and neck, and the **Brown-chested Conure,** *Aratinga aurea* [678], of Panama and South America, somewhat larger (11 in.) and coloured green with olive-brown-

677

678

ish breast, and an orange-yellow forehead and circle round the eye.

The well known **Jendaya Conure,** *Aratinga solstitialis jendaya* [677], of north-eastern South America has a green back, wings and tail, the remaining plumage being orange-yellow, so that the bird virtually "glows". This species is 13 in. long.

The pretty parrot of the United States, the **Carolina Parakeet,** *Conuropsis carolinensis* [679], was last seen in Florida in the 1920s. It was once plentiful in the woods of the east-central United States, but was destroyed because it caused much damage to fruit trees and wheat. It was a green bird with a yellow head and wing borders and a glowing red face.

A parrot of the plains is the 18-in.-long *Cynolyseus patagonus* [680] of Uruguay and Chile. The back, neck and head are a dark olive, the belly, upper tail-coverts and rump bright yellow. During the breeding season these birds dig tunnels in mud or sand banks which are broadened at the end to form a nest.

The 15 species of the genus *Ara* are large, gaudy parrots, with big hooked bills and a harsh screaming note, which inhabit the rain-forests of tropical America. All have long pointed tails, and naked cheeks and eye-rims. The larger species are gorgeous birds, but the smaller ones are more soberly coloured. They are monogamous, living with their mates to the end of their days. The **Red-blue-and-green Macaw,** *Ara chloroptera* [681, 682], is red with blue and green wings and a blue rump and tail. The naked face is adorned with several rows of red feathers. It occurs from Panama to Brazil. The **Scarlet Macaw,** *Ara macao* [683], has a striking black and white bill and pale naked cheeks. It is red with green and yellow markings on the blue wings, and measures about 36 in. It ranges from tropical Mexico to Bolivia. Found from Panama to Argentina is the

681

682

683

Gold-and-blue Macaw, *Ara ararauna* [colour plate XXIV], which has yellow underparts, blue back and tail, and several rows of black feathers on the bare, white face. It measures 32–36 in.

684

The next two macaws are not so gaudy and both have
black bills. The **Military Macaw,** *Ara militaris*
[684], occurs in Mexico, and also in Columbia, Peru
and Bolivia, but not in between, is grey-green with
blue flight feathers and a red forehead, and measures
about 25 in. This bird is found in the lowlands and

685

686

also in the mountains as far as the tree line. The
Hyacinth Macaw, *Ara hyacinthus* [685, 686], is one
of the largest, measuring up to 40 in. in length. It is
a lovely uniform cobalt blue with only a narrow strip
of bare orange-yellow skin at the base of the lower
bill. It inhabits the Brazilian forests south of the
Amazon, where it lives either in pairs or small groups.
Like all macaws it feeds chiefly on fruit but also on
small animal life.

Cuckoos and allies

The cuckoos and allies (order Cuculiformes) comprise two very distinct families: the turacos (Musophagidae), also known as the plantain-eaters, and the cuckoos (Cuculidae). The turacos are brightly coloured birds which occur only in Africa and are chiefly forest-dwellers. They have stubby bills, the upper mandible with a serrated margin, and fairly long tails with ten steering feathers (rectrices). The short round wings are adapted for light and silent flight. The toes on the strong feet are equipped with sharp claws. In some species the red flight feathers yield a pigment called turacin, which contains about 7 per cent copper and is soluble in water. The pigment known as turacoverdin is yielded by the green feathers and is found only in this family. The diet of these birds consists chiefly of vegetable food – fruit, young shoots and leaves – sometimes also insects and grubs. The birds, which are otherwise gregarious, separate into pairs during the breeding season. The nest is a simple platform of twigs in which the female lays 2 or 3 eggs. The largest of the family is the **Great Blue** or **Great Crested Turaco**, *Corytheola cristata* [688], of the west African forests. It is 26–30 in. long, pale blue and green below with chestnut under tail-coverts and a black crest.

In the 13 species of the genus Tauraco the red primaries are coloured with turacin, the remaining plumage is generally green and blue-black, and the naked eye-rim is red. The 17-in.-long **Helmeted** or **Knysna Turaco**, *Tauraco corythaix* [687], is distin-

687

688

349

689

690

691

guished by a thick erectile green crest bordered with white at the top.

The woods and rain-forests of west Africa are the home of the 17-in. **Violet-crested Turaco,** *Gallirex porphyreolophus* [689], whose green head is topped by a rounded, thick erectile crest, but without any white markings. The **White-cheeked** or **White-eared Turaco,** *Tauraco leucotis* [690], is green with a grey-blue back and a white patch in front of the eye and on either side of the neck.

692

693

The family Cuculidae is much larger than the Musophagidae, with 127 species. It has a worldwide distribution but is most plentiful in the Old World tropics. All the members of this family have two toes in front and two, the first and fourth, behind. The varying shape of the bill—from small and weak to large and strong—with its non-serrated margin, indicates that these birds feed not only on fruits and insects but also reptiles and small vertebrates. In one subfamily, each pair of birds builds its own nest, in another the species erect a communal dwelling in which eggs are laid by several females, but the typical cuckoos leave the incubation and care of the young to other birds.

The slender-billed, 13-in. **Common Cuckoo,** *Cuculus canorus* [691], shows little difference between the sexes. These long-tailed birds both have a pale grey head and neck. The male is dark grey above, white below with darker transverse markings. The female differs in having the head, sides of the neck and throat rather browner [692, 693]. The cuckoo is

xxii **Chinese Parakeet** *Psittacula derbyana*

xxiii **Cuban Parrot** *Amazona leucocephala*

695

696

widespread in forests and more open habitats in Europe, Asia and Africa. Its diet consists chiefly of caterpillars. It lays its eggs in the nests of other birds, leaving it to them to rear the young (social parasitism). It is interesting to note that the 12 or so eggs laid by each female at two-day intervals are usually similar in size and colouration to those of the foster parents. As the incubation period is 12½ days—less than that of some of its hosts—the young cuckoo may hatch sooner than they do. Its first instinct is to remove from the nest everything which comes in its way, be it

other eggs or the rightful progeny. Pictures 695–700 show a naked, blind newly-hatched cuckoo trying to get a fledgling warbler on its back and push it over the edge of the nest with its wings. The young cuckoo is insatiable and consumes all the food the foster parents are able to find [694, on previous page]. On leaving the nest it is fed for a further three weeks. It does not remain long in Europe, for cuckoos set out on the journey to their winter quarters in August. European cuckoos migrate to central and southern Africa, where there is also a native race.

697

698

699

700

701

The young cuckoo shown being fed by a shrike is the **Short-winged** or **Indian Cuckoo,** *Cuculus micropterus* [701], found from India and the Amur region to Java and Borneo. It has a white, black-barred breast. A species widespread in the tropics is the 18-in. **Chestnut** or **Squirrel Cuckoo,** *Piaya cyana* [702], coloured rust-brown above and grey below, and distinguished by its long tail. This bird belongs to the subfamily Phoenicophaeinae and ranges from Mexico to Argentina. Its characteristic note is "piaya". **Levaillant's Cuckoo,** *Clamator levaillantii* [703], ranging from Senegal and Abyssinia to Cape

Province, is distinguished by a pointed helmet on the head. It is black above, below white with black bars. The **Roadrunner,** *Geococcyx californianus* [704], 20–24 in. long, is one of 13 ground cuckoos (subfamily Neomorphinae), which have much stronger legs than their tree-haunting relatives. This species has a brown crest, upper parts streaked brown and white, pale underparts and a long, graduated, white-tipped tail which it frequently raises. It is resident in the southwestern USA and Mexico, living in the open desert where it runs down small reptiles and mammals. It can move as fast as a sprinter, but flies poorly.

702

703

704

Owls

The owls (order Strigiformes) are divided by virtue of their anatomical differences into two families: the typical owls (Strigidae) and the barn owls (Tytonidae). Though they have been dubbed nocturnal birds of prey by reason of their habits they have nothing in common with the true birds of prey. The typical owls, comprising about 120 species, are widespread throughout the world. Particularly well developed senses of sight and smell, and the rounded wings with their soft, fluffy feathers, make them efficient and silent hunters. Catching their prey unawares, they grasp it with their claws and swallow it whole, tearing the flesh in pieces only from larger animals. Undigested particles are regurgitated and make it possible to determine on what the owls were feeding. The large forward-facing eyes with glowing brown, yellow or orange iris catch even the slightest ray of light, owls being blind only in complete darkness. The eyes are set in a facial disk and are almost immobile in their sockets, but this is compensated by the ability of the birds to twist their heads around a full 270 degrees. The stout bill is surrounded by sensory bristles with which owls "feel" their prey, for they are long-sighted and can only discern it with difficulty at close hand. The base of the upper bill is covered with a cere which conceals the nostrils. The soft plumage with its grey, black and brown markings is an excellent protective covering. When danger threatens owls spread their wings wide and fluff up their feathers, making themselves appear larger than they are. Both sexes incubate from the time the first egg is laid. The clutch comprises 2–13 eggs depending on the species. Owls lay in cavities, on trees, cliffs, buildings, in old nests of other birds or in holes in the ground.

The barn owls comprise ten species marked by a number of peculiar features. The completely feathered legs are longer than those of the typical owls, the claw of the middle toe has a serrated comb and the facial disk is heart-shaped. Best known is the 14-in.-long **Barn Owl**, *Tyto alba* [705, colour plate XXV], its white facial disk edged with brown, the upper parts marked with brown, grey and white, and the underparts white or buff-brown. It nests mainly in the attics of old buildings, church steeples, barn lofts, also in hollows in trees and cliffs. The female

lays from 4-11 white eggs at two-day or longer intervals in the nest-scrape, sometimes incubating from
the first day. The young usually do not hatch at the
same time and show differences in their physical
development [706]. The Barn Owl is found in
Europe, southern Asia, Africa, Australia and from
the northern United States to Brazil.

The species which follow belong to the family
Strigidae. The **Tawny Owl,** *Strix aluco* [707, colour
plate XXVI], of Europe, west Siberia and southern
Asia, is coloured grey or brown and has a dark brown
iris [708]. The ear-openings of this 17-in. bird differ
in size and shape, evidently an adaptation for accurate
location of the prey. It inhabits woodlands, parks and
wooded country, even city squares, resting during
the day in a cavity or among thick foliage. The young
hatch with their eyes and ears closed; they are covered
with pale down which is replaced by juvenile plumage
[709].

708

709

361

710

The **Ural Owl**, *Strix uralensis* [710], is related to the Tawny Owl, but is larger and has a longer tail and lighter plumage. It inhabits the forests of northern Eurasia to eastern Russia but is also found in the Carpathians and the Bohemian Forest. It too is a cavity nester.

Tengmalm's or the **Boreal Owl**, *Aegolius funereus* [711], measuring only 10 in., is grey with white markings and a white facial disk. It occurs in the mountain forests of western and central Europe, and the northern coniferous forests of Asia and North America, but is a very rare visitor to Britain.

Owls are generally sombrely coloured. One exception, however, is the **Spectacled Owl**, *Pulsatrix perspicillata* [712], which has on its black head white markings resembling spectacles. The upper parts are brown, the underside yellowish. The white downy fledglings have a black facial disk. The diet consists of small vertebrates and crabs. It also wrecks the long, elaborately woven hanging nests of caciques and other icterids to get at the birds inside. Its range extends from Mexico to northern Argentina.

The **Little Owl**, *Athene noctua* [713], measuring only

711

712

714

715

9 in. is often found in the vicinity of human habitations and may hunt during the day. It has only sparsely feathered legs and an imperfect facial disk. The dark brown upper parts exhibit the usual mottlings. Characteristic of this bird is its habit of hopping about when upset. It inhabits temperate Europe (introduced to Britain), Asia and Africa where it is separated into several geographical races; one of these is *Athena noctua bactriana* [714], whose pale rust-brown colouration is adapted to life in the wilds of central Asia.

The smallest European owl is the 6½-in. **Pygmy Owl**, *Glaucidium passerinum* [715]. The 12 species of this group range throughout Asia, Africa and America. Their colouration is similar to that of the Little Owl. The Pygmy Owl does not sit as upright as other owls and when upset wags its tail. It inhabits the forests of northern Europe and Siberia; in central Europe it is found chiefly in mountain forests. The American counterpart is the **Northern Pygmy Owl**, *Glaucidium gnoma*, which occurs in the western mountains from Alaska to Guatemala.

The **Snowy Owl**, *Nyctea scandiaca* [716, 717] found in the arctic tundras of the Old and New Worlds, is a striking snow-white bird with black-brown markings, measuring 22–26 in. All-white

individuals [719] are also known to occur. It is a
diurnal (day-living) bird whose favourite food is
lemmings. Since the number of these rodents in a
given locality varies from year to year, the Snowy
Owl is not faithful to its breeding site but wanders
over the vast northern expanses nesting wherever
the food supply is sufficiently ample. At intervals of
about every fourth winter this species invades more
southerly regions, occurring as far south as central
Europe and the northern USA. The size of the clutch
also depends on the abundance of lemmings. The
eggs are laid in a small hollow on the ground and the
male brings the incubating female from 2 to 4
lemmings a day. The young show marked differences
in size. On hatching they are covered with white down
which later is replaced by the brown juvenile plumage [718]. The young owl in the foreground in
picture 719 is already acquiring the adult plumage.

717

The **Hawk Owl,** *Surnia ulula* [720], is definitely a diurnal bird. It watches for its prey – small birds and mammals – from a high vantage point. It is 14–18 in. long. The tail is long and rounded and the facial disk is imperfect. The upper parts are brown, the underparts white with distinct narrow bars. The white face is edged with black on the sides. The feathers are not as soft and delicate as in other owls. It inhabits the northern coniferous forests of Europe, Asia and America.

718

719

"King of the Night" is the name given to the **Eurasian Eagle Owl,** *Bubo bubo* [721, 723], with its conspicuous ear-tufts. Measuring 26–28 in., it is the largest of the European owls. Its large orange eyes are very striking. It is rust-brown above with dark brown mottling, pale below with longitudinal streaks and indistinct transverse markings. It nests on cliffs, steep banks and in the abandoned nests of other large birds. The Eagle Owl is a strong bird which can easily overpower a large hare. In all, there are 11 species of eagle owls, six of them found in Africa. The **Dusky Eagle Owl,** *Bubo coromandus* [722], of southern Asia has a more distinct facial disk, is a paler colour and smaller than the European species.

Gold and Blue Macaw *Ara ararauna*

xxv **Barn Owl** *Tyto alba*

724

fowls of the genus Gallus are its favourite food. All diurnal birds of prey and crows harbour an instinctive hatred for the Eagle Owl and attack it on sight. Such predators will converge from far and wide on a sitting solitary Eagle Owl. This fact is made use of by hunters who place a tame bird on a T-shaped perch, then lie in wait in a shelter from which they can shoot the crows and predators. This unsporting method of hunting greatly contributed towards destroying many rare and beneficial birds of prey in Europe. In picture 724 an Eagle Owl is being attacked by a buzzard.

725

726

The American counterpart of the Eurasian Eagle Owl is the **Great Horned Owl,** *Bubo virginianus* [72 726], measuring up to 2 ft in length. The black uppe parts are vermiculated and barred black-brown. Th face is edged with black. The upper picture shows female with a fledgling behind in juvenile plumag Its range extends from Alaska and northern Canad to the Strait of Magellan, but it is absent from th West Indies.

Its ecology is similar to that of the Eurasian bir It too inhabits rocky country where it nests on ou crops, in fissures or on trees. The eggs are laid on th bare ground or a platform nest, and the female supplied with food by the male; a reserve supply ma

often be found near the nest.
This owl also hunts chiefly in
the evening. Many races of the
Great Horned Owl are found
in America, including *Bubo
virginianus nacurutu* [728],
thickly barred on the underside, which makes its home in
South America, from Tierra
del Fuego to Peru and Brazil.
The **Cape Eagle Owl,** *Bubo
capensis*, is common throughout the whole of South Africa,
the race *Bubo capensis mackin-
deri* [727], extending to Tanganyika and Kenya. This owl,
which is thickly mottled
below, also unhabits rocky
country and usually takes over
the old nest of some large bird.
It is smaller than its American
relative.

The **Malaysian Eagle Owl,**
Bubo sumatrana [729, 730],
inhabiting both the lowland
and mountain forest of
Malaysia, is particularly fine-
looking. Its loud cries are believed by the natives of Papua
to belong to a cannibalistic
spirit. Unlike other members
of this genus it has a comparatively imperfect facial
disk and brown eyes. Its fine
transverse markings are particularly striking on the ear-
tufts. The upper parts are
brown-black, the feathers
bordered white, the underparts white or light reddish,
the breast a darker colour with
fine transverse wavy markings. It measures about 18 in

729

730

Rodents, snakes and smaller birds are the mainstay of its diet.

Closely related to the horned owls (genus Bubo) are the fish-eating owls of the genus Ketupa, soberly coloured with imperfect facial disks, naked legs, and only slightly feathered feet. The toes have rough scales on the underside which help them to hold their slippery prey – fish, crabs and frogs. The **Malaysian Fish Owl**, *Ketupa ketupa* [731, 732], is a uniform rust-brown with longitudinal streaks below and long ear-tufts. It inhabits south-east Asia and occurs in the vicinity of rivers, since fish are its chief food.

731

732

Showing a marked resemblance to the eagle owls is the **Long-eared Owl,** *Asio otus,* also with ear-tufts which can be laid flat on the head so that they can hardly be seen [734, colour plate XXVII]. It is much smaller than the Eagle Owl–about 19 in. long. The plumage is the mottled grey and reddish colour of the bark of a fir tree [733], and a bird resting on a branch in the daytime, pressed against the trunk, looks like the stump of a broken branch. As a rule it lays its eggs in the abandoned nests of crows or birds of prey. The future head-tufts are already apparent in the down-clad young [735]. At the age of a few weeks they adopt a ferocious attitude to frighten the enemy when danger threatens, their orange-yellow eyes a dominant feature in the ball of grey feathers [736]. The Long-eared Owl feeds on mice; it occurs in Europe, the forests of Siberia and in North America.

733

734

The **Short-eared Owl,** *Asio flammeus,* a 15-in., buff and brown bird with almost indiscernible head-tufts [737, 738], prefers a different environment – open country, chiefly marshes and moorland. It nests on the ground, in fairly long vegetation. Its distribution is widespread, encompassing all of Eurasia with the exception of its southernmost parts, and almost the whole of the Americas.

The leafy woods of south and central Europe are the habitat of the **Scops Owl,** *Otus scops* [740], a very handsome small owl with short, blunt ear-tufts. The colouration is a mixture of grey and brown, making the bird practically invisible against the bark of a tree-trunk. Insects are the mainstay of its diet. The

Scops Owl nests in holes in
trees, sometimes also in rock
fissures and in the abandoned
nests of other birds, in the
warmer regions of Europe,
central and western Asia and
north-west Africa. The
various subspecies in southern
and south-east Asia, such as
the **Nepal Scops Owl,** *Otus
scops sunia* [739], are smaller
but similar in colouration and
ecology. The **Flammulated
Owl,** *Otus flammeolus,* which
inhabits the western mountain forests from southern
Canada to Guatemala, is virtually identical to the Scops
in appearance and habits;
some believe it to be the same
species.

741

Nightjars and allies

Members of the order Caprimulgiformes – nocturnal or crepuscular birds – have soft fluffy plumage resembling that of the owls, sombrely coloured and with darker markings, making the birds practically invisible when perched lengthwise on a branch. They have long pointed wings, short feet and weak toes, so that they are incapable of grasping a branch. The bill is also insignificant, but the gape is tremendously wide, with stiff bristles which serve as a net trap for catching insects, the birds' chief food, on the wing.

Placed in this order for lack of anywhere better is the **Oilbird,** *Steatornis caripensis* [741], the only member of its family (Steatornithidae). Just over a foot in

742

length, the nocturnal Oilbird has a wing span of about 2½ ft; its plumage is a fairly uniform rich brown, with prominent white spots on the rather broad wings. Its feet are weak and it can only squat on a ledge or cling to a rock-face, but it is a master of flight, airy, buoyant and undulating. Its strong hooked bill enables it to detach the fruits of palm trees, which are its main food, while hovering on the wing. Oilbirds are strongly gregarious, flying miles by night in parties to their food trees and returning to roost deep in caves which they have occupied since time immemorial. Here they share the pitch darkness with bats and like them have evolved an echo-locating mechanism in the ear to guide their flights. This operates on a frequency audible to humans and sounds like a series of rapid clicks. The Oilbird's variety of cries and croaks earned it the Spanish name of **Guacharo** (wailer). Both adults incubate the 2–4 white eggs, which are laid in a nest of droppings and palm seeds. The young, born naked, grow enormously fat on their diet of oily fruits and it is just before they are able to fly that the Indians of Venezuela take them and extract cooking oil from them. The more important Oilbird caves are now protected, both in South America and in Trinidad, where this unique bird has been intensively studied in recent years.

The frogmouths (Podargidae) comprise 12 species found in Australasia, Malaya and the Philippines. They are distinguished from other families in this order by their large hooked beaks which they use to snap up a variety of invertebrate animals from the ground. Slow in movement and poor fliers, they are adapted to a strictly nocturnal life. When roosting in daytime along a branch, their heads raised but motionless, they are extremely difficult to see. The 20-in. **Tawny Frogmouth,** *Podargus strigoides* [742], of Australia and Tasmania, hunts owl-like by dropping on its prey from a perch. It has a beautifully marbled grey plumage; its booming call, repeated a number of times, carries far through the brush at night. The simple stick nest is usually built on a horizontal branch at some height; the female incubates the 2 or 3 round white eggs by night, the male by day, and the young stay in the nest until fledged.

743

A more typical representative of this order is the **European Nightjar,** *Caprimulgus europaeus* [745], of the family Caprimulgidae. It is a beautifully patterned, grey-brown bird measuring 11 in., with large eyes, like all nocturnal hunters. During the day it rests either on the ground as illustrated or perched lengthwise on the branch of a tree, becoming active at twilight. The two white, grey-mottled eggs are laid in a small scrape on the bare ground, their protective colouration making them inconspicuous. The Nightjar usually breeds twice in a season. When disturbed near the nest it flies up, hovering in one spot as it looks around [743]. It frequents the woods of the temperate and warmer zones of Europe and western Asia, migrating to tropical Africa for the winter. The **Whip-poor-Will,** *Caprimulgus vociferus,* which breeds throughout North America and winters in the southern USA, Central America and Panama, is essentially like the European Nightjar in appearance and habits. The **Jungle Nightjar,** *Caprimulgus indicus* [744], is a somewhat larger, darker-coloured bird with a white terminal band on the tail.

744

745

Swifts and Hummingbirds

The greatest masters of flight are the members of the order Apodiformes, put in three families; the swifts (Apodidae), the crested swifts (Hemiprocnidae) and the hummingbirds (Trochilidae).

The long, crescent-shaped wings and forked tail distinguish the **Common Swift,** *Apus apus* [746], and make it easy to identify in flight [747]. Covering over 600 miles in a day is no difficult feat for this bird, which attains speeds of over 60 miles per hour. It is nearly 7 in. long and the stiff feathers are sooty black with a white patch under the bill. The range of distribution includes Europe, Africa and southern Asia. It feeds only on insects which it catches in flight. The nest—a few dry stems and feathers secured together with saliva—contains 2 or 3 eggs and is located naturally in holes in trees and clefts of rocks, but in Britain is now usually under the eaves of houses. The female starts laying the eggs at the end of May and the young hatch after 18–20 days. If the weather is unfavourable and the food supply inadequate they fall into a stupor, their body temperature only 2–3 degrees higher than that of the ambient air; this is in no way harmful to the birds, if not too prolonged.

The **White-throated Spine-tailed Swift,** *Hirundapus (Chaetura) caudacutus* [749], has two distinct breeding grounds—one in east Asia extending west to Siberia, the other in the Malayan Penin-

746

sula and the Himalayas. It is brown and white, the wings and tail black with a greenish blue sheen. The small nest of moss and hairs glued together is generally placed in holes in trees. The 3–7 eggs are sometimes laid on the floor of the cavity.

There are three species of crested swifts (Hemiprocnidae) in India, Malaysia and neighbouring islands. The **Crested Tree Swift**, *Hemiprocne longipennis* [748], is a widespread resident in this region. The sexes differ in this 8-in.-long species, the male having the side of the face below the eye a bright chestnut. The crest and most of the upper parts are blue-grey, the wings and deeply forked tail are dark brown, the belly white. The loud call, uttered in flight or at rest, is parrot-like. Crested Swifts are able to perch and hunt their insect prey by flying out from a commanding point in a tree. But in the evenings they may fly round in noisy parties like typical swifts. The tiny nest of bark and feathers is fixed with saliva to a horizontal branch and the single bluish egg just fits it; the parent incubates sitting crosswise to the branch.

747

748

749

381

750

751

752

More than 300 species of hummingbirds (Trochilidae) are distributed throughout South and Central and to a lesser extent North America. They are tiny birds, the smallest measuring only about 2¼ in. in length and weighing about 2 grams, the largest over 8 in. (this, however, is an exception). No other group contains so many beautiful species; their iridescent colours are so brilliant and dazzling they are rightly termed the gems of the bird world. Their vivid colouring is often further enhanced by various ornaments, crests, ear-tufts, chin whiskers, long or deeply forked tails with long spiked or trailing feathers, and variously shaped bills.

Like the swifts, hummingbirds also have exceptional flying abilities, though different in character, theirs being a whirring flight. Like small helicopters they hover in front of a blossom; the human eye is unable to discern the rapid movement of the wings, it sees only an indistinct blur, which is accompanied by a delicate humming sound. Hummingbirds are able to change their direction of flight with amazing speed, and also to fly backwards. With the aid of a camera it was discovered that in normal flight there are 50–75 wingbeats per second and during the male's courtship display as many as 200 per second; picture 751 was taken by electronic flash at 1/7000 second. These spectacular powers of flight are coupled with relatively tremendous flying muscles and a breastbone relatively larger than in other birds, the muscles attached to it making up one-fourth of the bird's weight. Hummingbirds use their short, weak feet only to perch, resorting to flight when they wish to change their position. They feed on nectar and insects, capturing the latter on the blossoms, rarely in mid-air. The tongue is adapted for sucking, tubular at the tip in some species and with brushy tips in others. The horns of the hyoid apparatus, to which the muscles of the tongue are attached, pass around the whole head terminating in front of the eyes, as in the woodpeckers, thus allowing the tongue to be projected some distance beyond the bill. Some species feed only on the blooms of certain kinds of plants and their beaks exhibit a wide range of structural adaptation. Hummingbirds may survive several years in captivity on sugar or honey water with added fats and proteins. They frequent the most varied types of localities from sea-level to elevations of 13,000 ft from the southern tip of Alaska to Tierra del Fuego. The deep, thin-walled nest of moss and plant down is placed in the branches of trees and shrubs, underneath the top of a palm leaf, exceptionally on the sides of cliffs. The clutch consists of only two tiny pure-white eggs. The periods of incubation (2–3 weeks) and rearing (as much as 20 days) are rather long.

The number of hummingbirds is so large that mention can be made of only a few. One, the smallest of all birds, is the **Bee Hummingbird,** *Calypte helenae* [750], of Cuba, which measures about 2¼ in., the bill and tail comprising half of its length. The upper parts of the male are a brilliant blue and green. The female, shown sucking nectar in the picture, is blue-green above and grey below.

The **Ruby-throated Hummingbird,** *Archilochus colubris* [752], 3½ in. long, is the only species that nests in the eastern USA and Canada, where it is, of course, a summer visitor, often arriving in cherry blossom time after performing a phenomenal migration, which includes a flight of at least 500 miles over the Gulf of Mexico. Both sexes have iridescent green upper parts and are white underneath, with black and white under the tail. Only the male has the glittering ruby throat. The two young are fed mainly on insects. **Pucheran's Emerald Hummingbird,** *Chlorostilbon aureoventris* [751], represents a group of species in South America and the West Indies all distinguished by their predominantly bright green upper parts. The **White-tipped Sicklebill,** *Eutoxeres aquila* [753], measuring 5 in., is distinguished by the shape of its bill. Its plumage is greenish above, black-brown below with pale longitudinal streaks. It ranges from southern Central America to tropical South America.

753

754

Trogons

The members of the distinctive family Trogonidae (order Trogoniformes), birds inhabiting the tropical forests of the Old and New Worlds, differ from all other bird orders in the formation of the foot – the first and second, not the first and fourth toes being reversed. Trogons are not particularly active nor are they sociable birds, being inclined rather to sit motionless on a branch, darting off only to capture insects. They are dependent on their wings for procuring food as their legs are small and weak and unfit for walking. The exceptionally soft feathers glow with brilliant hues; the male and female show marked differences in colouration. The bill is short and strong with a curved ridge terminating in a hook; the mandibles are as a rule serrated. During the breeding season they are seen in pairs, both sexes sharing the duties of incubating the 3–5 blue-white or brownish eggs.

The **Slaty-tailed Trogon,** *Trogon massena* [754], about the size of a dove, is bronze-green above and on the neck, the breast and belly are white. The upper wing-coverts are beautifully vermiculated in grey and white. It occurs from Mexico to north-western South America.

755

The most ornate of the trogons is the **Quetzal,**
Pharomachrus mocinno [755], a bird of remarkable
beauty, coloured bronze-green with bright red and
white underparts. A full crest adorns the head, and the
tail-coverts of the male are extended to form plumes
over 3 ft long. The Quetzal breeds from southern
Mexico to western Panama but is most popular in
Guatemala, where it appears on postage stamps,
coins, and on the state seal. It has also given its name
to the country's monetary unit.

384

xxvi **Tawny Owl** *Strix aluco*

xxvii **Long-eared Owl** *Asio otus*

xxviii **Common Kingfisher** *Alcedo atthis*

756

Colies or Mousebirds

The six species of coly form a small order, Coliiformes, with a single family, Coliidae. They are all found in central and southern Africa and are remarkably alike, grey or brown in plumage – the sexes are similar – with long tails, red legs and bright bare skin by the eyes. From their curious mammalian gait along branches they are also called mousebirds. They are gregarious, the flocks flying about the forests where they live to feed on vegetation at all stages from bud to berry and on insects. The substantial nests contain 2–7 eggs, white sometimes with brown markings. Both sexes share parental duties. The young, fed by regurgitation, soon leave the nest by day to clamber about the neighbouring foliage, returning at night; they fledge when about three weeks old. The **Speckled Mousebird** or **Coly**, *Colius striatus* [756], of central and east Africa, is 14 in. long, with a slight crest, and a breast which appears speckled due to the pale tips of the feathers. It has harsh and twittering calls.

Kingfishers and allies

The order Coraciiformes comprises widely varied forms of birds which have been classed as independent orders by some authorities. They all have the three front toes united for part of their length. The distribution is mainly tropical and subtropical but they are also found in temperate regions. The seven families of this order number some 190 species.

Of the kingfishers (family Alcedinidae), only the 6-in. **Common Kingfisher**, *Alcedo atthis* [colour plate XXVIII], is found in Europe. The upper parts are a bright blue-green, the underparts rusty brown, the sides of the neck and the bill black. With its shrill whistling note it flies like an arrow along the courses of rivers and streams, perching on a branch overhanging the water to spot the small fish which are its chief food. The birds dig nesting burrows 3 ft deep

757

758

759

in mud or sand banks, terminating in a round chamber
where the 6 to 8 young are
reared. The Common King-
fisher is widespread in southern Eurasia, and from South
Africa east to the Solomons.
The small, 4½-in.-long
Pygmy or **Painted Kingfisher,** *Ispidina picta* [758],
ranging from Senegal and
Eritrea south to Natal, differs
from the usual conception of
the kingfisher in that it does
not perch above the water to
sight its prey but hunts in the
grass for the insects on which
it feeds; it occurs only exceptionally near water. The
crown is black with blue
transverse stripes, the back
and upper wing-coverts are
ultramarine, the throat white
and the underparts reddish
brown. The largest member
of this family is the 17-in.
Kookaburra or **Laughing
Jackass,** *Dacelo gigas* [757], a
common and very popular
bird in Australia, whose
laughing cries are heard
especially in the early morning. It feeds chiefly on small
mammals, young birds,
snakes and large insects, and
nests in hollow trees or in
termite nests. The upper parts
are dark brown, the wings
spotted grey-blue; a white
band separates the head from

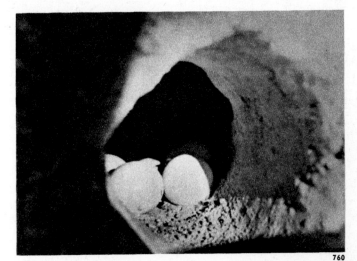

760

761

the body, there is a dark stripe
through the eye, the underparts are white and the strong
bill is blackish.

Members of the genus
Halcyon are distinguished by
a broad stout bill and somewhat longer legs. They often
frequent the banks of rivers
but their diet does not consist of fish, being more or less
the same as that of the Kookaburra. The **Black-capped
Kingfisher,** *Halcyon pileata*
[759], the only member of this
genus widespread in Africa,
the East Indies, Australia and
India, ranges north all the way
to Japan and Korea. The head
is black and the upper parts
ultramarine. The 4–6 white
eggs [760], are laid on the
mud banks of rivers.

The members of the genus
Tanysiptera are beautiful
kingfishers with two greatly
elongated, narrow, racquet-
tipped central tail feathers.
The exact number of species
is not known, but there are
not more than six. Their distribution is mainly limited to
New Guinea and the neigh-
bouring islands. One species
is found in Australia. The
Short-billed Kingfisher,
Tanysiptera microrhyncha
[761], of New Guinea, is blue-
black above with pale blue
head.

The motmots, family Momotidae, comprise eight species, of which one is shown here. The **Blue-crowned Motmot** or **King-of-the-woods,** *Momotus momota* [762], inhabiting the tropical forests of Central and South America from Mexico to Argentina, is green above with a blue head and a black crown and eye-stripe. The throat and flanks are rusty brown. The bird's most interesting feature is the 12-in.-long tail which it moves from side to side when excited; the two central tail feathers are greatly elongated with bare shafts and only small fans at the tips. This shape is produced by the bird nibbling off the vanes; the new tail feathers which grow after the moult are fully webbed.

The bee-eaters, 25 species of the family Meropidae, inhabit the warm and dry wooded and open steppes of the Old World. Only one species occurs in southern Europe and has nested in England and in the Channel Islands—the 11-in. rainbow-coloured **European Bee-eater,** *Merops apiaster* [763, colour plate XXIX]. The plumage is a magnificent combination of colours—white forehead, chestnut crown and back, green-blue underparts, bright yellow throat, rump and shoulder feathers, the wings tinged with blue, green and brown. The pointed central tail feathers extend beyond the rest. They are easily visible in flight and are a little reminiscent of the swallow [764]. The mainstay of its diet is bees and

762
763

wasps which the bird catches on the wing. The nesting burrows are dug by both sexes in sand or mud to a depth of 4–6½ ft. Unlike kingfishers, bee- eaters are colonial nesters. The 4–6 young rest on the indigestible hard body cases of insects which they cast up.

765

The family Coraciidae, found chiefly in Africa and extending through the tropics of the Old World to Australia and New Zealand, numbers 17 species in all.

One of these, the 13-in. **European Roller,** *Coracias garrulus* [765], is coloured green-blue with rusty back and shoulders, dark blue rump, lighter blue wing-coverts and the wing quills tinged dark red. The favourite nesting sites are old hollow trees, sometimes abandoned woodpeckers' holes [766], and as these are slowly disappearing from parks so is this bird.

767

A spring sound in regions with spreading meadows
and pasturelands, and here and there a hollow tree, is
the "hoop-hoop" of the **Hoopoe,** *Upupa epops* [767,

768

768], one of the six species of the family Upupidae.
This bird is so distinctive, with its orange-brown
plumage and black and white barred wings and tail,
that it can be mistaken for no other. The most prominent feature, however, is the long, black-tipped crest
which the bird expands and contracts when it is
agitated.

The nest is made in the hollows of trees, sometimes
in a pile of rocks or underneath a roof. The female
alone incubates the 5–10 greenish to brownish-grey
eggs for 15–16 days. The nest is foul and smelly
from the droppings of the young birds and also from
the black secretion of the preen gland which the
female and young exude when danger threatens. The
Hoopoe uses its long bill to probe soil and refuse for
its food–insects and worms and other small animal
life, including lizards. It inhabits Eurasia, except the
northern regions, Africa and Madagascar. It nests
occasionally in England, where it is seen regularly
on spring and autumn passage.

Most unusual nesting habits are displayed by the 45 species of hornbills (family Bucerotidae) found in Africa and the Indo-Australian Region. With one exception they all nest in tree cavities, the female being sealed in by the male. Sometimes the female also assists in the task from within. Mud, dirt, their own dung and even regurgitated food are used to plaster up the hole, leaving only a small slit through which the male feeds his partner and through which the female voids. The nest, unlike that of the hoopoes, is fairly clean. The hen goes through her moult while incubating the 1–6 eggs, remaining in her voluntary prison during the period the young are being fed before coming out to resume her normal life. The reason for this peculiar habit is doubtless to protect

771

772

The **Great Hornbill,** *Buceros bicornis* [769, 771], of India, Indochina and Sumatra, measures up to 40 in. in length and is distinguished by its black and white plumage. The yellow bill, unlike that of other members of this family, is not hollow but solid; the natives use it to carve ornaments.

The **Black-casqued Hornbill,** *Ceratogymna atrata* [772], of west Africa, measuring 3 ft in length, has a bare throat with a wattle. The plumage is black with white-tipped outer tail feathers. The male has a cylindrical casque, that of the female, whose head and neck are coloured red-brown, is less developed.

the young from enemies—monkeys and tree snakes. Hornbills are distinguished by the immensely developed downcurved bill surmounted by a horny casque. Both bill and casque are hollow or filled with cellular bony tissue so that they are light in weight (see cross-section of the bill of the **Rhinoceros Hornbill,** *Buceros rhinoceros,* in picture 770). A peculiar feature, rare among birds, is the hornbills' prominent eyelashes.

Hornbills vary considerably in size, ranging from 15 to 60 in. in length. Members of the genus Tockus are birds about the size of a magpie with comparatively long tails and less developed bills, and only a rudimentary casque or none at all. The **Red-billed Hornbill,** *Tockus erythrorhynchus* [773], measuring 20 in., is distinguished by a red bill, sometimes black at the base of the mandible. It is brownish black above with white markings and white below. It nests in Africa south of Senegal and Somaliland. The imprisoned female remains on the nest up to two months during which time she moults, the male bringing her food on 30–40 occasions. When she leaves the nest the young are already able to seal themselves in with wooden chips and saliva while both parents continue to supply them with food.

The **Pied Hornbill,** *Anthracoceros coronatus* [774], has the sides of the neck and the chin bare. The yellow bill is marked with black; the casque of the male ends in front in a point. The plumage is black, the underparts, tips of the wing quills and marginal tail feathers white. It inhabits India and Malaya, foraging for the various fruits which are its food in groups, rarely alone.

773

Woodpeckers and allies

Though the bills of toucans (family Ramphastidae) are as huge as those of the hornbills, these peculiar birds belong to the order Piciformes, all of whose members have feet with the first and fourth toes reversed, and all of which are cavity nesters. The eggs, needing no protective colouration, are pure white and the young, hatching naked and blind after 16–18 days, remain up to six weeks in the nest, cared for by both parents. The bill is big and simple without any excrescence, brightly coloured as a rule and with serrated edges. If the bill were of a solid horny substance the bird would have difficulty lifting its head and it would interfere with its powers of movement; however, as with the hornbills,

it is hollow and reinforced with a network of bony columns so that it is quite light. Nevertheless, one wonders why the bill is so large; it does not have any use as a weapon, nor is the size of any particular importance in procuring food or eating. The most convincing reason for it is that the shape and colour play some part in the bird's social life; many species clap their bills loudly in courtship. The tongue is comparatively narrow and extends to the tip of the bill, its sides fringed with bristles. The fruit which is the mainstay of their diet is plucked and eaten whole or else masticated with the aid of the bill's serrated edges.

A frequent inhabitant of zoos is the **Green-billed** or **Red-breasted Toucan,** *Ramphastos discolorus* [775], of south-east Brazil and north-east Argentina. Unlike others of this family it has a fairly short beak measuring about one-fifth of its total body length of 20 in. The back is black, the upper tail-coverts red, the throat, cheeks and foreneck yellow and orange, the chest, belly and naked eye-rims red. The bill, which has a black band at the base, is green. The smaller **Ariel Toucan,** *Ramphastos ariel* [776, 778], has a yellow and black band separating the black bill from the head. The throat is yellow, the breast and

780
781

upper and under tail-coverts red. Recent opinion has it that this bird is only a form of the **Sulphur-and-white-breasted Toucan,** *Ramphastos vitellinus,* a common inhabitant of the rain-forests of north-eastern South America to central Brazil. The native name Toco, from which the word "toucan" evolved, was used for the scientific name of the largest member of this family – the **Toco Toucan,** *Rhamphastos toco* [777]. This bird is black with white rump, throat and foreneck, red under tail-coverts and an orange-yellow bill with a black patch at the tip of the upper jaw [779]. This toucan frequents the rain-forests from Guiana to Bolivia and northern Argentina.

The **Spotted-billed Toucanet,** *Selenidera maculirostris* [780, colour plate XXX], of south-east Brazil has a whitish black-striped bill which is smaller than in most toucans. The bird, measuring 13 in., is green-black above with a black head, neck and chest. A yellow longitudinal band runs under the eye along the sides of the head.

The next two birds are the smaller toucans known as araçaris (genus Pteroglossus), comprising eleven species ranging from Mexico to Argentina. They are extremely gregarious, moving about in small flocks during the day and even roosting together at night in tree cavities. The **Lettered Araçari,** *Pteroglossus inscriptus* [781], of Guyana and regions bordering the Amazon, has a black head and throat, the remaining

underparts being yellow and
the upper parts green-black.
The white bill has black markings which are a little reminiscent of lettering. The brilliantly plumaged **Collared** or
Ringed Araçari, *Pteroglossus torquatus* [782], found from
southern Mexico to northern
South America, has a black
head and neck with a green
gloss, a chestnut neckband
and red lower back, rump and
upper tail-coverts. The remaining upper surface is
green-black. The under surface is yellow and red with a
black breast-patch and black
and red band on the belly. The
black and white bill has a
782 narrow white basal stripe.

xxx **Spotted-billed Toucanet** *Selenidera maculirostis*

xxxi **Green Woodpecker** *Picus viridis*

The **Black-backed** or **Levaillant's Barbet,** *Trac-hyphonus vaillantii* [783], is a member of another family of Piciformes – the barbets (family Capitoni-dae) which have heavy bills with conspicuous bristles. They inhabit the tropics of the Old and New Worlds but are absent in Australia and Madagascar. There are 72 known species, most of them found in Africa, which is the home of the barbet pictured here. It frequents the bushes of the dry steppes from Angola and Tanganyika to South Africa. It is a glossy blue-black and black, the forehead, sides of the neck and underparts yellow, and has a black crest.

The largest of the six in this order is the woodpecker family (Picidae), with 210 species. Woodpeckers are specially adapted to climbing the trunks of trees and chiselling wood in quest of food – chiefly the grubs of borers found in the wood and under the bark, but also ants and other insects and seeds. Their sharp curved claws enable them to cling to the bark and their strong, stiff pointed tail feathers (10–12) are used as props when on a tree trunk, the body tilted away so that it has a greater swing with its beak. The large wedge-shaped bill is covered with a thick horny layer, the tip shaped like a chisel. With this

beak the woodpecker uncovers the grubs in the wood, but it is the long tongue, specially adapted for this purpose, which is used to extract them from the tunnels. The tongue is in fact an extensile spear whose hard, pointed tip, equipped with barbs and a gluey secretion, hooks the grubs. Woodpeckers are mainly woodland birds widespread throughout most of the world with the exception of Australia and Madagas-car. The wings are well developed. The 2–10 pure white eggs are placed in unlined holes excavated in trees or in termite nests. Both sexes share the duties of incubation, which takes from 10 to 17 days; the young fledge after 19–28 days.

The above general description does not apply in all

786
787

details to the subfamily of wrynecks (Jynginae); these birds have soft tail feathers and small bills which are not used for pecking and boring, and they perch on a branch in the normal fashion, not lengthwise like the true woodpeckers. They do not excavate their own nests but utilize either natural cavities or holes made by other woodpeckers. When foraging for food the **Wryneck**, *Jynx torquilla* [784], hops about on the ground where it feeds on insects, chiefly ants. The plumage, grey with darker brown-grey markings, is somewhat similar to that of a Nightjar and it is difficult to distinguish a bird from the bark of the tree on which it is perching. When danger threatens it extends its long neck, twisting its head from side to side, at the same time erecting its short head crest [785]. A migratory bird, it inhabits Europe and Asia all the way to Japan, but is now very scarce in Britain, breeding only in south-east England.

The American continent is the home of several genera of woodpeckers of which Centurus, found from the southern United States to southern South America, is distinguished by the conspicuously barred upper surface. The **West Indian Woodpecker**, *Centurus superciliaris* [786], of Cuba and the Bahamas, has back, wings, shoulders and tail barred black and white, and a pale grey undersurface. In the male the crown and back of the head are red, in the female only the back of the head. The **Red-bellied Woodpecker**, *Centurus carolinus*, of the southeastern United States, and the **Golden-fronted Woodpecker**, *Centurus aurifrons*, found from Texas to Costa Rica, are essentially similar species.

The call of the **Grey-headed Woodpecker**, *Picus canus* [787], is commonly heard in spring in the woodlands of Europe. The picture shows two of these birds beside their nesting hole. They measure 10 in. in length. This species is distinguished from the similar **Green Woodpecker**, *Picus viridis* [colour plate XXXI], by the grey head and neck and narrow black whisker mark. The forehead of the male Grey-headed Woodpecker is red, but the female's head is uniformly grey. Its favourite haunts are broad-leaved woods and it is sometimes found in the mountains. It breeds in Europe, extending in a wide band through Siberia to Japan and thence southward through Burma to Sumatra.

Whereas the Green Woodpecker is frequently seen on the ground feeding on insects, especially ants, members of the genus Dendrocopos are much more arboreal, seeking their food by pecking at the trunks of trees. In spring can be heard the curious "drumming" noise produced by these birds instead of a

789

790

song. The **Great Spotted Woodpecker,** *Dendro-copos major* [788, 791], measuring 9 in., is one of the most plentiful European species, with characteristic black and white markings, the area around the vent coloured crimson. The male has a red patch on the nape. It inhabits the forests of Europe and Asia, both in the lowlands and in high mountains. The related **Lesser Spotted Woodpecker,** *Dendrocopos minor* [789], measures only 6 in. The front part of the crown

791

is red in the male, white in the female; in both sexes the upper surface is black thickly striped with white, the underparts pure white. It is a common though not plentiful inhabitant of Eurasian woodlands. Old stands of conifers, particularly when mixed with beech in the west, and stretching from Europe through northern Asia to Kamchatka in Siberia, are the home of the **Black Woodpecker,** *Dryocopus martius* [790]. In this species the plumage is entirely black with the exception of the red-topped head in the male (in the female only a red neck-patch). The 4–5 eggs are laid on the floor of the excavated cavity, which is lined only with a layer of woodchips. Incubation takes under three weeks. The Black Woodpecker seeks its food on trees but, like the Green Woodpecker, it also feeds on the ground on ants and their pupae. In old decaying trees it sometimes bores huge holes in its search for grubs, being joined in this task by the Great Spotted Woodpecker [792].

Among the largest of woodpeckers are the handsome crested American birds of the genus Campephilus, some of which are on the verge of extinction, like the **Ivory-billed Woodpecker,** *Campephilus principalis,* which once inhabited Cuba, Mexico and the woodlands of the south-eastern United States, but of which there have only been a few records in recent years. As the name indicates, these birds have strong, ivory-coloured bills. The largest of all is the black and white **Imperial Woodpecker,** *Campephilus imperialis* [793] which measures 22 in. This bird frequents the mountains of north-western Mexico. The male has a red, the female a black crest. Like the other members of the genus, this bird is fast disappearing as the old forest giants are being felled.

Perching Birds

The last bird order, the perching birds (Passeriformes), contains more than 5,000 species, many more than all other orders combined. They are birds of small to medium size–for example, of the European song-birds the smallest is the Goldcrest (weighing 5 grams) and the largest the Raven (1,250 grams–nearly 3 lb). All have one toe behind and three–the second, third and fourth–in front. Otherwise they show marked variations in structure–shape of body, wings, feet, tail and bill. This great diversity results from the adaptation of the different species to various environments. Passerines were probably tree-living birds originally. Today they are found in all parts of the globe from the arctic tundras to the tropical rain-forests, in deserts and high mountains. An important characteristic of these birds is their power of song, produced by a syrinx (voice organ) of great perfection controlled by as many as 5–8 pairs of song muscles. This power of song, with a few exceptions, is exercised only by the male although the syrinx of the female is almost identical in structure. The eggs are coloured, as a rule, with various markings, the clutch comprising 4–6 eggs with often several broods in the year. Both sexes usually share the duties of incubation. The young are blind on hatching and usually covered with only a thin layer of down. They are fed by the parents until they are able to fend for themselves.

Ornithologists are not agreed on the classification of this order but as a rule it is divided into several suborders: the Eurylaimi, Clamatores, Menurae and Oscines.

794

The first of these, the Eurylaimi, comprises the single family of broadbills (Eurylaimidae) with its 14 species of brightly coloured birds distinguished from the other passerines by the simple syrinx and by having 15 instead of 14 neck vertebrae. Of the species widespread throughout south-east Asia and Africa, **Whitehead's Broadbill,** *Calyptomena whiteheadi* [794], coloured a glossy green with black markings and with a black patch under the bill, makes its home in the mountain forests of Borneo.

795

796

408

The family of ovenbirds (Furnariidae, suborder Clamatores), comprising 215 species, extends from southern Mexico to Patagonia. They are plain-coloured birds distinguished by their unusual types of nests. The **Rufous Ovenbird** or **Baker,** *Furnarius rufus* [795], is the best known of all. Measuring about 8 in., it is rust brown above, lighter below. It is a common inhabitant of the open country of southern Brazil, Paraguay and Argentina. During the rainy season from December to February it is known to build its nest of mud, grass and straw in as little as three weeks. The nest is located out in the open on fence-posts and bare branches or on the eaves of houses. It is 12 in. long, 10 in. high and weighs about

797

798

799

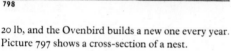

20 lb, and the Ovenbird builds a new one every year. Picture 797 shows a cross-section of a nest.

Only a few feathered inhabitants of tropical forests have white plumage. Certain species of bellbirds (family Cotingidae) are one example. The white male **Naked-throated Bellbird,** *Procnias nudicollis* [799], of north-east Brazil has the bare face and throat coloured bright green; the female's plumage is a soft green-grey. Similar in colouration is the **White Bellbird,** *Procnias nivea* [796], of Guiana and Venezuela, which has a long, slightly feathered fleshy caruncle on the forehead. Both birds measure about 11 in. Even more remarkable is the ornament of the **Three-wattled Bellbird,** *Procnias tricarunculata* [800], a red-brown bird whose white head, as the name indicates, is adorned with three long wattles. Its range extends from Nicaragua to Panama. The note of the bellbirds is a loud, clear peal said to carry for a distance of over half a mile.

The region from southern Mexico to Paraguay is the home of the manakins (Pipridae) – lovely, active little birds of the tropical and subtropical forests, number-ing in all 59 species. The males are not only brilliantly coloured, but are often adorned with various feathered ornaments, all of which they put to good use during their courtship display. This is quite unique in the avian world, consisting of intricate dances both on the ground and in trees, performed in special territories cleared for the purpose – the court-ing male even removes the leaves on a branch so that they do not interfere with his movements. The dances are generally performed before the female. Manakins are polygamous and the males do not take part in rearing the young nor in building the nest. The sounds they make are usually very un-bird-like, for example, smacking and clapping. In addition the males of some species produce various rattlings and buzzings by the vibration of specially constructed flight feathers.

The **Blue-backed** or **Sharp-tailed Manakin,** *Chiroxiphia pareola* [798], measuring only 3½ in., occurs in the Amazon region, Venezuela and Guiana. The male is black with a cobalt blue mantle and crimson crest. In this species the green-coloured female is courted by two males, sometimes more, at one time.

800
801

Cocks-of-the-rock, genus Rupicola, inhabit the moss- and fern-covered ground of South American mountain forests and valleys. They gather in forest clearings to perform their courtship display, in which their bright colours, large, disk-like crests and voices all play a part. The courtship dance is communal, as a rule, with as many as twenty males showing off before the brown-coloured females. The hens build shallow nests of mud, grass and moss which they fasten to the walls of rocks, in crevices, caves and clefts. The clutch consists of two whitish, dark-spotted eggs. According to some authorities there are three species. The **Smaller** or **Common Cock-of-the-rock**, *Rupicola rupicola* [801], is bright orange with a narrow black border on the crest. The large, 14-inch **Scarlet** or **Peruvian Cock-of-the-rock**, *Rupicola peruviana* [802], has scarlet plumage. The wing quills and tail of both species are black or brownish black. Their range of distribution extends in the Andes from Bolivia to Ecuador. The **Colombian Cock-of-the-rock,** *Rupicola sanguinolenta*, which is also found in west Ecuador, is very similar, though an even brighter red, and may only be a geographical race of *Rupicola peruviana*.

The tyrant flycatchers (Tyrannidae) are a New World family of over 360 species and are not at all closely related to the Old World flycatchers, though some of the smaller species show a remarkable convergence both in appearance and habits. The tyrant flycatchers are noisy, conspicuous birds in spite of generally dull plumages; they make up for this by aggressive behaviour. The males of some larger species have prominent crests and others have long tails, but the majority are under a foot in total length. The family is distinguished by weak legs suitable only for perching, and by broad, often hooked bills with bristles— the sign of aerial insect hunters—at the base. Nests vary from neatly slung baskets on slender twigs to elaborate domes in the tropics, while several build in holes of all kinds, natural and man-made. Eggs are also variable, from white to well-marked, and clutches run from 2 to 6 eggs. Both sexes build and feed the brood, but usually only the female hatches the eggs, which may take under a fortnight or up to three weeks, according to size, with similar fledging periods. One of the most striking and abundant tropical species is the **Great Kiskadee**, *Pitangus sulphuratus*, 9 in. long and found from the southern parts of Texas to Argentina; the bird illustrated [803] is the **Rufous-winged Kiskadee,** subspecies *rufipennis*, which occurs in Colombia and Venezuela. The name Kiskadee comes from its strident call. The flycatching life of this species suits open habitats with trees, such as parklands. It also catches fish, diving after them like a kingfisher.

802

803

All the colours of the rainbow are to be found in the plumage of the pittas (family Pittidae), small birds inhabiting the thick undergrowth of Old World jungles and tropical forests and resembling round bundles with long legs. The large head is attached to the plump body by a short neck and the tail is also extremely short, a mere stump in some species.

The pittas spend most of the time on the ground, though powers of flight are well developed in the migratory species. They are distributed throughout south-east Asia and the neighbouring islands; two species occur in Africa, three in Australia. The **Blue-winged** or **Fairy Pitta,** *Pitta brachyura* [804], extends from south Japan through southern

China and Malaysia to northern India. With its bill and feet it rummages in fallen leaves in search of the small animal life it feeds on. It perches on branches only at night and when calling. The plumage is a combination of brown, black, white, green, red and blue. Like the other members of its family, it builds a large globular nest of twigs, roots, bark and grass with an opening at the side.

The New Zealand wrens (Acanthisittidae) were a family of four very small insectivorous birds, superficially like the European Wren with their stumpy tails, round bodies and thin, slightly curved bills. One species is now extinct, two are rare, but the **Rifleman,** *Acanthisitta chloris* [805], is widespread in the native beech forest of the North and South Islands, each having its distinctive race. The Rifleman is also, at 3 in., the smallest native New Zealand bird and perhaps the commonest. The males are mostly green, the females streaked olive and dark brown; the white underparts are flecked with yellow and dark brown. The Rifleman has virtually no tail, but flicks its wings continually. It runs up a trunk like a Treecreeper and the nest may also be like a creeper's under bark, or in a hole of small entrance diameter. The height ranges from ground level to 60 ft and the nest is built in October and November. Both parents incubate the clutch of 4 or 5 eggs, and they will visit the nest boldly when the young are hatched. Polygamy has been recorded.

804

805

The lyrebirds, classed as an independent suborder (Menurae) and family (Menuridae) consisting of two species, were originally thought to be pheasants because of their strong legs and long tails, but they were soon found to possess a fairly complex syrinx. This and their wide vocal range indicates their relation to the songbirds. Not only do these birds have their own distinctive notes but they are also able to mimic other bird songs and sounds such as the hooting of a railway locomotive, the honking of a motor horn, or the barking of dogs. The **Superb Lyrebird,** *Menura novaehollandiae* [806], inhabits the forests of southeast Australia. The male measures up to 52 in., including the tail which is about 28 in. long and consists of 16 feathers. Of these the two exterior feathers are curved like a lyre, their outside webs narrow, the inner webs broad, light coloured with darker bands. The next six pairs of feathers lack barbules to hold the vanes together and therefore hang loosely. The central pair, long and narrow, cross to sweep outwards. The courting cock spreads his tail and lays it on his back so that almost his entire body is covered by it, and the silver white underside of the feathers glows in the dusk amidst the thick forest undergrowth. The male usually performs his display on a mound of mud and humus which it scrapes together for the purpose. The female's tail is much shorter and has only 12 quills. She alone builds the large domed nest in which she deposits her single egg. 806

413

807

The last passerine suborder comprises 4,000 song-birds (Oscines) whose syrinx has generally 5–9 pairs of song muscles. The larks (family Alaudidae), containing 75 species, are a truly distinctive group, with the tarsus scaled not only in front, as in the other oscines, but also along the sides, and with a syrinx operated by five pairs of muscles. That they are ground birds is borne out not only by their sombre colouring but also by the long claw on the large hind toe which enables them to run with ease in the steppes

808

and deserts of Africa where the majority of larks make their home. The long broad wings make them good fliers, able to soar high up in the air and remain almost motionless in one spot. Their diet consists of insects, with their larvae and grubs, and also seeds. The open, cup-shaped nests, placed in slight depressions in the soil, are built by the female alone. There are 2 or 3 clutches in the year, with 2–6 eggs which hatch after 11 or 12 days. The female incubates while the male provides her with food. The duties of rearing the young, which are able to fly at the age of 10–12 days, are shared by both sexes. Larks' haunts are the deserts, fields and moors of the whole world.

The **Skylark**, *Alauda arvensis* [807, 810], measuring 7 in., is earthy brown, barred with black above and creamy white below, with a small crest on the head. It is a partly migratory bird which leaves its winter quarters along the Mediterranean in early spring, sometimes in February, to sing high in the sky above its nesting ground. It is found in Europe, north-west Africa and temperate Asia, and has also become established in Australia, New Zealand and Vancouver Island, British Columbia, where it was introduced by immigrants.

Whereas the Skylark sings during the daytime hanging almost motionless high up in the sky, the related **Woodlark**, *Lullula arborea* [808], describes wide arcs in the air as it sings, and its melodious, somewhat melancholy voice can be heard also on clear nights. Some consider its song to be even better than the nightingale's. The Woodlark has a shorter tail than the Skylark and a pale stripe above the eye. It frequents the edges of forests and heaths ranging throughout Europe, south-west Asia and north-west Africa. Like Skylarks, many winter in western Europe and the Mediterranean region, migrating to their breeding grounds in February and March. The nest, located on the ground, is a deep cup shape lined with vegetable fibres and hairs, the sides strengthened with roots, grasses and moss. The first clutch of 3–5 whitish, dark-speckled eggs is laid in March or April.

810

The **Crested Lark,** *Galerida cristata* [809, 811, 812], is the same size and colouration as the Skylark but has a longer bill and a more prominent crown. It frequents dry, unattractive locations such as garbage-dumps, outskirts of human habitations, untilled land and railway embankments, where it runs tirelessly to and fro, occasionally flying short distances. Its simple song, not nearly as lovely as that of the Skylark, can be heard in flight or when the bird is seated on some higher vantage point. The nest, built in April, is placed in a depression in the soil, sometimes quite near railway tracks or on the roofs of low buildings and often, like other larks, in the grass [809]. The 3–5 eggs, resembling those of the Skylark, are white, spotted a darker colour. The Crested Lark is a resident species extending throughout much of Europe and temperate Asia to Korea and southwards to north Africa.

Song Thrush *Turdus philomelos*

xxxiii **Rock Thrush** *Monticola saxatilis*

The **Shore Lark** or **Horned Lark,** *Eremophila alpestris* [813, 814], has an interesting range of distribution. One population inhabits the far northern tundras of Eurasia, another the high mountains of south-east Europe, still others the mountains of inner Asia, always far above the timber line where the climate resembles that of the arctic tundra. All the more surprising is the extension of its breeding range to the dry and warm regions of north Africa and Syria. Some authorities consider this desert race to be a distinct species. It also inhabits the fields, plains and deserts of North America. from the arctic tundra to Mexico in the west and the middle Atlantic states in the east. Isolated populations are also found above the tree-line on certain peaks of the Andes in South America. The plumage is brown above, the face and throat yellow, a black stripe on the forehead extending to the black horns, and with a black patch on the breast and cheeks. The female

815

is duller. In winter the Shore Lark may be seen also in central Europe, and some come to the east coast of Britain.

The swallows and martins (75 species of the family Hirundinidae) are slender, elongated birds with long pointed wings and forked tails. They are past-masters in flight, shooting like arrows up into the sky, where they soar and swoop, performing all sorts of manoeuvres. Their keen eyesight enables them to spot the smallest insect and the wide gape equipped with bristles indicates that swallows feed on insects caught on the wing. On the ground, where they alight only to gather material for their nests, they move clumsily for they have weak legs. Their song consists chiefly of twittering and chirping. They are wide-

816

817

spread throughout the whole world with the exception of New Zealand, the Arctic and the Antarctic. The five species native to Europe are migratory birds. Though showing a marked resemblance to the swifts, there is no relationship between the two groups; the superficial likeness is the result of a parallel development, adaptation to the same way of living.

The **Common** or **Barn Swallow**, *Hirundo rustica* [818], glossy blue-black above with a brownish red forehead and throat, a dark blue band on the breast and creamy white underparts, and measuring about 8 in., builds an open nest of mud strengthened with grass and straw and lined with feathers, both sexes taking part in its construction. The 4–6 eggs are incubated mostly by the female while the male may sleep at night perched on the edge of the nest [815]. Sometimes he too sits on the eggs in the female's absence, but his services are only temporary as he lacks the bare brood patch which provides the eggs with the temperature necessary for their successful hatching. Incubation takes 14–16 days and another 21 days are needed for the young to fledge [816]. They return to roost in the nest for several more nights before leaving it permanently. The breeding

distribution includes almost all of Eurasia and North America as well as part of north Africa. Being dependent on insects for its food, the Swallow is a migratory bird; European Swallows migrate to central and southern Africa, eastern birds to south-east Asia, and North American individuals to South America. Widespread in southern Europe, Africa, and southern and eastern Asia is the **Red-rumped Swallow,** *Hirundo daurica* [817], a little smaller than the Common Swallow. It is easily distinguished by the rusty yellow rump and creamy underparts without the dark breast-band. The pointed outer tail feathers are shorter and the wing tips more blunt than in the Swallow. It is not found exclusively near human habitations but nests also in rocks and sand or mud banks. The nest is shaped like a retort with a tube for entrance at the side instead of a simple hole. These swallows also gather in large flocks before migration, often perching on telephone wires as in the illustration.

The **House Martin,** *Delichon urbica* [819], is confined to Eurasia and Africa. It has a deeply forked tail like the Swallow and is completely white on the underside. Its clean white rump is conspicuous in flight. The covered nest, with a narrow entrance at the upper edge, is placed under leaves and cornices; in some regions, as was the original habit, also on rock faces. The House Martin is somewhat smaller than the Swallow. The smallest European species is the **Sand Martin** or (in the USA) **Bank Swallow,** *Riparia riparia* [820], 4¾ in. long, which is interesting for its nesting habits – large colonies of nest holes are dug in vertical sand or clay banks [821], one entrance hole practically on top

820

of another [823]. It is amazing how a bird with such delicate feet and bill is capable of scraping out the tunnel, which is about 2 ft long, in the hard sand or clay. The chamber at the end of the slightly up-turned tunnel holds the nest where the eggs are laid and the young reared. Both parents share the duties of incubation and feeding. Like all swallows, they will return to the same nest the following year if they survive their migration. The Sand Martin inhabits Eurasia and North America and in some regions the nesting colonies hold thousands of pairs. Its plumage is quite distinct from that of the Swallow and House Martin, with brown upper parts and breast-band. It is slightly smaller than the House Martin and the tail fork is so shallow that it is not visible even when the tail is outspread.

The drongos (family Dicruridae) are forest birds about the size of a thrush, sometimes larger, with a stout bill resembling a raven's. They are usually black and many have a crest or ornamental plumes. They watch for the large insects which are their main food from high exposed sites, then dart out to catch them in the air as well as on the ground. Like the orioles, they build shallow, saucer-like nests in the forks of branches. They attack savagely any bird that trespasses on their nesting territory. The voice is harsh, though some males have a melodious song and some are good mimics of other birds. **821** The drongos, a family of 20 species, inhabit Africa south of the Sahara and extend from India and China to north Australia and the Solomons. The **Large Racquet-tailed Drongo,** *Dicrurus paradiseus* [822], ranging from the Himalayas to Java and Borneo, has wire-like outer tail feathers whose bare shafts terminate in flags or racquets. The bird measures 27 in. from the bill to the tip of these tail feathers.

There are 34 species of orioles (family Oriolidae), all of which inhabit the forests and forest steppes of the Old World, mainly in the tropical zone. These birds are typical tree-dwellers which feed on various insects, their larvae and pupae, as well as on fruits of various kinds. The cup-shaped nest, built chiefly by the female, is placed high up in the forks of horizontal branches [825[.

822

823

823

824

825

424

Only when spring is well advanced does the **Golden Oriole,** *Oriolus oriolus* [824], utter its song, which may be mistaken for a boy's whistling by the uninitiated, from the tops of broad-leaved trees. The bird is more often heard than seen, for it rarely leaves thick cover. Only when it flies across open spaces is there a glimpse of the male's bright yellow plumage with contrasting black wings and tail. The female is more soberly coloured in yellow-green. It breeds in Europe and southwest Asia, including India, and is among the last of the migratory species to arrive in Europe; in August it is off again to central Africa. It is a rare summer visitor to England, where it nests occasionally.

The crows (family Corvidae) are often placed at the top of the avian family tree because of their high intelligence. In the bird world they frequently play the role of police, heralding the approach of danger, and are able to judge a situation to a certain extent. Every sportsman knows that he can come up much closer to a sitting crow when he is without a gun. Their high intelligence is best demonstrated by captive birds which have been taught to perform various tricks as well as to pronounce words, thanks to their powers of mimicry. The crows are the heaviest of the passerine birds, and their 100 species are distributed throughout the entire world.

In many species the nostrils are covered with bristles, as can be seen in the close-up of the **Raven,** *Corvus corax* [826, 827], a large, robust bird measuring about 25 in. At one time

826

827

it ranged throughout the whole northern hemisphere, but was completely exterminated in many places, thus becoming a rare bird in central Europe. But in recent years it has begun to make new inroads from the east. Its favourite haunts are cliffs, where the nest is built on a ledge, but it is also frequently placed in high trees.

The **Carrion Crow,** *Corvus corone corone,* and **Hooded Crow,** *Corvus corone corvix* [828], are considered great pests by game-preservers. They are two geographical

831

832

races of the same species. The "Hoodie" is ashy grey with black wings, tail, head and chest, the "Carrion" is black with a green and purple gloss [831, 832]. The River Elbe forms the line of demarcation between the distribution of the two in Europe, the Carrion Crow inhabiting the territory to the west and the Hooded Crow that to the east. In Britain Hoodies are found in the Scottish Highlands and Ireland. Where they overlap the two races interbreed to produce hybrids of greatly diverse colouration. It is not unusual to see mixed pairs. The crow is very vigilant in the vicinity of the nest and rarely betrays its location by its behaviour. The nest is generally placed in the forks of tall trees but also in bushes or on a rock-face in hill country. It is a substantial structure of twigs, reinforced with turf and mud and lined with wool, hair and grass [830]. The blue-green, dark-spotted eggs are incubated only by the female, which is fed by the male. The young are cared for for by the parents for 30 days, after which time they leave the nest for good [829]. Crows are omnivorous birds. They also attack small mammals and cause much damage by their fondness for the eggs of other species. The **American Crow,** *Corvus brachyrhynchos,* found throughout North America, is virtually identical to the Carrion Crow.

The **Rook,** *Corvus frugilegus* [833], is often mistaken for a Crow. At closer quarters it is distinguished by the narrower bill and smaller head, and by the loose feathers covering the shank. A distinctive feature of adult birds is the bare, white skin, the cere, at the base of the bill. The gloss of a Rook's plumage is blue whereas that of the Carrion Crow is green and purple. The Rook inhabits central, north and east Europe and temperate Asia all the way to the Far East. Rooks are gregarious and form large colonies during the breeding season, and there may be as many as 50 nests in a single tree; single nests in isolation are rare. A rookery soon makes its whereabouts known by the loud harsh cawing of the birds. They are noisy creatures even in flight, and when coming to roost in the evening. In Europe Rooks migrate in large flocks. The Rook is not as destructive as the Crow and, even though feeding flocks sometimes cause considerable damage to newly sown grain fields, most people would like to see it protected.

834

835

The bright and active **Jackdaw,** *Coloeus monedula* [834, 835], is one of the smaller species of crow. It is coloured black with a grey nape, grey ear-tufts and dark grey underparts. Some eastern races have more grey on the neck. These birds are found where there are old, hollow trees or tall, old buildings, ruins and cliffs, from western Europe far into Asia. In the lowlands of Asia and in parts of Europe the Jackdaw builds its nest in mud banks; it is a colonial breeder. It almost always flies in flocks which herald their presence with loud cries; the bird's "jack-jack", however, is not nearly as harsh as the call of the Crow or the Raven. The courting season begins in late February or early March, following which the birds seek cavities in which to build their nests—sometimes whole mounds of twigs, turf and straw lined with hair and other soft material. The 4–6 eggs, paler in colour than those of other crows, are incubated by the female for 17 or 18 days. Young fledglings remain with the parents and other families to form large groups which wander over the countryside but always return to the nesting colony. For much of the year Jackdaws join flocks of Rooks and roost with them. In milder regions, like Britain, they are resident, that is, they remain throughout the whole year, whereas in the north and east of Europe they are migrants. Jackdaws feed on the ground, their diet being three quarters animal food and one quarter vegetable food. Picture 836 shows young Jackdaws in a hollow oak.

837

838

In winter, in the leafless tops of isolated trees or in a thick tangle of bushes, bulky domed structures of sticks with a side entrance become visible. These are the nests of the **Common Magpie**, *Pica pica* [837]. The Magpie is not brightly coloured but it is a handsome bird. The head, breast, back, wings and tail are black with a blue, green and purple gloss, the remaining plumage, including the shoulder-patches, is white. It is further distinguished by its long, graduated tail. The Magpie does not nest colonially but in single pairs, though it cannot be said that is not gregarious. In autumn or winter, following the breeding season, Magpies gather in flocks; such companies, especially when roosting, may number several hundred birds. They usually build several nests, but only one is used. In April the female lays 5–8 eggs, incubating them for 17 or 18 days. Several races range from Europe, temperate Asia to Kamchatka, northwest Africa and western North America. Picture 838 shows a view of the open nest of the related **Azure-winged Magpie**, *Cyanopica cyanus*, of Spain, Portugal and the Far East. This bird, measuring 14 in., has blue wings and tail, and a black head. Its haunts are the same as those of the common Magpie.

Members of the genus Kitta (Urocissa) are distinguished by a long tail, twice the length of the wing. The **Red-billed Blue Magpie**, *Kitta erythrorhyncha* [839], of China, Nepal and Siam, has a bluish back and hyacinth-blue wings and tail. The tail-feathers have a black band above the white tip, the head and neck are black and the bill red. It is often kept as an ornamental bird in aviaries.

The **Jay,** *Garrulus glandarius* [840], of Eurasia, measuring 14 in., is as brightly coloured as many exotic birds. It is reddish brown with a white rump, black tail, white wing-patches and lovely-blue-and-black barred wing-coverts. When agitated it can erect the black-striped feathers on its crown [841]. It is very astute and sights intruders long before other birds, and with its harsh grating voice warns the forest inhabitants of approaching danger. Jays nest in young trees and bushes. They remain in one territory, straying farther afield only when there is a shortage of food. Some years, inhabitants of more northerly regions set out on lengthier journeys to the south, large numbers of them visiting areas where the acorn harvest is abundant, this being the birds' chief

839

840

433

841

food; such instances are called invasions or irruptions by ornithologists. Jays, like some other crows, often store food; these caches, containing acorns, beech nuts or other seeds and fruits, may be forgotten by the birds and sprout into small seedlings [842]. Thus the Jay contributes to the natural dissemination of certain trees. Its diet consists chiefly of vegetable food, but the Jay also eats small vertebrates. It fre-

quents the forests of Europe and Asia but is absent in southern Asia.

A fairly common inhabitant of the forests of northern Europe and the arctic taiga to Sakhalin is the **Siberian Jay,** *Perisoreus infaustus* [843], about the size of a small jackdaw. It is olive-brown above, grey below with a black-brown cap and red-brown wing feathers, rump and tail. It is a typical forest dweller, only rarely venturing beyond its boundaries. During the breeding season it makes itself inconspicuous and frequently passes unnoticed; at other times of the year, however, it wanders about the forest, flying back and forth with its tail widespread calling "kuk-kuk" (hence *kukscha*—the bird's Russian name). The male's song is quite pleasant. The Siberian Jay is not a shy bird, on the contrary it is quite inquisitive and will fly very close to humans. There is only one brood in the year, the sturdy and warm nest containing 3 or 4 grey-white or green-grey eggs.

842

Inhabiting the region from southern Texas through
Central America to Bolivia are several races of the
Green Jay, *Cyanocorax yncas* [844], whose exotic
colouring making it a favourite cage-bird in Europe.
The crown is blue, there is a blue patch above the
eye and another reaching from below the eye to the
bill, the sides of the neck and head are black, the back,
wings and central tail feathers green, the outer tail
feathers yellow. It measures about 11 in. The nest is
placed in dense thickets, less frequently in trees.

843

844

845

846

The **Blue-naped** or **Urraca Jay,** *Cyanocorax chrysops* [845], of south Brazil, Uruguay and Paraguay has a thick cap of short, upright black feathers covering the forehead, lores and head. The head and neck are black, the hind neck pale blue, the underparts and the tip of the tail white, the back black-brown with a purple gloss. There is a blue patch above and below the eye. This is also a popular cage-bird.

A typical inhabitant of the conifer forests of Europe and Asia is the **Nutcracker,** *Nucifraga caryocatactes* [846], which nests in the mountains of central and eastern Europe, It is absent from a large region north of this territory but its distribution is again continuous from northern Europe through northern Asia to Kamchatka in Siberia. Isolated populations of these brown, pale-spangled, jay-sized birds are also found in the mountains of inner Asia. The brown tail has a broad white terminal band. The voice is harsh, like that of the Jay. The Nutcracker eats insects and various other small animals; its favourite foods are hazel nuts or evergreen seeds which it picks from the pine cones with its strong bill. Wherever there is an abundant crop of nuts these birds will gather from far and wide in great numbers. In some years the northern populations of Nutcrackers invade central and western Europe, apparently because of a lack of sufficient food in the north.

A typical inhabitant of the highest mountains of southern Europe, north-west Africa and western and central Asia is the **Alpine Chough,** *Pyrrhocorax graculus* [847], a black bird with a yellow bill and red feet. Groups and flocks of these birds perform all sorts of aerial acrobatics around the peaks of the cliffs on whose ledges they nest. Sometimes whole colonies nest together inside deep caves. They feed on alpine meadows and on rubbish-heaps near mountain chalets, showing little fear of man.

The extinct **Huia,** *Heteralocha acutirostris* [848], of New Zealand is the only bird known in which the male and female had bills of distinctly different shapes. Pairs of these birds used to wander through the forest undergrowth on their long, strong legs. The male with his stout, straight beak chiselled away the bark of decayed trees and the female with her longer, thin down-curved bill probed the crevices for insects. The plumage was black with a green gloss, the large wattles on the cheeks were orange. The long, white-tipped tail feathers were one of the reasons for the bird's destruction in the 19th century, for these were used by the Maoris for their chiefs' ceremonial headdresses; another cause was collecting by Europeans. The Huia was a member of the family Cal-laeidae.

347

348

437

849

850

When in the 16th century two magnificent bird skins were brought back to Europe aboard Magellan's ship "Victoria" they created quite a sensation; so beautiful was the plumage the Spaniards believed them to be "birds of paradise" and that is the name they are known by to this day. Forty-three species inhabit Australasia, their distribution centred in New Guinea. They are medium-sized birds no larger than a crow, with strong feet adapted for perching, and variously shaped bills. It is difficult to describe their remarkable beauty. Long and short, narrow and rich trailing plumes, short feathers like velvet, magnificent collars of various shapes, delicate fluffy, divided feathers, feathers terminating in large racquets, wire-like with curved shafts, feathers resembling bands of hammered metal, these and many other kinds adorn the various parts of the body and also play their role in the courtship performance. The females, in comparison, are drab creatures and it is difficult to believe that they are the mates of the glorious males. The males have their established courting territories where they show off to the females. The dances can be described as "quite out of this world". Perched on a branch, the birds sway from side to side, crouch low or stand proudly erect, tilt forward and backward, some even hang upside down or revolve around a branch, always trying to make the most of their gorgeous attire. Every species naturally has its own specific movements as well as combinations of colour and shape of feather ornaments. But not all are of such splendour; some are quite inconspicuous. All birds-of-paradise are forest dwellers inhabiting the high treetops or lower scrub. The open nest is placed in the branches of trees, sometimes in holes. Nest-building, incubation of the one or two eggs and rearing the young are attended to by the female, as the male is busy courting and is often polygamous. Their diet consists of animal life such as insects, worms, small vertebrates, and also fruits and seeds. The voice, as in most birds of great beauty, is not remarkable. The best known and handsomest are the members of the genus Paradisea. The **Great Bird-of-paradise**, *Paradisea apoda* [849], of Aru is reddish brown on the back with a yellow head, metallic green throat and long, thick extensile tufts of golden-orange feathers on the sides. The two elongated central tail feathers are narrow and wiry. When courting it spreads its wings wide and hangs upside down. The related **Lesser Bird-of-paradise**, *Paradisea minor* [852], of New Guinea has back and wing-coverts the colour of straw. The females of both species are rust-brown above, paler below.

The **Little King Bird-of-paradise**, *Cicinnurus regius* [850], measuring 6½ in., is one of the smaller members of this family; it makes its home in New Guinea and neighbouring islands. The male is cherry-red above with a red throat and emerald-green breastband; the underparts are white. On either side of the chest is a fan of grey-brown plumes tipped with green and the two central tail feathers are long curved wires terminating in curly green racquets. The female is grey-brown and yellow-brown.

The **Ribbon-tail** or **Wire-tailed Bird-of-paradise**, *Astrapia mayeri* [851], is the last species of these birds to be identified (in 1938). It inhabits the high mountains of New Guinea. The plumage is black with a bronze and green gloss in the male, and it has an extraordinarily long tail of narrow feathers. The central ones may measure as much as 3 ft in length.

851

852

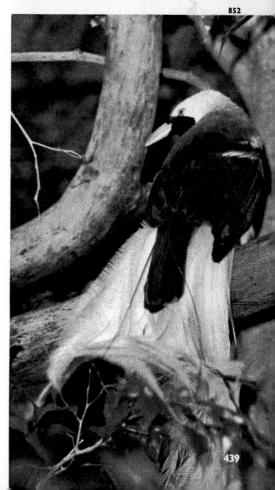

439

853

Bowerbirds (Ptilonorhynchidae) are closely related to the birds of paradise, though not nearly as brightly coloured. They are distinguished by their courtship behaviour. Some of the 19 species, not satisfied with selecting a certain territory for their courtship display as is the habit with most birds, make clear spaces and build domed bowers of sticks and moss, decorating them with shells, berries, leaves and flowers, and here they perform their dances. The birds mate in these bowers but the nest is built in a nearby tree. Bowerbirds inhabit forest regions and spend little time on the ground. They fly strongly. The largest of the family is the **Great** or **Red-crested Bower-bird,** *Chlamydera nuchalis* [853], of tropical north Australia. It is brown-grey above and yellow-grey below, and the male has a reddish crest on its nape. Most of these birds are natives of New Guinea or northern Australia.

The small, bright-eyed titmice or tits (family Paridae) are alert birds, constantly on the move, hopping about among the treetops and thickets in search of the eggs, caterpillars and adults of many insects. About 65 species are found in Europe, Asia, North America and Africa, most often in woodlands, orchards, gardens, and parks, wherever trees grow. The sexes are very similar and only in a few species is it possible to distinguish between the male and female in the field. The nesting habits vary–most titmice nest in holes but some build globular or pear-shaped nests. Tits lay large clutches but the mortality rate is high, especially in the first autumn and winter, so numbers fluctuate from year to year. Their main enemy may be winter cold, for tits are resident birds and do not migrate but roam about in groups joined by other birds such as Goldcrest, Nuthatch and Treecreeper. Ringing, however, has revealed that

some individuals do undertake more lengthy journeys, sometimes travelling hundreds of miles, and that certain species can be spoken of as partial migrants.

The **Great Tit,** *Parus major* [854], measuring 5½ in., is a handsome little bird with an olive-green back, yellow belly, glossy black head and white cheeks. The black longitudinal stripe down the breast and belly is more marked in the male. At the first breath of spring the winter groups break up and the courting season begins, the males repeating continuously their simple song. Tits nest in natural cavities in trees or man-made nestboxes, also in such odd places as letter-boxes, old pipes, even in an old forgotten shoe. The structure is neat and warm, made of a thick layer of moss and a thinner layer of animal hairs and wool [855]. The parents are kept busy after the eggs have hatched for the brood is a large one (6–13) and some of the young are hungry all the time [856]. The daily food intake of a large brood in broad-leaved woodland may be up to a thousand small caterpillars. Apart from insects and other small animals, Great Tits take fruit and seeds, and food put out by man. The Great Tit occurs throughout all Eurasia, Indonesia and north-west Africa.

854

855

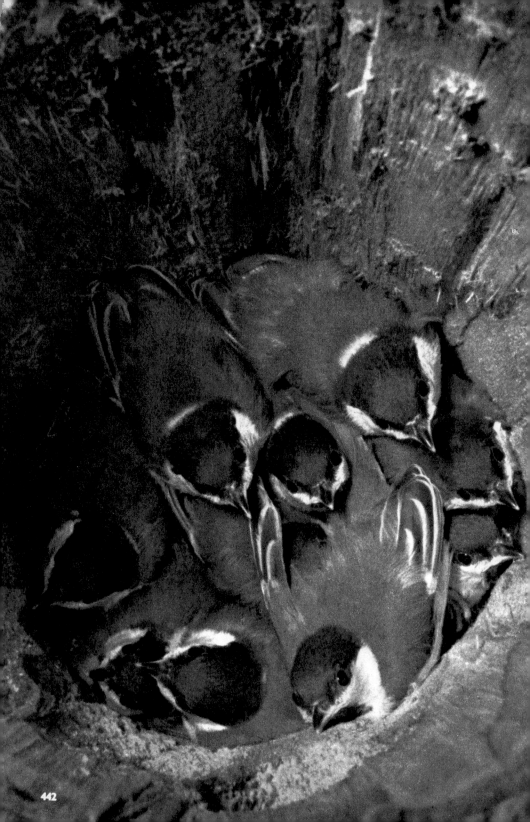

857

The **Blue Tit,** *Parus caeruleus* [857], is a charming little bird measuring only 4½ in., with crown, mantle, wings and tail a lovely cobalt-blue. Its note can be heard the whole year round and in spring the male's song, ending in a lengthy trill. The nesting habits are like those of the Great Tit except that in Europe it keeps to the woods, farther away from human habitations, though this is far from the case in Britain. The well-lined nest contains upwards from seven eggs, a large number for so small a bird. The clutch of 16 eggs shown in the picture [858] is about the upper limit. The Blue Tit does not range as far east as the preceding species, the Urals marking the eastern boundary of its distribution.

The **Coal Tit,** *Parus ater* [859], shown bringing food to the nesting cavity, is even smaller than the Blue Tit. It has a black head with white cheeks and a white patch on its nape. The chin and upper breast are black, the upper parts olive-grey. It inhabits evergreen forests in lowlands and mountains and if it does not find a suitable cavity in trees or tree-stumps it will appropriate an abandoned mouse-hole. Next to the Chaffinch it is the most plentiful denizen of Europe's coniferous forests. All these tits will nest in man-made nestboxes.

Even the **Crested Tit,** *Parus cristatus* [860], essentially a forest dweller, will sometimes use a suitably placed nestbox. This bird has a handsome black and white streaked crest and a white face bordered with black; the upper surface is brown-grey. In eastern and central Europe it nests in evergreen and mixed forests, in western Europe also in broad-leaved woods. To the east its range extends beyond

859
860

445

861

the Urals. In Britain it is confined to the north-east Highlands of Scotland. Like the other tits it is a bright, active, noisy little bird whose deep purring call is characteristic. The young birds do not have a crest but the streaked feathers on the head show evidence of the future ornament [861].

The behaviour of the **Marsh Tit,** *Parus palustris* [862], a little ball of grey with a black cap and chin and pale cheeks, clearly points to its membership in

this family. Its name is somewhat misleading for it is chiefly found in woodlands where it can be recognized by its typical "pitch-u" note. It ranges from England and Wales to the Urals and from central Siberia to Japan. In North America the genus Parus is represented by the chickadees, which include the familiar **Black-capped Chickadee,** *Parus atricapillus,* found over most of the northern half of the continent, and the **Carolina Chickadee,** *Parus carolinensis,*

which is an inhabitant of the south-eastern USA. The next two species can be said to be master-builders. The **Long-tailed Tit,** *Aegithalos caudatus* [863], differs markedly from tits of the genus Parus both in the shape of the nest and in the silky, fluffy feathers. The photograph shows the northern race. It measures 5½ in. from the bill to the tip of the 3-in.-long tail. The upper surface is reddish, mixed with black, the lower surface whitish. It ranges from Europe and the central zone of Siberia to Japan and Kamchatka in Siberia. The Long-tailed Tit of central Europe belongs to a mixed population; the young birds have distinctly striped heads like the British race [865]. The nest shown in picture 864 is

864

a comparatively large, egg-shaped structure with only a small side entrance. The thick walls are woven of mosses, lichen, spider webs and other fibres. The lining may contain 2,000 assorted feathers.

The **Penduline Tit,** *Remiz pendulinus*, is shown at work [866]. It is easily recognized by its chestnut

865

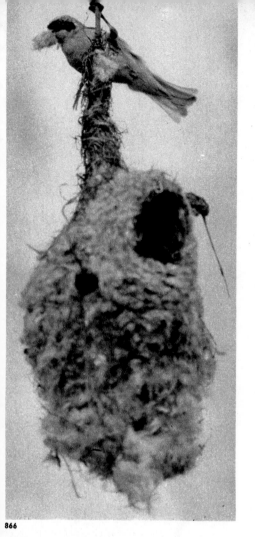

866

867

back and the broad black band on either side of the grey-white head. Its sharp squeaky note can be heard only near rivers, lakes and marshes for that is where, on the end of branches, usually above the water's surface, it hangs its nest—a long bag with a short tunnel-like entrance [867]. The fabric of the nest consists of the fluffy seeds of poplars and willows. The building instinct is well developed, especially in the male who starts several nests one after the other. Suspended where it is the nest sways in the slightest breeze. The Penduline Tit breeds in southern and eastern Europe, thence to central Siberia and China.

868

The **Nuthatch**, *Sitta europaea* [868–870], is a true acrobat. Its loud whistling call is heard in the early spring, but it has a variety of notes, some uttered throughout the year. Sometimes it climbs tree trunks upwards like woodpeckers, without having to support itself with its tail, while at other times it hunts head downwards. The strong bill is used to ferret insects out from under the bark. It is blue-grey above, creamy yellow below, with chestnut flanks and a black eye-stripe [870]. The bill is not strong enough to hew a hole in the trunk and so the Nuthatch takes over old woodpeckers' holes and other cavities; it sometimes lays its eggs in nestboxes. If the entrance is too large the Nuthatches brick it up with mud [868], making the nest safe from larger enemies. The cavity is lined with bits of bark, in this case the red-brown bark of the pine [869]. The female sleeps in the nest even before it contains any eggs, whereas the

male sleeps elsewhere. The Nuthatch is a resident bird feeding on insects in summer and on the seeds of trees in winter, chasing other birds away from window-box feeding places and taking the food from them to its hiding place. It inhabits Europe and Asia as well as India, but is absent in the central Asiatic regions.

The Nuthatch is a member of the family Sittidae, which comprises in all 15 species.

869
870

451

Whereas the Nuthatch is a loud-voiced acrobat, the creepers (family Certhiidae) are little unobtrusive birds which often pass unnoticed in the wild. They climb like woodpeckers using their tails as props, but upwards and around the trunk in a spiral. On reaching the top of the tree they flutter down to the ground and start working their way up from the base of the next tree, exploring the crevices under the bark with their long curved bills. This is repeated over and over again. When the bird stops to rest, which does not happen often, its brown-flecked plumage is practically invisible against the bark. Two species occur in Europe; they are best identified by their note. Illustrated here is the **Treecreeper** or **Brown Creeper**, *Certhia familiaris* [871], distinguished from its relative the **Short-toed Treecreeper**, *Certhia brachydactyla*, by a greater contrast between the colour of the upper and underparts, a slightly shorter bill and a longer claw on the hind toe. The nest of both species is placed in crevices, under a piece of loose bark, in crannies, piles of wood and other cavities [872]. It is made of twigs and various soft, fine materials. The eggs are white with small reddish brown dots. Both sexes share the duties of

incubation. The diet consists of insects and their eggs, larvae and pupae. Whereas in Europe the Tree-creeper inhabits dense, mostly evergreen forests, the Short-toed Treecreeper lives in gardens, parks and tree avenues, but does not occur in Britain. The Tree-creeper is widely distributed in Europe, a large part of temperate Asia and in North America, where it is called the Brown Creeper. The Short-toed Tree-creeper occurs in the Old World.

The large family Timaliidae, comprising 280 species of passerine birds, is a very primitive and diverse one, its members including birds resembling tits, jays, wrens and pittas. All have soft, fluffy feathers, short, rounded wings (they are not good fliers) and strong legs and feet. They are found in woodlands and scrub areas, generally living in the undergrowth. The largest number of species nests in south and south-east Asia, but they also occur in Australia and Africa; in Europe the Bearded Tit may now be classed in this family. The Timaliidae are separated into 73 genera of which the largest is that of the laughing thrushes, common and undistinguished birds of south and south-east Asia.

The **White-crested Laughing Thrush,** *Garrulax leucolophus* [873], is brown with a white head, neck and breast, a broad black eye-band and a high, broad white crest. It lives in forests of all kinds from the Himalayas through Indochina to Sumatra. These birds are very gregarious and, except for the breeding season when they go about in pairs, they are always to be found in groups which, though hidden from sight in the thickets, reveal their presence by their occasional loud choruses of laughter. They forage for their animal food under leaves like thrushes or among the branches of trees; they also eat small fruit and seeds. The flat nest is generally placed near the ground. The female lays 4 or 5 eggs and both sexes incubate.

Living in southern China, Indochina and Formosa is the related **Hwamei** or **Spectacled Laughing Thrush,** *Garrulax canorus* [874], coloured brown and rust-brown with a white eye-rim and a white stripe on the temples. It frequents jungles and forests.

873
874

The eastern Himalayas and western China are the home of the **Chinese Black-chinned Yuhina** or **Black-crested Babbler**, *Yuhina nigrimentum* [875], measuring about 4 in. and sporting a peaked black crest. The upper parts are dark olive-brown, the underside pale yellow-brown, the wings and tail dark brown. The two sexes are alike.

Also classed in the family Timaliidae is the **Bald Crow** or **Bare-headed Rockfowl**, *Picathartes gymnocephalus* [876], somewhat resembling a magpie, and until recently a rather mysterious species. It lives in virgin African forests interspersed with rocky cliffs. It is essentially a ground bird, seeking insects and other invertebrates as well as small vertebrates among the leaves, hopping about as it does so. It builds an open nest, in which it lays two creamy white, mottled eggs, in clefts, crevices of rocks and caverns 6–17 ft above the ground. This species measures 16 in. and has a bare, yellow head with a large black spot behind the eye. The bill, upper parts, wings and tail are black, the underside white. It ranges from Sierra Leone to Ghana.

875

876

The **Bearded Tit,** *Panurus biarmicus* [877], as its name indicates, was formerly classified with the titmice. Today, some ornithologists classify it in the family Timaliidae, as an independent family Panuridae, or else among the Paranoxornithidae, even though the bill is markedly high and compressed. This 6½-in. bird with its long tail is difficult to discern among the thick yellow reed-beds. The upper parts and tail are cinnamon-brown, the underparts reddish grey. The male has a grey head and black moustachial stripe [879]. Its favourite haunts are thick reed-beds where it also nests and forages for food. The nest is placed among reeds, either on the ground or just above the water's surface. Both sexes build the nest, incubate and feed the young. The inside mouth markings of the young, which act on the parents as a signal for feeding, are red with yellow margins. Pale dots cover the red patch in the centre [880]. As the Bearded Tit inhabits only reedy marshes, its distribution in Europe, central Asia and the Far East is discontinuous.

The bulbuls (Pycnonotidae) are an Old World family of some 120 species distributed throughout Africa and Asia south of the great mountain ranges, on which they are found up to 10,000 ft. As a group they are distinguished by hair-like feathers on the nape of the neck, though in some species these are hard to see. Bulbuls range in size from that of a finch to a thrush; the sexes look alike but males tend to be larger than females, and the plumage is generally some shade of green, yellow or brown, enlivened by bright-coloured patches on the head or under the tail. They are forest birds, more often heard than seen, but some species have colonized gardens and parks where their noisy parties are prominent outside the breeding season.

The **Yellow-vented Bulbul,** *Pycnonotus goiavier* [878], 7½ in. long, is probably the commonest bird of Singapore and is well-known throughout Malaysia. The upper parts, including the tail, are brown, the underparts brownish white. Much of the head is dark brown with a white streak over the eye and a white throat; the yellow patch under the base of the tail gives the bird its name. It has a simple song and

878

877

879

881

882

feeds on fruits, especially wild figs and berries, and on insects. It builds at no great height in a bush and lays a clutch of two eggs; both parents sit on them and also feed the young.

The **Golden-fronted Leafbird,** *Chloropsis auri-frons* [881], ranks with those birds which are distinguished by brightly coloured plumage. The male is pale green, the underside a lighter shade, the area from the forehead to the centre of the crown orange-yellow, the cheeks, throat and breast velvety black, the chin blue. There is a turquoise-blue patch at the bend of the wing. The female has a green forehead. Its length is 8 in. It is a popular cage-bird but requires plenty of space and branches, as in the wild it frequents the thick branches of trees. It and 13 other species belong to the family Chloropseidae, widely distributed throughout south-east Asia. They are all tree-dwellers which seldom alight on the ground. They build open cup-shaped nests either in bushes or on the tree canopy. The nest of the lovely **Fairy Bluebird,** *Irena puella* [882], is a frailer structure coated on the outside with moss. The male of this species has the crown, hind neck, back, rump and upper tail-coverts coloured a brilliant turquoise, the remaining plumage being dark cobalt-blue. The female is blue-green. These birds inhabit the forests of the Himalayas, northern India, Burma and Indo-china.

457

Of all the passerine birds only the four species of dippers (Cinclidae) can be said to be aquatic. Their favourite haunts are clear, rapid flowing streams where they hunt insects and small fish. Even when making a lengthy journey they fly close above the surface of the brook or river as if loth to leave the water. Although they do not swim well on the surface (the toes are not webbed) they dive expertly with the aid of their wings, capturing water insects even at a depth of nearly 20 ft. Like most aquatic birds, the dippers have thick plumage with a layer of down beneath, and their preen gland, whose secretion makes the feathers impervious to water, is ten times as large as that of other passerine birds. The picture shows the **Common Dipper,** *Cinclus cinclus* [883], a dark brown bird with white gorget and short tail, a feature common to all the members of this family. The distribution is discontinuous, extending through Europe to the Himalayas. Dippers build large domed nests close to the water, on rocky shores, between the roots of trees, sometimes even behind waterfalls so that the bird has to fly through the curtain of water. It is one of the few birds whose pleasant song can be heard even when the countryside is blanketed in snow. The **American Dipper,** *Cinclus mexicanus*, is identical in habits and shape, but is uniformly slate-grey in colour. It is found throughout the west from Alaska to Panama, mostly along rapid mountain streams.

883

884

A winter singer whose voice is remarkably strong for its size is the **Wren,** *Troglodytes troglodytes* [884, 885], a tiny bird only 4 in. in length. Coloured brown with dark streaks, it creeps through dense thickets, roots and cracks between rocks, and flies short distances close to the ground. The nest is a round, domed structure [885]. It is found over most of Europe, and parts of Asia; in North America, where it is known

885

as the **Winter Wren,** it is confined to far northern and far western mountain forests. Through the rest of the continent it is replaced by the **House Wren,** *Troglodytes aedon,* a paler, greyer bird. Of the 63 members of this family (Troglodytidae) only *Troglodytes troglodytes* occurs in the Old World. All the rest inhabit the Americas, mostly between Mexico and northern South America.

Intermediate between the wrens and the true thrushes
are the mimic thrushes (Mimidae), an American
family of some 30 species, of which the best known
is the **Mockingbird,** *Mimus polyglottus* [886], "state
bird" five times over in the southern USA, which is
its stronghold. Like a slim, greyish thrush, 10½ in.
long, it has become a familiar bird round houses and
gardens, aggressive towards possible enemies of all
sizes and singing its famous imitative song at all
hours, even under a full moon. The Mockingbird's
powers in this respect are remarkable and it quickly
acquires new notes from other birds and from man
and his machines. Its diet, like that of its relatives, is
partly animal, partly vegetable. Both sexes, which
look alike, build the substantial nest in a shrub or
tree but the female alone incubates the 3–6 red-
spotted greenish eggs. The whole nesting cycle takes
about a month, which allows at least two broods in a
season.

The **Catbird,** *Dumetella carolinensis* [887], 9 in. long,
has a more northerly breeding distribution but winters south to Panama. It is also a common garden
bird in the USA and Canada, with its uniform dark
grey plumage relieved by a black cap and a chestnut
patch under the fanned tail. A cat-like mew earns its
name but it is not as versatile a mimic as the Mockingbird. The nest, often at no great height, contains 4–6
glossy blue-green eggs which hatch in under two
weeks; the male's share in helping his mate seems
to vary.

The thrushes (Turdidae), comprising over 300
species distributed throughout the world, are as
numerous as the Timaliidae. They include a number
of excellent songsters, like the **European Blackbird,** *Turdus merula* [889]. The adult male, measuring 10 in., is black with a bright orange bill and
eye-rim. Originally a forest bird, the Blackbird has
become accustomed to the presence of humans and
today, at least in western and central Europe, its song
can be heard almost in the centres of the biggest cities.
Its distribution follows a zone from north-west
Africa, through Europe and Asia to China. It nests
in evergreen and deciduous forests, gardens, parks,
farmland and well up hillsides. The nest is a massive
structure cemented with mud [888]. The Blackbird's
song is mellow, contemplative and flute-like.

886

887

888
889

463

890

891

464

The familiar **Song Thrush**, *Turdus philomelos* [890, colour plate XXXII], is an excellent but loud-voiced songster, its song consisting of several often repeated phrases. Easily distinguished from the Blackbird, it is 9 in. long, brown, with thickly speckled throat and breast. Both species feed largely on the ground and their diet is more or less the same – insects and their larvae,

892

worms, and, in late summer and autumn, berries and fruit. The Song Thrush also specializes in opening snail shells against stones. Its nest is usually placed in forks or near the trunk of coniferous and deciduous trees and shrubs and resembles that of the Blackbird, though inside the cavity is lined with a mixture of wood shavings and wet mud, cemented with saliva.

The clutch consists of 3–5 blue-green or blue, dark-spotted eggs [891]. Picture 892 shows the young 12 days after hatching. Two days later they abandon the nest. The Song Thrush occurs throughout Europe and western Siberia to Lake Baikal. It is a migrant over much of its range, wintering in Africa and southern Asia.

893

Birds of this family rarely nest colonially. The **Fieldfare,** *Turdus pilaris* [893], however, though it does nest by itself occasionally, is a social breeder, a large number of nests sometimes being found on a single tree. Fieldfares breed on the margins of forests and clearings, more often in deciduous than coniferous trees. The bird is more distinctively coloured than the Song Thrush; the head is grey, the back dark brown and the rump pale grey. It breeds in central and northern Europe as well as throughout almost the whole of Siberia. It is a winter visitor to the British Isles where in cruel winters these otherwise wary birds visit gardens in search of food.

The **Redwing,** *Turdus iliacus* [894], is often mistaken for the Song Thrush though it is distinguished by a creamy white stripe over the eye and in flight by its chestnut flanks and underside of the wings. It occurs in northern Europe and Asia, appearing in central Europe only in winter.

The **Mistle Thrush,** *Turdus viscivorus* [895], the herald of spring in European forests, is grey-brown above with thickly speckled yellow-white underparts. Its ringing song, coming from the very top of a tree, may be placed somewhere between the mellow note of the Blackbird and the harsher one of the Song Thrush. The nest is often built high on a horizontal

896
897

branch. Its distribution includes Europe, western Asia and north-west Africa. It feeds chiefly on the ground, forming parties in late summer and autumn. It measures 11 in., and is noticeably larger than the Song Thrush.

The **Ring Ouzel**, *Turdus torquatus* [896], is distinctively coloured. The male is almost black, the female brown, and both have a white patch the shape of a half-moon on the breast. Compared to the Mistle Thrush its range is quite limited. The darker race makes its home at high altitudes in Scandinavia and Great Britain, while birds with pale-edged feathers are typical inhabitants of the mountains of central and southern Europe, ranging eastwards to Transcaucasia.

Stony hills, rocks and ruins are the favourite haunts of the **Rock Thrush**, *Monticola saxatilis* [897, colour plate XXXIII]. Measuring only 7½ in., it is the smallest of the thrushes mentioned here and has a shorter rust-coloured tail which is brown in the centre. The male in his mating plumage has the head, neck and upper mantle slate-blue, the rump white. The female is brown above, the underparts yellowish and spotted. The nest is built in rock crevices, between stones, places which are usually difficult of access, with the male singing his pleasant melody nearby. The Rock Thrush breeds in southern Europe and central Asia.

898

The female of a lesser known related species, the **White-throated** or **Forest Rock Thrush,** *Monticola gularis* [898], is shown feeding its offspring. This small thrush, the size of a starling, lives in the Far East in the region of the Amur River, at rather high altitudes, but only in forests—it is not a cliff-dweller. The simple nest of grass is placed in holes in the ground, often between the roots of trees. The male has a blue-grey head and lesser wing-coverts, black wings and rusty underparts. The female has an olive-grey back, spotted a darker colour.

The **Western Red-legged Thrush,** *Mimocichla plumbea* [899], is a favourite cage-bird which occurs in several races in the Bahamas and Greater Antilles. It is grey with a rust-red belly, black throat and white chin, and measures about 10 in.

899

900

901

Another thrush often seen in captivity is the **Orange-headed Ground Thrush,** *Geocichla citrina* [901], whose note resembles that of the Golden Oriole. It measures 8½ in., the upper surface is grey-blue, the head and under-surface yellow-brown. The central wing-coverts have white tips so that when folded the wing shows a white transverse bar. It is a common forest bird from western China and the Indian Himalayas to Indonesia.

The **Whinchat,** *Saxicola rubetra* [900], a small bird with a short tail and a pale stripe over the eye, is shown in its typical stance. It inhabits several types of open country –heaths and grassland–with isolated bushes, often near streams. Here it can frequently be seen perching on telephone wires, whence it

swoops down every now and then to catch a small animal on the ground or swerves sharply in pursuit of a flying insect. The male in his nuptial dress is brown above with broad rust-coloured margins on each feather, the throat and breast creamy white, the outer tail feathers white at the base. The female [902] is a paler colour with a less distinctive stripe over the eye. The call-note is grating and the song is a brief jingling phrase; occasionally the Whinchat imitates the voices of other birds. It nests in Europe and western Asia to the ●Yenisei River in Siberia.

Drier habitats are favoured by its relative the **Stonechat,** *Saxicola torquata*, which is found on hill slopes, near railway embankments, on heaths and, in the eastern part of its range, on dry, stony sites

471

with low shrubs. In winter it may be found much more widely. The head, neck and upper parts of the male are almost black, the rump white, the under-parts chestnut, and the belly a paler shade. The female is browner, without white on the neck, but both sexes have white wing-bars. Juveniles look like dark-plumaged females. Both Stonechat and Whin-chat nest on the ground in well-concealed sites. The Stonechat lives in Europe, Asia and Africa, where it occurs in several races. Pictures 903 and 904 show two birds (a pair) of the east Siberian race *Saxicola torquata steinegeri* which is darker above and lighter below than the European form *Saxicola torquata rubicola* [905].

A typical inhabitant of the east European and Siberian taiga is the **Red-flanked Bluetail,** *Tarsiger cyan-urus* [906], measuring about 5½ in. The male is blue above with bright cobalt-blue shoulder feathers, rump and tail, the underside creamy white with conspicuous orange flanks. It has a white stripe on the forehead. The female is olive-brown. The young

905

906

473

907
908

are spotted [907], as are most of the young of this family. The nest is placed in thick coniferous woods. Finland marks the westernmost boundary of its present range. Besides its northern nesting grounds, it is also known to breed in the region of the Himalayas. When resting on the ground or perched on a rock the **Wheatear,** *Oenanthe oenanthe*, is an inconspicuous bird, the size of a sparrow, until it starts bobbing up and down, occasionally flirting and spreading its tail. Further distinguishing marks are the white rump and base of the tail, which has a black terminal band. It is a typical inhabitant of quarries, dunelands, boulder-strewn hillsides and other rocky situations. During the breeding season the male is grey above with a white stripe over the eye and a broad black mask. In winter the two sexes are similar [908]. The young,

909

when they leave the nest, are spotted [909]. The Wheatear sings on the ground or from a stone, occasionally taking a few turns in the air. The nest is always placed so as to be protected from above. The diet consists chiefly of insects. The range includes Europe, all Siberia, Alaska and the coast of Greenland. It winters in Africa and southern Asia.

The **European Robin,** *Erithacus rubecula* [910], is easily identified by its orange-red face and breast and olive-brown upper parts. The spring song of the male, the simple phrases continuing until late in the evening, is musical and pleasant. The nest of dry leaves, grass and moss, lined inside with hairs and feathers, is placed in a hollow in the ground between tree roots, in banks and various nooks and crannies. The female incubates the 5 or 6 eggs alone. It breeds in Europe and western Asia and in most areas is a migrant, although British Robins are mainly resident.

910

911

Renowned for its powers of song, the **Nightingale,**
Luscinia megarhynchos [911], is visually an un-
impressive bird. The plumage is russet-brown, the
upper parts darker, the breast and belly lighter and
the tail a redder shade. It measures $6\frac{1}{2}$ in. It occurs in
deciduous or mixed woodland with thick under-
growth; when this is cleared the bird soon disappears.
The Nightingale sings both at night and during the
day. Each tone is clear and pure and the song is very
rich and varied, soft tones alternating with joyous,
bubbling phrases. Young birds are believed to learn
the refinements of the song by listening to adults in
their vicinity. The courting note is harsh and
unpleasant.

The nest is built of whatever is at hand – grass, leaves,
moss – so that it is practically invisible in the thick
undergrowth [912]. The 5 or 6 eggs, densely spotted
with olive-green or brown [913], take 11 or 12 days

914

to hatch. The female incubates alone but both sexes share the duties of feeding the young. The distribution of the Nightingale extends from north-west Africa, through southern Europe and Asia Minor to central Asia. In winter it migrates to central Africa. An area stretching from central Europe and Asia far to the north is the home of the **Bluethroat,** *Luscinia svecica* [914], which spends most of its time on the ground. The male has a bright blue throat-patch separated from the white breast by a black, white and red stripe. In the centre of the blue patch is a smaller one which may be either white or russet (white in the south European and russet in the north European race). In non-breeding plumage both sexes have a whitish throat. The upper parts are bluish grey-brown and a conspicuous distinguishing mark in the wild is the bird's red-brown tail, which it has the habit of flirting.

915

A red chin and throat distinguish the **Common Rubythroat,** *Luscinia calliope* [915], whose brown head is also adorned by a white moustache and a white stripe over the eye. The female has a white throat; both sexes otherwise are olive-brown. The nest is placed in thick shrubs growing in the taiga and at the edges of forests from the Urals to Kamchatka, and in an isolated area in northern China.

The redstarts are slender, long-legged birds about the size of a sparrow. They are in the habit of hopping about and flirting their tails. They always sing from an elevated post, either a dead branch, a tree-top or the ridge of a roof; they also sight their favourite prey – small insects – from these high vantage-points. The male **European Redstart,** *Phoenicurus phoenicurus* [916, 918], has a white blaize above the black forehead, face and throat, a slate-grey upper surface and a russet-red breast. The red tail is nearly always in motion. The nest is placed in tree cavities, often rather exposed, wall crevices and man-made nestboxes. Picture 917 shows the yellow and brown-grey female beside a nestbox. The Redstart's song is heard in the early morning hours in deciduous as well as coniferous woodland, in river valleys and on hills as far as the tree line, also in parks and gardens. The 5–7 green-blue eggs are laid in a feather-lined nest and incubated by the female alone, though both

916

917

918

919

sexes share the duties of feeding. There are usually two broods in the year and they eat a large quantity of insects. The range extends from north-west Africa, through Europe to central Siberia and Persia. The Redstart is a migratory bird which arrives in Europe in April and leaves in September for its winter quarters in central Africa.

The **Black Redstart,** *Phoenicurus ochruros* [919], is more simply coloured. The plumage is generally grey-black, and the male in his nuptial dress has a pale speculum and sometimes forehead; the tail and rump are red-brown in both sexes. It is plentiful in central Europe, arriving in March and leaving in October for north Africa, though some winter in Britain. Originally the Black Redstart frequented only cliffs and high mountain peaks above the tree line, but today the majority of these birds are to be found in towns and cities, their nests placed in sheds ruined buildings, brick-works, etc. The 5 or 6 white eggs, hidden in some dark corner, hatch after 14 days

920

the female lays two clutches a year. The speckled young ·[920] abandon the nest after two weeks, scattering all over the garden or farmyard. The hurried, rattling song of the male can be heard from fences and rooftops well into the summer.

The Caucasus, northern Persia and the mountains of central Asia are the home of the big **Güldenstädt's** or **Red-bellied Redstart,** *Phoenicurus erythrogaster* [921], which is found on the highest peaks. The male has a white head, black back, and bright russet-red belly.

The Indian counterpart of the Nightingale, which often figures in the poetry of that country, is the **Shama,** *Copsychus malabaricus* [922]. It is one of the world's best songsters, the note strong and clear and the melodies many and varied, unlike the repeated song of the Nightingale. If properly fed, this species will live a long time in captivity and will even breed successfully. It inhabits the thick jungle undergrowth in India, China, Malaysia and Indonesia. The male has blue-black upper parts, neck and tail. It measures $10\frac{1}{2}$ in. The female is grey-brown instead of black.

921

922

The Old World warblers (Sylviidae) are a large family comprising about 400 species of small, active birds, very widely distributed. All have slender bills slightly downcurved at the tip and soft, thick plumage. Animal life is their main food though they also eat berries and other small fruit. They spend most of their time concealed in foliage from the tree canopy to low scrub and reed-beds. There are marked differences between the nests and eggs of the various species. They are placed on the ground, in thickets, reeds and tree-branches and may be open cup-shaped nests or domed structures. The young, unlike those of the thrushes, are unspotted. Some are excellent songsters, for example both of the birds pictured on this page.

The **Garden Warbler**, *Sylvia borin* [923], measuring 5½ in. (body length) and coloured olive-brown above and pale yellow-brown below, frequents thickets at the edge of woods, often near lakes and rivers. It nests in Europe and western Siberia. The male has a pleasing voice though the strong flute-like song of its relative the **Blackcap**, *Sylvia atricapilla* [924], is even more beautiful. The latter is distinguished by the crown or cap, glossy black in the male and red-brown in the female and juvenile. It is found in similar habitats, especially where there are brambles and nettles. Its range is practically identical with that of the Garden Warbler; in the south, however, it extends all the way to north-west Africa.

The **Whitethroat**, *Sylvia communis* [925], is the same size as the Blackcap. The head of the male is grey-brown, the back russet-brown, and there are large russet patches on the wings. It sings its song perched on an exposed sprig, often on telegraph wires, concluding it with the nuptial flight, singing as it wings its way upwards before returning again to cover. The nest is placed fairly near the ground; it is a light cup, woven of grasses, horsehair and other materials, the edges lined with spider webs or plant fibres [926]. The adult birds incubate for 11–13 days; the young then remaining in the care of their parents for about the same length of time. It breeds from Britain, Ireland and western France to east Siberia.

923

924

925
926

485

927

Somewhat smaller (5½ in.) is the **Lesser White-throat,** *Sylvia curruca*, coloured grey-brown above, dirty white below, with dark ear-coverts. It has no rust-brown on the wings. It is easily identified by its song which begins with a soft chattering and ends in a loud rattle. The nest with incubating female is shown in picture 927. The range of distribution is roughly the same as that of the Blackcap. All these warblers are migrants, arriving in Europe in April and May and leaving for east and central Africa in September.

We have already said that some warblers build covered nests. One such group are the leaf or willow warblers which, though searching shrubs and leafy tree branches for food, build their nests in a tussock or on the ground. They are restless, active birds. Some are difficult to identify in the field and experts depend more on their song than their plumage to tell them apart. The **Chiffchaff,** *Phylloscopus collybita* [928, 929], is readily identified by its repeated "chiff-chaff, chiff-chaff". It measures 4½ in., and is green-grey above, whitish below. It is not easy to locate the nest, as can be seen from picture 928 which shows the female feeding the young; she undertakes the major share of this duty. The Chiffchaff breeds over most of Europe and western Asia.

929

The southern regions of east Siberia are the home of the related species **Radde's Bush Warbler,** *Herbivocula schwarzi* [931], which frequents the margins of the taiga but is not to be seen deep in the forests. It measures 5¼ in. Both sexes are grey-brown above, white tinged with yellow below. It is distinguished by the pale stripe over the eye and the dark brown eye-band. The covered nest, resembling that of the Willow Warbler, is placed near the ground. The life history of this species has not yet been fully

930

studied. The bird winters in south-east Asia, coming to its nesting grounds fairly late – in May – and leaving again immediately after the young have fledged – in August and September.

The **Rufous Warbler,** *Erythropygia galactotes* [930], occurs here and there in southern Europe, throughout the northern half of Africa, except the desert, and in south-west Asia. In size (6 in.) and with its fairly long legs, it looks rather like a thrush. It is easily identified by the long chestnut fan-shaped tail, bordered black and white at the tip. It nests in open country, steppes or semideserts dotted with shrubs. In cultivated areas it nests in orchards, vineyards and olive groves. The male sings his song from the tops of isolated trees, fences, telegraph posts, and now and then performs a slow, dance-flight close to the ground. It winters in India, South Arabia and central Africa.

The grasshopper warblers, members of the genus Locustella, have a retiring mode of life. They hide in thick tangles of grasses, nettles, undergrowth or reeds. Only when singing their courting songs do the males perch momentarily on a branch or reed stem, otherwise these birds remain near the ground, keeping out of sight like mice. The monotonous, reeling or buzzing song is more like the note of an insect than a bird. Unlike their other relatives, grasshopper warblers have a graduated tail, and their plumage is very plain. The territory extending from the Ob River in western Siberia eastwards to Sakhalin Island north of Japan, is the home of **Gray's Grasshopper Warbler,** *Locustella fasciolata* [932], which lives in the thick grass, the nest being placed between

933

934

tussocks. It is larger than the European grasshopper warblers and is coloured brown above and pale grey below. The voice is not as monotonous as in the other species, the note being a bell-like "tuti-ruti . . .ruti-tuti". In the Far East, somewhat further south than the last species, is found the **Thick-billed Warbler,** *Phragmaticola aëdon* [933], which is reminiscent of the Great Reed Warbler. The upper parts are rust-brown, the underparts white, tinted ochre. The song of the male is rich and varied, including imitations of other birds and a special note which sounds like "tschok-tschok", which is its name in Russian. The nest is built in shrubs.

Thick reed-beds on the shores of ponds, lakes and other bodies of water in temperate Eurasia are occupied by several species of reed warblers. Their nests are like deep baskets, expertly woven between reed stems either above the water's surface or near the ground. As a rule the female builds the nest un-aided by the male, but he assists in the feeding of the young.

The **Great Reed Warbler,** *Acrocephalus arundinaceus* [934], and closely related species breed throughout southern and central Europe, north Africa, in Asia to the Malay archipelago, and also in Australia. The upper parts are brown; the underparts brown-white without spots. The bird measures $7\frac{1}{2}$ in. The nest, 6–8 in. high, is woven of wet vegetation pierced by reed stems. The 4–6 greenish

to blue eggs hatch after 14 or 15 days, and the
young abandon the nest after another 12 days, before
they can fly very well. The food consists of caterpillars, spiders and small beetles. The journey to the
winter quarters in eastern and southern Africa is
made in August and September. The song is easily
identified–a loud and strident "karre-karre-karre-
krrik-krrik-korr-korr-korr".

The **Reed Warbler,** *Acrocephalus scirpaceus* [935],
has a similar, though not so strident note. The
colouration is the same but it is somewhat smaller
(5 in.) than the Great Reed Warbler. Large reed-beds
are not essential for its nesting; it may be satisfied
with a few square yards and it sometimes builds in
shrubs far away from water. The nest is similar to that
built by its larger relative, but of dry material [936].
The young hatch in 11–12 days, remaining in the
nest for another 11–13 days; when still unable to fly
they are very adept at moving about on the reed
stems. The Reed Warbler breeds in Europe, and in
south-west and central Asia.

937

938

The **Marsh Warbler,** *Acrocephalus palustris* [937], is almost identical in appearance but can be distinguished by its song, which is more musical and varied. It also mimics the songs of other birds. Its haunts are thick growths of grass, osiers and nettles, as well as grain fields. The nest is built above the ground, not above water, and is slung from its supporting stems like a basket, rather than woven round reeds like a Reed Warbler's nest. The male and female share the task of building the nest. The eggs are bluish or greenish, with ashy or brown spots. The Marsh Warbler breeds in west and central Europe east to the Urals.

The **Moustached Warbler,** *Lusciniola melanopogon* [938], is distinguished by a very dark crown, a pale stripe over the eye and darker cheeks. The song resembles that of the Reed Warbler, though more pleasant, interspersed with melodious notes reminiscent of the Nightingale. The nest is placed either on reed stems or on the shrubs scattered among the reed-beds. The short, rounded tail is often held erect. Its range of distribution is limited to southern Europe, north into Czechoslovakia, and east to Turkestan and Persia.

The **Sedge Warbler,** *Acrocephalus schoenobaenus* [939], is found in abundance on the banks of rivers and ponds overgrown with reeds, tall grass and thickets. The golden-brown upper surface is streaked a darker colour, the underparts are creamy yellow, the stripe over the eye contrasting with the dark-striped crown. Its length is 5 in. The

940

941

male sings his song perched on the tip of a reed stem or shrub, occasionally flying up in the air with widespread tail and then diving out of sight again. The nest is placed in thick, low vegetation. The Sedge Warbler breeds in Europe and western Asia.

The vast family of Old World flycatchers (Muscicapidae) is so numerous that it is possible here to name only a few. The 378 species occur in the Old World, including Australasia, but not in America. All have a broad, flat and relatively wide bill, and stiff gape and nostril bristles assist the birds in catching insects in flight. The short feet are used primarily for perching, their structure making running on the ground difficult. The young are usually spotted like young thrushes. The adult birds are rather plainly coloured, many species being black and white, as the **Pied Flycatcher,** *Ficedula hypoleuca* [940], and the **Collared Flycatcher,** *Ficedula albicollis* [941]. The male Pied Flycatcher shown in the picture has not yet attained its full plumage, and lacks the white forehead and the intense colouring of the upper parts found, for example, in males of Scandinavian origin. Both species are the same size (5 in.). The Collared Flycatcher has a white neck-band which in the female, coloured brown-grey above, is scarcely visible. The Pied Flycatcher ranges from north-west Africa through Europe and western Asia to Altai; the Collared Flycatcher does not occur in Africa or in western and northern Europe, and does not extend as far east. Both species

are migrant, flying to central Africa in August and September and returning in April to their haunts in broadleaved woodland, parks and old gardens. The male Collared Flycatcher [941] is shown perched next to a natural nesting cavity; the plain female [942] built her nest within a few days in a wooden nestbox. From the middle of May the female lays 5–7 unspotted, blue-green eggs [943] which it incubates for 12–15 days. Another 14–16 days are needed before the young leave the nest. Like all flycatchers this species feeds chiefly on insects; in late summer it occasionally eats berries. It hunts its prey in the treetops, sometimes diving to the ground in pursuit of a beetle or spider.

944

945

The **Spotted Flycatcher**, *Muscicapa striata* [944], measuring 5½ in., is coloured grey-brown above, the pale underparts streaked a darker colour. The picture shows a young bird. It is generally seen perched upright on fence-posts, railings, dead branches and other elevated positions whence it has a good view, jerking its tail and wings every now and then. As soon as it sights an insect it darts off in pursuit, returning to its perch after catching it. The Spotted Flycatcher leaves Africa for central Europe in early May, rather later in the more northerly parts of its range. It nests in wooded habitats rather than woodland, e.g. parks, margins of woods, forest clearings, gardens, orchards and cemeteries. The male's simple song phrase easily escapes the notice of the untrained ear. The nest is built of moss, grass-stems and cobwebs, lined with fine grasses and hair; it contains 4–6 blue-white eggs thickly spotted with red-brown. The parents feed the young with flies, mosquitoes, beetles and spiders one at a time, their task much more tiring than the swallows', which carry not one but several insects in their bill on each trip. These birds can be seen till late September when they all leave for the warmer climate of Africa. The Spotted Flycatcher ranges from north-west Africa to northern Scandinavia and eastwards as far as eastern Asia.

The best songster of this family is the **Japanese Blue Flycatcher**, *Muscicapa cyanomelana* [946], of easternmost Asia and Japan. The male is cobalt-blue above with black cheeks and throat, the female is brownish. The nest is placed in various cavities or recesses in trees, though the female is also known to scrape moss off rocks with her feet and use it to build a nest in rock cavities. In winter it is found in southern Asia.

East Asia is also the home of the **Narcissus Flycatcher**, *Ficedula narcissina* [947], extending north to Sakhalin. The male is coloured yellow, black and white: yellow throat, breast, lower back and over-eye stripe, white patch on the folded wing—altogether a handsome little bird. The female is brownish and olive-green above [948]. It occurs in both coniferous and deciduous forests subtropical in character. It is quite plentiful in some localities and winters mostly in Indonesia and Malaya.

946

The paradise flycatchers (genus Tersiphone) are exquisite and beautiful birds of Africa, southern Asia, Indonesia and the Philippines. The adult male has greatly lengthened central tail feathers measuring up to 2 ft. They build well-formed cup-shaped nests in the forks of branches, not very high above the ground. The **Paradise Flycatcher,** *Tersiphone paradisi* [945], is all white with only the head, crest and neck blue-black. The long tail feathers are absent in the female and in the young. The bird breeds from Afghanistan through India and Ceylon east to Korea and Borneo.

947

948

949

950

Most of the 12 species of accentors (family Prunelli-
dae) are inhabitants of the high mountains of central
Asia, and only a few have left their original home. In
appearance and mode of life they approach the
finches; their food, especially in autumn and winter,
also consists of berries and seeds – in summer they
eat chiefly insects. That they are seed-eaters is also
evident from the well developed crop where the
seeds are predigested. There is little or no difference
between the sexes. The longitudinal streaks on the
back are reminiscent of the buntings and in the wild
serve as protective colouring. Most accentors nest
high in the mountains above the tree line; those which
occur at lower altitudes frequent tundras where there
are few trees. An exception to this rule is the

Dunnock or **Hedge Sparrow,** *Prunella modularis* [949], which, though common above the tree line, also inhabits scrub and undergrowth at lower altitudes. Here, in spring, the male warbles his rapid song with its sharp, metallic notes, perched on the top of a bush or hedgerow. The head and neck are slaty-grey, the upper parts dark brown, the underparts slaty-grey, both with dark streaks. The female builds the nest in thick cover, of twigs and moss with a soft lining [951]. The clutch is of 3–5 eggs and there are usually two broods in the year, beginning in mid-April. The Hedge Sparrow is a European species, occasionally found in western Asia. In Britain it has become a typical garden bird.

The **Alpine Accentor,** *Prunella collaris* [950], re-sembles a lark both in size and in its song. Its chin and throat are whitish spotted black, the flanks are streaked with russet, the breast is greyish. The nest is placed above the tree line on rock-strewn mountain slopes, in crevices of rocks, or beneath flat boulders. Always well concealed, it is made of dry grass, leaves and moss and lined with hair and feathers. The male frequently makes a brief courtship flight as he sings. Accentors are not shy and will let an observer come quite close to them. They inhabit the highest mountains from the Atlas in north-west Africa through south and central Europe and Asia to Japan. The Dunnock is resident in the British Isles, but migratory elsewhere in its range; the Alpine Accentor only makes local movements.

The wagtails and pipits are members of the family Motacillidae. The former have a world-wide distribution except for the islands of the Pacific. They spend most of their days on the ground, where they move by running, not hopping, continually pumping their long tails up and down. The outer tail feathers are always white. Their favourite haunts are open country, meadows, clearings, treeless grassy mountain slopes, often close to water, although some species occur in dry situations in steppe and even desert regions. Being predominantly ground birds they have fairly long legs and strong toes and claws. They are also good fliers, with a typically undulating action.

The pipits show a marked resemblance to the larks. They are unobtrusive birds with a long claw on the hind toe. The bill and scaly plates on the legs, however, differ from those of larks.

A common inhabitant of the margins of forests is the **Tree Pipit,** *Anthus trivialis* [952, colour plate XXXVI], whose plumage greatly resembles a lark's. It runs well both on the ground and along branches. Its song is commonly heard on bright sunny days,

the male perching on a tree and now and then taking to the air, flying high and descending slowly to alight again on a branch or on the ground without pausing in his song. The bird measures 6 in. and is coloured olive-brown above with dark, longitudinal streaks, and whitish below, also with dark streaks. It ranges from northern Spain throughout Europe to eastern Siberia, wintering in south-west Asia and Africa.

The **Water Pipit**, *Anthus spinoletta* [953], is shown among the scrub in the pose it typically takes up when threatened with danger. Measuring 6½ in. it is somewhat larger than the Tree Pipit. The nuptial plumage of the Water Pipit is unspotted below with a pinkish breast; the upper parts are dark brown, and there is a pale stripe above the eye. The Rock Pipit, which is the coastal race, is like a rather large grey-brown Tree Pipit. It flies up in the air as it sings, concluding its song as it alights with tail cocked. The nest, larger than that of most pipits, is generally placed under overhanging grass beside a stone, so that it is covered from above [954]. The 4 or 5 eggs are grey or grey-green, with darker streaks and spots. Adult birds become very upset when an intruder approaches the nest, flitting here and there and running short distances, calling sadly as they run. Besides the Water Pipits nesting in the high mountains of south and central Europe, Asia and North America, other populations of Rock Pipits nest at lower altitudes on the coasts of France, the British Isles and Scandinavia. In winter and on migration, Water Pipits occur all over North America south to El Salvador.

955

The **Tawny Pipit,** *Anthus campestris* [955], inhabits sandy country, regions with sparse vegetation and heaths, where it runs about flipping its tail rather in the manner of wagtails, although its carriage and movements place it somewhere between wagtails and pipits. The upper surface is more or less uniformly tawny, the underparts yellow-white, thinly spotted. It performs its courting flight above the nesting ground accompanied by the characteristic, repeated note "zirluih". It ranges from north-west Africa through Europe, the central zone of Asia to Mongolia, wintering in Africa and southern Asia. The 6½-in. **Forest Wagtail,** *Dendronanthus indicus* [956], occurs in Eurasia, extending south to Burma. It is olive-yellow above, yellow-white below, with a black breast and distinct black markings. It frequents light deciduous forests, showing a special preference for oaks. It is a tree-dweller and also builds its large sturdy nest on horizontal branches. It winters in India, the Malay Peninsula and Indonesia. The **Blue-headed** and **Yellow Wagtails,** *Motacilla flava* [957], measuring 6½ in., inhabit wet meadows,

956

pastureland and the low shores of lakes and ponds. The tail is not as long as that of the following species but it continually moves up and down in the manner characteristic of the group. The underparts and chin of males are yellow, the upper surface olive-green. The colouration of the head is different in each of the several races and may be anywhere from yellow to grey, to powder-blue or black, with or without a pale stripe over the eye. The heads of British males are brilliantly yellow in spring. Females of all races are mostly alike, their heads matching

their olive-brown upper parts. The flight is not so undulating as that of the Grey Wagtail; the note is a single syllable "tsweep". Races of this species occur all over Europe and part of north Africa, also in Asia north of the Himalayas and on the coast of Alaska. In August-September and April-May migrating flocks forage for insects on pastures where cattle graze. The **Grey Wagtail,** *Motacilla cinerea* [958], is nearly an inch longer, with a very long tail. It is a handsome bird often seen near clear mountain streams, on the banks or on boulders in the water, pumping its tail up

959

and down, or moving from one spot to another with its undulating flight. In summer the male has a bright yellow breast, a black throat with a white stripe dividing it from the grey cheeks and another white stripe passing over the eye. The upper surface is blue-grey, the wings and tail black-grey, the under tail-coverts yellow. In winter the throat is whitish; the

960

female's throat is never black, not even in spring. Though its favourite haunts are clear mountain streams, the Grey Wagtail is also found here and there in the lowlands. Its distribution in Europe and Asia is discontinuous and it does not occur in southern Asia.

Partly resident in the British Isles, migrant Grey Wagtails return to their nesting grounds in central Europe in March and the nest may be found in April either in the steep bank of a stream or very near the water among stones, between the roots of trees or in the masonry of old bridges, etc. [959]. The nest varies in size, depending on where it is located, but the cup itself is fairly small. It is made of grass, moss and fine twigs, and lined with animal and vegetable fibres. The first clutch of 4–6 eggs [960], coloured pale brown on a white ground, is laid in April or early May, the second in June.

The **Pied** or **White Wagtail,** *Motacilla alba,* is perhaps the best known of all wagtails because it occurs near human habitations. In spring it can be seen on the roofs of houses in towns and villages, hopping about alongside rivers, brooks and on freshly ploughed fields. It is coloured white, black and grey. In spring the White Wagtail of Europe has the back of the crown, the nape, chin, throat and breast coal black, the back grey and the remaining plumage white or grey [961]. The female has less black on the head and breast. The male Pied Wagtail of Britain and Ireland has a black back, while that of the female is dark grey. The great adaptability of the

962
963

species shows in its range of distribution from the south of Europe and Asia to the shores of the Arctic Ocean – from the subtropics to the Arctic region – in Iceland and in north-west Africa. In temperate and warm climates it is resident, sometimes given to roaming; in more northerly regions, however, it is seasonal, migrating regularly to the Mediterranean or even South Africa and southern Asia. It is a fairly hardy bird and thus is among the first spring arrivals. Both sexes build the nest which is made of small twigs, bits of leaves, plant stems, rootlets, wool and moss. The inside is softly lined. It is usually placed in recesses between rocks [963], in banks, beneath the roofs of houses, under bridges and on rock-faces, also in wooden nestboxes. The first clutch is laid in April-May, the second in June. The eggs are whitish, thickly spotted and streaked with dark grey to brown. The young birds on leaving the nest do not have the elegant black and white plumage of the parents and the intense black is absent [962]. The non-breeding plumage of adult birds is also less striking – they have a white throat and black breast-band the shape of a horseshoe.

The **Waxwing,** called **Bohemian Waxwing** in North America, *Bombycilla garrulus* [964], is an attractively coloured bird with soft, silky plumage, inhabiting the northern forests of both the Old and New Worlds. Its most distinctive features are a red-brown crest and a short tail with a yellow terminal band. It is liver-coloured above, chestnut brown under the tail with a black throat and black eye-band. The red wax-like pellets on the tips of the secondary flight feathers are remarkable. The rapid flight is reminiscent of the starling's. The Waxwing is a gregarious bird which is usually seen in flocks; even during the nesting season the breeding pairs stay fairly close to one another. The nest, made of lichen, small twigs, grass and moss, is often placed on an exposed tree branch. The 4–7 blue, dark-spotted eggs rest on a layer of feathers and reindeer hairs. The male feeds his mate throughout the period of incubation. During the nesting season the Waxwing eats chiefly insects but its favourite food is berries and small fruits, which are digested very rapidly. A berry takes 20–40 minutes to pass through the alimentary tract during which time only its outer surface is digested. At intervals of 4–7 years flocks of waxwings leave their northern range and wander like nomads far to the south and west, penetrating to the British Isles, southern France and the Balkans. No fully adequate explanations have as yet been found for these "invasions", but the main reason is probably a

964

lack of food when numbers are high in their native habitat.

The Bohemian Waxwing is not a well-known bird in North America, being confined for the most part to the far northern forests. Through the rest of the continent it is replaced by the **Cedar Waxwing,** *Bombycilla cedrorum,* a smaller but very similar-looking species. Both are members of the family Bombycillidae, which comprises nine species distributed throughout the northern hemisphere. All except one have soft, silky plumage, short legs, rather broad bills, and all are fruit-eaters.

The wood swallows (Artamidae) of Australia are known as swallow-shrikes in south-east Asia. They form a distinctive little family of ten species, not closely related to any other passerines, among which they are unique in possessing powder-down feathers. The soft, generally rather dull-hued plumage of both sexes may be relieved by patches of white. The rather long, somewhat curved bill, opening to reveal a wide gape, is well-adapted for catching insects in flight or at rest; and the rather long tail and wings are further aids to expertise in the air. The feet and legs are more powerful than might be expected in largely aerial birds. Found from India and the Philippines to Tasmania, the family is typified by the **Dusky Wood Swallow,** *Artamus cyanopterus*, one of six Australian species; it shows the family tendency to a social life, roosting close together in unfavourable weather [965]. About 8 in. long and mainly brown, with blue and white on wings and tail, it is a familiar bird near habitations, where it is regarded as the gardener's ally because it takes insect pests. The rather frail nest may be built in a tree-fork or under bark at heights up to 40 ft. Both parents share incubation of the 3 or 4 white eggs with zoned markings, and also tend the young.

965

966

The most predatory of the passerine birds are the shrikes (family Laniidae), comprising 73 species. They are widespread throughout most of the world,

967

and the only places where they do not occur are South America, Australia and Madagascar. Africa, where the greatest number of species breeds, is the centre of their distribution. Only two species are native to North America. Shrikes are not large birds, about the size of a sparrow or thrush, with fairly large heads and stout bills hooked at the tip. The upper bill is notched [969], enabling the birds to hold and crush the hard chitinous armour of the insects they feed on. They also hunt and eat small vertebrates such as frogs, lizards, snakes, rodents and other birds, killing their prey with the beak even though they have fairly strong claws. Some shrikes have the curious habit when food is plentiful of impaling their prey on thorns or other spiked objects [967], and establishing quite large caches (larders) when the hunting is good.

The **Red-backed Shrike**, *Lanius collurio* [966], measuring 7¼ in., is one of the smaller members of the family. Like almost all its allied species it frequents open country dotted with numerous shrubs, which provide it with a good view. It does not usually conceal itself in cover but perches on the topmost spray, moving its long tail from side to side and dropping to the ground now and then to seize a small

beetle or grasshopper. It also catches insects in mid-air. Although an occasional mouse or small bird may be found impaled on a thorn nearby [967] analyses of the bird's food have shown that insect pests are the mainstay of its diet. The bulky nest of grasses and rootlets is built by both sexes, among the thickest foliage of a bush or small tree. Incubation is performed by the female, the male relieving her for only a brief spell; but he provides her with food during the whole period. The eggs, numbering 4–7, are reddish white, speckled dark red [968]. The young hatch in 14 or 15 days and fledge 12–15 days later. The fledglings are fed by the parents for another three weeks.

The sexes differ in colouration; the female is brownish above, her breast vermiculated like that of the young birds, while the male has a chestnut back, grey-blue nape and rump and a broad black eye-band. The underparts are pink. It breeds from northern Spain and England to southern China and Kamchatka in Siberia, but does not extend beyond the Himalayas. It winters in central and southern Africa and in southern Asia.

The somewhat larger **Lesser Grey Shrike**, *Lanius minor* [969], has a broad black eye-band and a black forehead, grey back and pink-tinged underparts. It measures 8 in. Unlike the preceding species it builds its nest high in trees. It is generally found in sunny open country dotted with trees or with tree-lined roads, breeding from France through central and southern Europe to Altai. The **Loggerhead Shrike,** *Lanius ludovicianus*, widely but somewhat irregularly distributed through North America, is virtually identical to the Lesser Grey Shrike in appearance and habits.

Starlings (family Sturnidae) have a world-wide distribution, excepting South America, having been introduced to many of the various countries by man. The original home of all the species, numbering about 110, is the Old World, mainly Africa and the Indo-Malayan Region. The members of this family have several characteristic features. The feathers are firm and close fitting, the bill strong and comparatively long, straight, or slightly downcurved. Some species can force the bill open when it is inserted in a crevice or loose soil to grasp their prey. The legs are strong and stout for running on the ground, where the birds seek their food, and for perching in trees where most species nest. The two sexes are generally more or less alike; the plumage is dark with a metallic sheen, though some species are brightly marked with coloured bare patches or wattles on the head. They moult once a year immediately after the breeding season. The plumage varies not only as a result of moult but also because the feathers wear. Starlings

970

971

are very noisy birds, and besides producing their own distinctive song they are able to imitate the songs of other birds; some can even learn to repeat certain words.

The best mimic of the family is the **Hill Mynah**, *Gracula religiosa* [970, 971], occurring in eleven races throughout the whole Oriental region. It is a stout, glossy black bird with a white speculum on the wing and a yellow bill. There are two large yellow wattles on the nape and two small ones below the eye. It measures 10–15 inches, depending on the race. It lives in pairs or small groups on the margins of forests, building its nest high in the cavities of trees and feeding mainly on fruit, especially figs.

An unusually bright sheen distinguishes the African starlings of the genera Lamprocolius and Lamprotornis. Thus the **Splendid Glossy Starling**, *Lamprocolius splendidus* [972], ranging from Senegal to Abyssinia and Angola, is a glossy green and blue above with black patches on the wings, and iridescent violet and copper below. It inhabits the treetops of river-valley forests, occurring in pairs during the breeding season and otherwise in small flocks. The nest is located in the hollows of trees. The primaries are curved and make a peculiar whistling sound in flight.

The **Black-winged Starling**, *Sturnus melanopterus* [973], of Java and Bali is coloured black and white. The young are grey and brownish. In their native habitat the birds nest in the cavities of trees and beneath roofs.

972

973

974

975

The **Superb Starling**, *Spreo superbus* [974], measuring 8½ in., has remarkably bright colouring—green upper parts, greenish blue breast, reddish brown underside, a white band across the chest and white under tail-coverts. It inhabits the steppes and savannahs of central Africa, building round domed nests of twigs in bushes or treetops and occurring in flocks, as a rule, on the ground.

The twittering song of the **Common Starling**, *Sturnus vulgaris* [975], includes less of its own notes than those of other birds. This well-known species, measuring 9 in., seems to be entirely black with a yellow bill, but on closer inspection shows fine white spots and a bronze, purple or reddish sheen. During the spring months these spots disappear due to feather-wear and in June the Starling is almost uniformly black. From July, after the moult, the plumage is again speckled. The young are dusty brown from the time they leave the nest till August when they begin moulting and acquire the spotted plumage. A juvenile, aged about 3 months, which has almost completed its moult except for the head, is shown in picture 976. If there is no nestbox available, the Common Starling makes a loose nest of straw and grass in a hole of some kind, in buildings, trees or rocks. The first clutch, comprising 4–6 pale brown eggs, is laid in April, the young hatching in June. Incubation takes at least 12 days, and for the ensuing three weeks the nestlings are fed in the nest by the parents.

Worms, snails and insects form the mainstay of their diet. After nesting, starlings gather in large flocks which wander over fields and meadows in search of food; in the autumn they are unwelcome visitors to vineyards where they feast on the ripening grapes, and also cause damage to fruit orchards. In the evening they gather from far and wide, twittering and chattering noisily before settling down to roost in woods, reed-beds and, increasingly, in the middles of cities. They are extremely noisy and gregarious birds, especially before their migration to warmer climes, when huge flocks can be seen perching on branches or telegraph wires [978]. Most British Starlings are resident but in September and October, when they leave central Europe, the flocks of Starlings become a great problem in southern and western Europe, and in north-west Africa, where they cause considerable damage to the olive harvest. In spring these birds are the first to return, arriving in central Europe during February. The Starling breeds from Iceland to northern Spain, throughout the whole of Europe and western Asia to Lake Baikal; away from habitations it generally builds its nest in natural cavities. Introduced into North America in the late

xxxiv   **Scarlet Tanager** *Piranga olivacea*

xxxv   **Brazilian Cardinal** *Paroaria capitata*

xxxvi **Tree Pipit** *Anthus trivialis*

976

nineteenth century, it is now an abundant bird in
the east and central parts of the continent and is
rapidly spreading westwards.

The **Spotless Starling**, *Sturnus unicolor* [977],
occurs only on a small area which includes the Iberian
Peninsula, north-west Africa, Corsica, Sardinia and
Sicily. It is about the same size as the Common
Starling, but is entirely black without the white
spots. It is a resident species nesting in holes in sand
and mud-banks, loose masonry, under eaves and in
the cavities of trees.

The **Bare-eyed** or **Pied Starling**, *Sturnus contra*
[983], the same size as the Common Starling, differs
from the other members of the genus in having naked

977

978

979

980

eye-rims. The male has a black head and neck, white cheeks, blackish brown back, white rump, black wings and tail, and pale rust underparts. It ranges from India to Java. The **Rosy Starling** or **Rosy Pastor,** *Pastor roseus* [979], inhabits the wide steppes of central Asia, wandering sometimes in huge flocks to Mongolia and China in the east and Europe in the west, following the swarms of locusts which are its chief food. After such an invasion of new territory it often nests there but is not seen again in the following years. After a brief turbulent courtship it builds an untidy nest in cavities or rock clefts where the female lays 4–6 eggs. These hatch in 12 days and after a further 14–19 days the young are fully fledged and join the adults in their quest for locusts. The Rosy Starling is a handsome bird with black and rose plumage. The back, rump, and underparts are pink, the remainder is black; it sports a broad black crest on the head. Juveniles are like Common Starlings but lighter in colour.

South-east Asia is the home of the mynahs (genus Acridotheres), dark-coloured birds with rounded tails and without any spots. They have erect frontal plumes which often cover the nostrils and some have bare patches of skin around the eye. The **Common** or **Indian Mynah,** *Acridotheres tristis* [980], is a common inhabitant of south-east Asia. Its range of distribution is expanding in much the same way as in the case of the Collared Dove, though not quite as rapidly. Originally it occured only in India and Burma, but it has now spread through Afghanistan all the way to Uzbekistan north of Tashkent. In its native land it is found in the close vicinity of towns and villages, nesting in holes in sand and mudbanks, beneath the roofs of houses, sometimes building round, domed nests on the branches of trees. It feeds on the ground, frequently alighting on the backs of grazing cattle to feast on the insects which victimize them. This mynah has become acclimatized in a number of countries, including Australia and New Zealand, where it is established and breeds. The plumage is chiefly brown, the head and tail are black; there is a white patch on the back wing quills and the belly, under tail-coverts and terminal band on the tail are also white. The bare patch of skin around the eye is yellow. The related **Maldive** or **Bank Mynah,** *Acridotheres ginginianus* [981], of Afghanistan and northern India, measuring 8½ in., is grey, the eye-patch, wing-patch and terminal tail-band are yellow instead of white. The **Crested** or **Chinese Jungle Mynah,** *Acridotheres cristatellus* [982], measuring 10½ in., is black or grey-black with an intensely black head and a short bristly tuft on the forehead. The tips of the tail feathers are white. It breeds from central China to Indochina. It has been introduced and is well established in the vicinity of Vancouver, British Columbia; occasionally it strays to Washington and Oregon.

981

982

983

984

The sunbirds (family Nectariniidae), comprising 104 brightly metallic coloured species, are closely related to the honeyeaters, differing from them, however, in the structure of the long and narrow extensible tongue. This is forked, the two sections forming one or two tubes used to suck up nectar, much as in the case of the hummingbirds. The edges of the bill near the tip are serrated. Sunbirds are active birds occurring either singly or in groups in the tops of trees and bushes, where they feed on insects, spiders and nectar. When taking nectar, however, they do not hover before the blossom like the hummingbirds, but prefer to perch beside it. If the flower has a large corolla they pierce it from the side with their long bills. These birds show marked plumage differences between the sexes, the females usually being dull. The ragged untidy nests of delicate fibres are made, most probably, only by the female. They usually hang from a branch and the side entrance is covered by a small portico. About half the species of this family live in Africa, the remainder are found in India, the Philippines, Indonesia and northern

985

Australia. The **Ceylon Sunbird,** *Cinnyris zeylonicus* [984], of Ceylon and southern India, measuring 4 in., is coloured a metallic blue above, on the head and neck, yellow on the underparts.

Most of the known 160 species of honeyeaters (family Meliphagidae) make their home in the forests of Australia. They also occur, however, in New Zealand, Indonesia, the Philippines and the South Pacific islands. They feed in the same way as the sunbirds and the bill and tongue are very similar in structure. The bill is narrow, pointed and slightly downcurved; the tongue cannot be extended as far as in the sunbirds, but it, too, is divided to form a tube for sucking nectar and the bushy tip serves to collect pollen and small insects. Many honeyeaters are excellent songsters. The **Cardinal Honeyeater,** *Myzomela cardinalis* [985], one of the small members of this family, makes its home in Micronesia, Samoa, the Solomons and New Hebrides. The male is red and black.

The white-eyes (Zosteropidae), a family of 85 species, are nectar-feeding birds of the Old World, found throughout southern Africa, across southern Asia to China and Japan and south-east to Australasia and the Pacific, where they have colonized some islands and been introduced to others as far as Hawaii. Under 6 in. in length, most species are yellow-green above and white below, with a white ring round the eye which gives the family its name. For such small birds they fly very strongly and reach new territories in roving flocks. Typical of the group is the **Oriental White-eye,** *Zosterops palpebrosa,* with perhaps twenty races in India, Malaysia and the Philippines; the bird shown [986] is a **Malayan Coast White-eye,** *Zosterops palpebrosa aureiventer.* The species is a common inhabitant of gardens and woodland, hunting the foliage of tall trees for insects and berries which it takes as well as nectar. In the breeding season the male has a rather feeble jingling song. The sexes are alike in plumage and share nesting duties, sitting very tightly on two or three pale blue eggs in a hammock nest a few feet up in a bush. The eggs hatch in about ten days, the young fledge in a similar period and flocks of up to 100 birds form after breeding is over.

The New World equivalents of the white-eyes are the vireos (family Vireonidae), mostly about the same size and with predominantly green plumage.

986

The forty or so species, divided into three subfamilies, range from Canada to Argentina. The **White-eyed Vireo,** *Vireo griseus* [987], of the eastern USA, the West Indies and Central America, has a reasonably varied song-phrase, beginning and ending with a "click". It is the only species with a white iris to the eye and has bright yellow flanks and two showy white wing-bars. Haunting gardens, thickets and the woodland edge, it builds a rather large nest, generally in low cover, and lays three or four white, brown-spotted eggs.

The closest relatives of the vireos belong to another New World family, the Parulidae or wood warblers, with which are included the conebills and bananaquits. The hundred or more kinds of wood warbler have superficial resemblances to the Old World warblers (pages 484–493) in size, shape, song, diet and nesting habits but are quite distinct anatomically. In spite of their smallness, individuals of several species have reached Europe, especially Britain and Ireland, in recent years, possibly with some help from ships. Unlike the true warblers, wood warblers have distinct plumages in spring and autumn, when they become confusingly similar. In breeding dress males are usually more striking than females. The family shows great variety in plumage patterns, but grey and yellow occur frequently and are well exemplified by the **Canada Warbler,** *Wilsonia canadensis* [988], about 5 in. long. The sexes are basically alike, with a white eye-ring, but the male has bolder markings, notably the black gorget of spots on his yellow breast. This is a common breeding species of the northern forest shrub-layer as far as Labrador, making a nest of leaves, bark and grass close to the ground and laying 3–5 eggs, well-marked on a white base. The song is a rapidly uttered, rather variable phrase.

987

The Canada Warbler winters in Central America. The **Prairie Warbler,** *Dendroica discolor* [989], breeds in the eastern USA and migrates to the West Indies and Florida. Its English name is misleading: in the breeding season it inhabits thickets of young pine and the edges of woods. Only 4 in. long, its dominant shades are olive-green above and yellow below and both sexes look much alike with black streaks on their faces. The male's song, uttered from a tree top, consists of notes in a rising scale and of rather lisping quality. The elegant little nest is built under the canopy of a bush and contains 3–5 whitish eggs with speckles.

988

989

990

991

New World counterparts of the starlings are the icterids (family Icteridae) which exhibit many differences in appearance and way of life. Icterids differ from starlings in the number of primaries (nine instead of ten). All have a pointed, slightly compressed bill, sometimes widening to a frontal shield extending to the forehead, generally straight but sometimes slightly downcurved. The legs are stout, well suited for moving about among branches as well as on the ground. Most icterids are tree-dwellers, though some forms prefer the ground during the day. The mainstay of their diet is invertebrate animals, seeds and fruit, larger species feeding also on small vertebrates.

Starlings generally build their nests in cavities whereas those of icterids are placed in trees. The nests are of two types: one group of birds, the size of starlings, build conventional open cup nests either in trees, bushes, reeds or on the ground; others, generally larger species, for example the caciques, members of the genus Cacicus, build long hanging nests, up to 6 ft in length, placed next to each other to form whole colonies [992]. Some icterids do not build any nests at all, but use nests abandoned by other species. The young are reared by the female, who also builds the nest and performs the duties of incubation, the male merely assisting and frequently acquiring another mate. Some icterids are brood parasites like the cuckoos (page 352). The 94 known species of this family are widespread throughout the New World, ranging from Canada to Patagonia and

992

993

994

the Falkland Islands and occurring also in the West Indies; one species has been introduced on Easter Island.

Members of the genus Agelaius are widespread in America. The males are usually black relieved by red, brown or yellow shoulder patches. They nest near water, in reeds or bushes, the colonies sometimes numbering several thousand birds. As a rule the nest is placed close above the water. The clutch comprises 4 or 5 bluish eggs with brown blotches, and incubation, performed by the female, takes eleven days. The male helps to look after the young, but is sometimes polygamous. The **Tawny-shouldered Blackbird,** *Agelaius humeralis* [990], of Cuba and Haiti, measures about 7 in. The male is glossy black with a greenish tinge; the lesser wing-coverts are reddish brown. In the **Red-winged Blackbird,** *Agelaius phoenicus*, an abundant species throughout North America, the shoulder patch is brilliant red, bordered yellow.

The 30 gaudily coloured species of the genus Icterus include excellent songsters as well as architects – the females weave intricate nests on horizontal branches in which they rear their 4 or 5 young practically unassisted by the male. One species is even known to pierce holes in the leaf of a banana tree, to anchor the strands supporting the nest, which hangs beneath its broad canopy. These icterids live in pairs. The bill is rather pointed; the food consists of insects and fruit. They are very active, and make engaging and attractive cage-birds. Their range is from Canada to Argentina; those which breed in the north are migrants. The **Black-cowled Oriole,** *Icterus dominicensis* [991], measuring 8 in. is black with yellow upper and under wing-coverts, flanks and shanks. It ranges from southern Mexico to north-western Panama and to islands of the Caribbean.

The **Bobolink,** *Dolichonys oryzivorus* [994], is one of the best known North American birds, not only for its plumage and remarkable song, but also because on migration it is a notorius crop-damager, large flocks alighting to feed on the grain in Southern rice fields. Formerly, when their numbers were much larger, whole flocks of these birds were sold on the market for their meat; today, however, they are protected by law. The Bobolink nests in southern Canada and the northern United States, migrating to southern Brazil and Argentina, flying in flocks across the Caribbean. In spring the males arrive first, selecting the nesting territory without the aid of their mate. There is only one brood in the year, the clutch comprising 5–7 eggs. The nest is placed on the ground in thick grass. The male is black below and on the head, with a yellow-white nape; the back, rump and upper tail-coverts are coloured grey to white. The short tail feathers are pointed at the tip. The female is brown above streaked with black, ochre below. The male's non-breeding plumage is similar to that of the female. The Bobolink measures about 8 in.

Comparatively little is known about the **Cuban Blackbird,** *Dives atriviolaceus*, an icterid native to Cuba, [993], which is black with a purple sheen.

Tanagers (family Thraupi-
dae), comprising 222 species,
are another distinctive group
of New World birds occurring
in the tropical and subtropical
parts of the Americas. They
are about the size of finches,
with which they have many
features in common, meas-
uring 8–10 in. at the most.
Like the icterids, they have
nine primaries, the wings
being as a rule short and
rounded.

In some genera, the bill resembles that of a finch, but is
not so strong at the base;
others have bills like warblers
or thrushes. The food consists chiefly of fruit of all kinds,
also soft seeds and insects.
In most species, the two sexes
are alike or very similar, the
female being just as brightly
coloured as her mate. A few
species build covered nests,
but an open cup nest, placed
high in the tree, is the most
common; some tanagers also
build their nests in bushes
close to the ground or in
cavities. As with the icterids,
it is the female who builds the
nest and incubates with some
assistance from the male. The
1–5 spotted eggs take 12–16
days to hatch; the young are
fed by both parents.

The exotic colouring of the
Orange-rumped or **Paradise Tanager,** *Tangara fastu-
osa* [995], of east Brazil makes
it a favourite cage-bird. The
forehead and back are velvety
black, the lower back and
rump orange; the head and
hind neck are covered with
scaly, glossy, blue-green
feathers, the throat is black,
the underparts silvery blue,
the wings and tail black, the

995
996

520

wing tips red. The bird measures 5½ in.

South America is the home of these beautiful tanagers. A native of southern Brazil, northern Argentina and eastern Paraguay is the **Green-headed** or **Golden-naped Tanager,** *Tanagara seledon* [996], measuring 5¼ in. and very like the preceding species in colouration. The forehead is black, as are part of the back, the chin and the breast-band, which reaches to the back. The chest is silvery blue, the remaining underparts yellow-green. The head and neck are golden-green. It is a forest dweller.

The male **Scarlet Tanager,** *Piranga olivacea* [colour plate XXXIV], of eastern North America has a brilliant nuptial dress but unobtrusive non-breeding plumage. It winters in South America. One individual was seen in Northern Ireland in 1963.

The **Blue-Grey Tanager,** *Thraupis episcopus* [997], occurring from southern Mexico to Brazil in several races, measures 6 in. and is almost uniformly blue-grey. These tanagers go about in pairs, the two partners remaining together throughout the whole year. The female, as is generally the case in this family, builds the nest and incubates alone.

The **Stripe-headed Tanager,** *Spindalis zena* [998], of the West Indies has a black head with white longitudinal stripes; the nape, rump and breast are red-brown, the chin and central belly yellow, the back yellow-green, the wings and tail black.

997

998

999

Certain genera of this family have downcurved, hooked bills adapted for piercing the corollas of flowers and sucking the nectar. One of these is the well-known **Blue** or **Red-legged Honeycreeper,** *Cyanerpes cyaneus* [999]. Its long downcurved bill is used to suck nectar and pick small insects from inside blossoms. The bird also feeds on soft fruits. The Blue Honeycreeper, measuring 6 in., is coloured turquoise-blue on the crown, elsewhere purplish blue with black wings, back, lores and tail. After the post-nuptial moult the male has the same olive-green plumage as the female. This active and gregarious bird ranges from Cuba and southern Mexico to Ecuador and southern Brazil, where it frequents lowland forests, nesting in treetops or bushes. The two eggs are incubated by the female for 12 or 13 days during which time she is not fed by the male. The young eat fruit, and to a lesser extent insects.

The related **Shining Honeycreeper,** *Cyanerpes lucidus* [1000], has a blue back and black throat; it is found in South America from Guatemala to Panama. The honeycreepers, together with another group of tanagers known as flower-piercers, comprise the subfamily Dacninae, considered by some ornithologists as a separate family (Coeribidae). The flower-piercers do not have bills as slender and downcurved

1000

1001
1002

as the honeycreepers. The **Sulphur-bellied Honeycreeper** or **Splendid Dacnis**, *Dacnis egregia* [1001], is a brilliant metallic blue, the sides of the head, nape and back black, the centre of the belly yellow. The female is olive-brown above. This species is a native of Colombia and western Ecuador, where it feeds on soft fruits, showing a marked preference for bananas, and small insects found on leaves.

Birds of the genus Tachyphonus, are distinguished by a more slender bill. The **Red-crowned Tanager,** *Tachyphonus coronatus* [1002], measuring about 7 in., is glossy black with a red crown and white under wing-coverts. It is a native of south-east Brazil.

523

1003
1004

It has already been mentioned that the seedeaters (family Fringillidae), which originated in the New World, are birds with a stout, strong bill adapted for eating seeds. This family, comprising 315 species, includes birds who are even able to crack the hard shell of fruit stones. The seeds do not pass directly to the stomach but remain for a time in the crop where they are pre-digested. Though seeds are the mainstay of the diet, these birds feed on insects, buds, young shoots and other greens. The legs are fairly well developed, enabling them to perch in trees as well as to hop and run about on the ground. The shape of the wing differs among the various groups of this family indicating varying degrees of flying ability. It has nine primaries and there are twelve tail feathers. All seedeaters moult once a year, in the autumn. The lovely colouration of their plumage in spring is not produced by the growth of new feathers but by feather wear. Finches are widespread throughout the whole world, with the exception of Australia, Oceania and Madagascar, both in the far north and in the tropical regions of the equator. They are found in high mountains, on the sea-coast, in deserts, forests, fields and near human habitations. In warm and temperate regions most species are resident birds, but further north they are migratory. They are not usually colonial nesters. They build open cup nests in branches, low bushes, on the ground and sometimes even in cavities. The

female lays 5–8 eggs in temperate zones, in tropical zones usually only two.

The male **Common Cardinal**, *Richmondena cardinalis*, is entirely scarlet with a narrow black band across the forehead and black gape, chin and throat. The female [1003], measuring 8 in., is yellow-brown above, dull yellow below tinged red on the belly, with a red crest and yellow-tipped feathers. The Cardinal is well known for its lovely colouring and pleasant song. Its range of distribution extends throughout North America, from southern Canada, and to Guatemala.

The **Indigo Bunting**, *Passerina cyanea* [1004], measuring 5 in., is a brightly coloured bird. The male in summer is entirely blue; in winter the upper parts are rust-brown, the underparts yellow-brown. The female has a brown back, the throat and underparts dull white with faint streaks. It breeds from the eastern parts of southern Canada to northern Florida and Texas, wintering in Cuba and Central America.

The **Cuban Grassquit**, *Tiaris canora* [1005], a fairly small bird with a small bill, is coloured yellow-green above with a grey crown, black face and throat and a yellow band extending from above the eye to the throat. The mountain areas above the tree line in Chile, Bolivia, Peru to Patagonia are the home of the **Mourning Finch**, *Phrygilus fruticeti* [1006], coloured slate-grey above with black forehead and gape; the throat, breast, central part of the belly and under tail-coverts are white.

1005
1006

1007

1008

A red head crowned with a crest of the same colour, red throat and breast, grey upper parts and white underparts distinguish the **Red-crested Cardinal,** *Paroaria coronata* [1007], of South America, which ranges from southern Brazil to Argentina and Bolivia. The female is similarly coloured. The bird measures 7½ in. It breeds and thrives quite well in captivity. The **Brazilian** or **Yellow-billed Cardinal,** *Paroaria capitata* [colour plate XXXV], is a species which

1009

ranges from northern Brazil to northern Argentina. The next two species are circumpolar in their distribution, inhabiting the far north of Eurasia and America. The first is the **Snow Bunting,** *Plectrophenax nivalis* [1008], penetrating farthest north of all the finches and buntings. It occurs near the seashore, which can provide it with necessary food in this unhospitable country, though it breeds in the inland tundra as well. It measures 6½ in. Only the back, shoulders, wing quills and central tail feathers of the male are black in spring; the remaining parts are white. The female has a grey-brown head and back and the winter plumage of the male is also darker. The nest is placed in rock crevices and on the ground. With the arrival of autumn the Snow Bunting travels south, sometimes as far as North Africa, central California, the Ohio Valley and the middle Atlantic states of the USA.

The **Lapland Bunting** or (in North America) **Longspur,** *Calcarius lapponicus* [1009], is shown near its nest in the tundra. This is placed in a depression in the ground among low vegetation or dwarf trees. The bird is 6 in. long, and the male is distinguished by characteristic markings on his black head. A white band extends from below the cheeks to the eye, the upper parts are striped dark brown, the cheeks are a bright chestnut. The female is duller. In the short northern summer it feeds on the insects which are to be found in abundance at this time; in

autumn and winter it eats seeds. It also ranges to the USA and central Europe in winter.

The buntings of the subfamily Emberizinae, found chiefly in the Old World, are sombrely coloured birds with a preference for open country. Here they feed chiefly on grain seeds which they open with their strong bills. A typical example of these seed-eaters is the **Yellowhammer,** *Emberiza citrinella* [1010–1013], measuring 6½ in. The difference between the male [1010] and female [1012] varies. Some males have a bright yellow head and underparts, a chestnut rump, the back and flanks streaked with brown. But others resemble the female and juvenile and show less yellow; all plumages show the bright-coloured rump. Yellowhammers inhabit almost the whole of Europe, except for some parts of the south, and a large part of Siberia. They breed in hedgerows, round

fields and in wilder open country, chiefly on the edges of woods; in the east they may be found in mountains at altitudes up to 6,500 ft. The male's song can be heard in early spring. Having staked out his territory he defends it against all other males; but he will return to the flock if the weather becomes cold again. The female selects the spot for the nest herself

1012

and also builds it alone, usually on the ground, hidden by grass, a bush or tree. It is a neat structure woven of hair, grass, twigs, and sometimes leaves. Both sexes share the duties of incubation. It has even been recorded that, on the death of a female, the male has incubated the eggs himself. The young hatch 12–14 days after the laying of the last egg. There is a second brood in June or July and sometimes even a third brood may be produced later in the year. Besides grain seeds, the Yellowhammer also eats the seeds of various weeds; during the nesting season a quarter of the diet consists of small insects and other small animal life. A resident bird, it remains even in severe winters, when it usually frequents the outskirts of villages where a seed or two is always to be found, chiefly in horse dung and haystacks.

1013

xxxvii   **European Linnet** *Carduelis cannabina*

xxxviii   **Hawfinch** *Coccothraustes coccothraustes*

xxxix **European Goldfinch** *Carduelis carduelis*

1014

The **Corn Bunting**, *Emberiza calandra* [1014], just under an inch larger than the Yellowhammer, is a typical resident of open arable farmland with isolated bushes. The male can often be seen perched on the tip of a tall plant or on telephone or electricity wires where he sings his simple jangling song phrase for hours on end. Located somewhere nearby, in the grass or corn, is the nest sheltering the eggs or young birds. The Corn Bunting is a uniform brown, rather darker above and lighter below, with dark brown longitudinal streaks. It lacks the white outer tail-feathers of most buntings. The female has the same colouration as the male, which is an exception among the Emberizinae. The nest is located in a hollow among grass or grain. The female incubates the eggs alone for 12–14 days, leaving the nest now and then to find something to eat; the male does not feed her but accompanies her to the feeding ground. Only after the young are four days old does he help in caring for them. On the ninth to twelfth day the young birds leave the nest, though still unable to fly. They remain hidden nearby and the parents continue attending to their needs. The diet is more or less the same as the Yellowhammer's. The Corn Bunting

1015

breeds in Europe, and in south-west and central Asia. It is a resident species, given also to local migration. In autumn and winter the birds may gather in large flocks, though this is unusual in Britain.

The **Reed Bunting**, *Emberiza schoeniclus* [1015], makes its home near water by lakes and rivers and in marshes. The male, as in the case of the Yellow-hammer, sings his melody perched on some elevated spot–either on the dry twig of a bush or on a reed stem. He measures 6 in. and is coloured black on the head, chin and breast. A white band separates the head from the body, the back is brown with black streaks, the underparts grey-white. The female has a brown head with a pale stripe over the eye, and dark-brown and white moustache stripes. In winter, when his head is not black, the male looks very like the

1016

female. The nest is generally built by the female in
April in a dry spot near the water, concealed in
rushes, grass or sedge tussocks, or beneath a bush.
The 5 or 6 brownish-red, dark-spotted eggs [1017]
are incubated mostly by the female, though her mate
sometimes relieves her [1016]. The Reed Bunting is
found in suitable situations throughout Europe and
in northern and temperate Asia all the way to Kamchatka. In winter Continental birds migrate to
southern Europe or southern Asia.

The **Rock Bunting**, *Emberiza cia* [1018], has a grey,
black-striped head, chestnut upper parts, and
cinnamon underparts. Its name derives from its
preference for rocky, sparsely covered slopes facing
south. It favours warm climates and is found mainly
in southern, occasionally in central Europe and in
central Asia to northern China. The nest is usually
located under or among rocks, sometimes also in
clumps of vegetation.

1017

1018

The **Grey-headed Bunting**, *Emberiza fucata* [1019], of Asia, shown bringing food to its young, has three separate areas of distribution: Japan, Korea and the territory along the Amur River, southern China, and the Himalayas. It measures about 6½ in. The male is grey on the crown, with black spots, the back is yellow-brown, the underparts white tinged with ochre. The female is duller. Both have a dark breast-band. It appears that shrubs and bushes are important in its habitat. The little known **Yellow-headed** or **Elegant Bunting**,

1019
1020

Emberiza elegans [1020], is limited in its distribution to the territory bordering the Amur, to Korea and southern China. The male of this species is distinguished by a lemon-yellow throat and small crest at the nape, a broad black eye-band, a yellow stripe over the eye, chestnut back and white underparts tinged with yellow. Its favourite haunts are young oak woods. The nest is always placed on the ground under the overhanging twigs of a bush or clump of grass. The clutch consists of 4 or 5 dirty white, speckled eggs [1021]. There are two broods in the year.

The **Ortolan Bunting** [1022] derives its name from the scientific *Emberiza hortulana*, which means garden bunting; it shows a marked preference for gardens, but is also found in hedgerows between fields and in large orchards. In the eastern part of its range it frequents rugged, shrub-grown regions and occurs high up in the mountains – in Altai at altitudes

1021

up to 6,500 ft. The Ortolan measures 6½ in. and is distinguished by the grey-green head, yellow throat and plumbeous-yellow moustache streak. The female is more soberly coloured, with a spotted throat. The nest, identical with that of the Yellowhammer, is placed among vegetation beneath low bushes or under stones, as in the picture. The adults are very wary in the vicinity of the nest, taking great care to scan the neighbourhood from some high vantage point before approaching it. The Ortolan breeds in Europe and western Asia, migrating in large flocks to northern Africa in the autumn.

1022

1023

The small, dark **Crested Bunting,** *Melophus lathami* [1023], is coloured black with red-brown wings and tail; the female is brownish. Both sexes have a crest on their crowns. This species is found in southern Asia, occurring at altitudes of up to 6,500 ft. It is a solitary bird and is only rarely seen in small groups.

1024

The commonest bird over much of Europe is the **Chaffinch,** *Fringilla coelebs* [1024]. Its world range of distribution is not very great, including Europe, western Asia and a small section of north-west Africa. It occurs wherever trees are to be found – in woodlands, hilly country, wooded hillsides, gardens, parks and hedgerows. The song is loud and characteristic, though exhibiting certain regional variations. It can be heard in February and March when the males stake out their individual territories, where the female then selects the nesting site, often in the fork of a branch on a tree or shrub [1025], sometimes in ivy or other creepers. The nest may be practically invisible when the outer layer is made of lichen growing on the tree. It is a neat, compact cup of

moss, lichen, grass, roots and horse-hair. This is lined with hair, down, wool. In Britain the Chaffinch has only one brood a year. As a rule only the female incubates, fed during this period by the male, but instances are known where the male regularly relieves his mate. Both parents share the duties of rearing the young. Though most Chaffinches are migratory, many remain through the winter. Northern European birds winter in western and southern Europe. Two white bands on the wing are a characteristic feature of the Chaffinch; these are already evident in the fledglings [1026]. The male is red-brown below with a chestnut back, grey-blue crown and nape, the female pale olive-brown above. The bird measures 6 in.

1026

About the same size and with much the same habits is the **Brambling,** *Fringilla montifringilla* [1027]. The breeding plumage of the male is glossy black on the head and back. The shoulder-patch and the breast are orange-yellow, even in the winter garb

when the black on the head is largely replaced by grey. It nests in the birch and conifer forests of northern Europe and Asia. From October on, huge flocks of these birds arrive annually in central Europe where they frequent beech woods and fields. They also

1027

form mixed flocks with other finches and sparrows. In March, or April at the latest, they return to their nesting grounds.

The most marked characteristic of the **Hawfinch,** *Coccothraustes coccothraustes* [1028, colour plate XXXVIII], is its bill, which seems quite out of proportion to its 7-in.-long body [1029]. The male is brown above with yellow-brown underparts and head, the nape grey, wings blue-black, throat and gape black. In spring the bill is blue-black, in winter pale grey. The female is much duller. A wide white patch is visible on the black wings in flight and the tail is terminated by a white band. The Hawfinch occurs in broad-leaved woodlands, large gardens, orchards and parks, where it feeds on buds, seeds and kernels which it extracts by cracking the hard stones. In summer it also captures large quantities of insects with which it feeds its young. The nest is located high up in trees. The 5 or 6 eggs are incubated by both sexes. The Hawfinch breeds from north-west Africa through Europe and Asia to Japan.

1028

1029

537

1030

The **Black-tailed Hawfinch** or **Asiatic Bullfinch,**
Eophona migratoria [1030], of eastern Asia has a very
limited distribution, breeding only along the Amur
in northern and southern China. It measures 8 in.
The bill is not as stout as in the Common Hawfinch;
the male's head and wings are black with a metallic
gloss, the tips of the folded wings are white, the back
brown, the underparts grey. The female, shown
feeding the young, does not have a black head. This
bird is a typical inhabitant of broad-leaved and mixed
woodlands. It does not occur in the interior of the
taiga. The nesting season is fairly late, the young
hatching at the end of June and in the first half of
July. The 3–5 eggs are incubated only by the female,
who is fed by her mate throughout this period.
The **Bullfinch,** *Pyrrhula pyrrhula* [1031, 1032], is a
quiet, unobtrusive bird with a soft call, which frequently escapes notice in the wild. But the male has
quite distinctive markings. The breast and sides of
the head are red, the crown, chin, wing-tips and tail
black, the back grey and the rump white. In the
female the breast and the sides of the head are liver-
brown instead of red. Several racial populations
breed in the woodlands of Europe and the Siberian
taiga all the way to Japan and Kamchatka. The sweet
piping call is heard far more often than the twittering
note. The female also sings in captivity, when the
Bullfinch can be taught simple melodies. Where they

538

are migrants, Bullfinches arrive at the breeding grounds in pairs sometime in March and begin building the nest, usually near the ground, in April. The female weaves a shallow structure of twigs from both conifers and deciduous trees, which she lines with roots and hair. The eggs, numbering 4–6, are a clear pale blue with dark red and purple-grey streaks and blotches. For 12–16 days after hatching the young are fed seeds and insects by the parents, otherwise Bullfinches favour the seeds and buds of various trees, in autumn, for example, the berries of the mountain ash [1032]. In the south they are resident birds but the northern races migrate to warmer climes in winter.

539

1033

1034

The **Scarlet Grosbeak,** *Carpodacus erythrinus* [1033], is the same size as the Bullfinch (6 in.) and also has a short stout bill. The male in spring is crimson with two indistinct bands on the dark brown wings and a grey-brown tail. The female and the young are brown above and yellow-brown below. It occurs in Europe and temperate Asia southwards to the Caucasus, Persia and the central Asian mountains. Currently it is spreading westwards and has been found in several places in central Europe. It frequents thickets near water, and edges of woods with thick undergrowth; in Asia it occurs at altitudes up to 12,000 ft. The call consists of 4 or 5 strong flute-like notes. As a rule the male sings perched on the tip of a bush close to the nest. The **Purple Finch,** *Carpodacus purpureus,* of eastern and northern North America, and the **House Finch,** *Carpodacus mexicanus,* of the west, are both essentially similar to the Scarlet Grosbeak in appearance and habits.

The well-known **Greenfinch,** *Chloris chloris* [1034], also has a stout bill. It is the same size as a sparrow and is often mistaken for it, especially in cities where its plumage is dulled with grime. Otherwise it is an attractive olive-green bird with a yellow rump and bright yellow patches on the wings and tail. The female is greyer, with little yellow in its plumage. The Greenfinch has a pretty bell-like song—a rapid series of notes "gigi gi gi" terminated by a descending "shooah". The male perched on a branch a he sings, flies up a

1035

mes to make his courtship display. The female
uilds the nest in various sites, including treetops up
50 ft above the ground. Except for deep forests,
ne Greenfinch nests wherever trees are to be found,
hedges, gardens, orchards, parks, cemeteries and
n the margins of woods. The nest is a fairly large,
hallow structure made of twigs, moss, rootlets and
ry grass lined like those of other finches. The 4–6
lue or yellowish white, red-speckled eggs are laid
late April and the beginning of May. The duties of
cubation are performed by the female, the male
ringing her food during this period of 12–14 days
nd for some time after. Both parents then feed the
oung–chiefly on seeds partially digested in the crop;
ost seedeaters feed their offspring young insects.

Greenfinches, though not yet strong on the wing,
leave the nest 12–17 days after hatching [1035]. Their
plumage is grey-green with dark streaks. They void
over the edge of the nest where the droppings remain,
as the parents do not remove them. There is a second
brood in July. When the young have fledged the
family joins other families and even other species to
forage for seeds in the fields. Favoured are oily seeds,
rape, sunflower and hemp. The Greenfinch is found
in Europe, also in north-west Africa, Asia Minor and
central Asia. Birds breeding in northern Europe
migrate south and south-west in winter; central
European birds are only partial migrants. They are
common visitors to window-box feeding places in
winter.

1036

The **Eurasian Siskin,** *Carduelis spinus* [1036, 1039], frequents the coniferous forests of north and central Europe, occurring higher and higher in the mountains the farther south it ranges, whereas in the north it can be found in lowland woods as well. It also occurs in the mountains of the Caucasus and northern Persia and in the Far East. The plumage is yellow-green with dark upper parts and light, striped under-parts. The male has a black crown and chin. It is a lively little bird which is gregarious and forms into large flocks after the nesting season. These roaming flocks cover large distances, the largest numbers occurring wherever there is an abundant harvest of alder cones from which they extract the seeds, balancing on their tiny feet or sometimes hanging head downwards [1039]. Pairs of these birds arrive

1037

1038

1039

at the nesting grounds in March or early April, but even in February one can observe the courtship performance when the male flies up and sings with wings outspread. The song is a pleasant combination of soft chirps and twitters. The female builds the nest high up in trees, sometimes as much as 65 ft above the ground, concealing it among the needles so well that it is hard to find, the birds' quiet unobtrusive behaviour adding to the difficulty. In June and July, when the second clutch is laid, the young siskins of the first brood are already to be seen flying about in the woods. The mainstay of the winter diet is alder and birch seeds, in summer, seeds of all kinds.

The **European Goldfinch,** *Carduelis carduelis* [1037, colour plate XXXIX], measuring about 5 in., has a lovely head – the face is red, the sides of the head and cheeks white, the crown and nape black. Also striking are the black, white-tipped wings with broad yellow bands. The back is brown, the underparts brownish and white, the black tail has white markings. The two sexes are very similar. Its range is about the same as that of the Greenfinch. The male sings his lovely song, which consists of a series of clear notes, from the branches of a tree or some other elevated perch. Birds reared in captivity from the time they are fledged are very tame but must learn to sing properly from other Goldfinches. The nest is generally located in deciduous trees, rarely in conifers, often on the topmost or on horizontal branches, where it can be reached only with difficulty. The compact cup-nest of moss and rootlets, with a layer of wool, thistle down and hair, is attached to the branch with fibres. Both parents feed the young, first with insects and later with seeds partially digested in the crop. The juvenile plumage lacks the colourful head pattern of the adults. In central Europe the Goldfinch migrates locally, to the south and south-west; in Britain and elsewhere, it often stays the winter.

Nineteen different geographical races are to be found throughout its range, those nesting in the east differing from the western species in the pale grey upper parts and in having no black on the head. Picture 1038 shows a bird of the grey-headed race *Carduelis carduelis subcaniceps* of Tadzhikstan and Persia.

1040

It is difficult to judge which of the passerine birds have the finest songs, but without doubt in captivity the **European Linnet,** *Carduelis cannabina* [1040, 1041, colour plate XXXVII], ranks among the best. The grey-headed male has a crimson cap starting just above the bill and a breast-patch of the same colour. The underparts are grey-brown, the back dark brown. The female is much like the male but without the crimson patches. The pictures show young linnets in their striped plumage. The song consists of metallic, flute-like and chirping notes. The Linnet generally frequents dry farmland, heaths and open country with bushes. It shows a preference for gorse and evergreen shrubs, and nests in parks, gardens and hedgerows–practically everywhere, except continuous woodland. The range of distribution is about the same as that of the Greenfinch, extending in the east to Turkestan and West Pakistan.

xl **Gold-fronted Finch** *Serinus pusillus*

xli **Chestnut Mannikin** *Lonchura ferruginosa*

Linnets come to their breeding grounds in April. The
nest, which is sometimes built
within 48 hours, is situated
close to the ground in thick
bushes or small trees [1042].
Seeds are the chief food, more
so than in the case of any other
bird, and the Linnet only
occasionally eats insects.
When the young have fledged,
the birds form flocks which
visit fallow fields overgrown
with weeds.

A red forehead and black chin
distinguish the **Common
Redpoll**, *Carduelis flammea*
[1043]. The upper parts are
brown, the underparts whitish
1042 with darker streaks; in the

1043
1044

male the breast is tinged with pink. The bill is well suited for extracting seeds from the small cones of birches and alders, which is also the chief food of these lively birds in winter. The Redpoll is a northern species which breeds in the arctic tundras of Europe, Asia and North America; smaller, darker races are found also in the mountains of central Europe and in the British Isles. In winter the mountain race descends to the lowlands and the northern Redpolls journey south, sometimes in great numbers, to central Europe and the northern USA.

1045

A distinguishing feature of the crossbills (genus Loxia) is the bill with its overlapping tips [1047]. In the young the bill is straight but begins to overlap at the age of three weeks. The two sexes are dissimilar in appearance.

The adult male of the **Common** or (in North America) **Red Crossbill**, *Loxia curvirostra* [1044], is brick-red with brown wings and tail, the female olive-green with a yellow rump. The juveniles are green-brown, striped black below. Yellow males are probably young birds. Crossbills breed very early in the year even in severe frosts and so build a solid, snug nest high up in the branches of conifers. The incubation period is about 15 days and the eggs are hatched by the female. At first she receives food for the young via the male and passes it on. The food consists of seeds from fir cones, and for that reason crossbills establish their nest in areas where there is an abundant supply of these cones. The range of continuous distribution encompasses the northern coniferous forests of Europe, Asia and North America. These birds also have a discontinuous distribution extending to north-west Africa, the Himalayas and in the New World throughout the northern coniferous forests, south in the mountains to North Carolina in the east and Nicaragua in the west. In some winters they invade the northern USA in great numbers, but in other years may be virtually absent.

The **Serin,** *Serinus serinus,* is the canary's closest living European relative. It resembles the Siskin but has a more robust short conical bill, and is yellower with no black markings on the head. Its yellow rump flashes brightly as it flies up in the air. The male is yellow with longitudinal streaks [1045], the female greyer and more thickly streaked [1046]. The Serin measures $4\frac{1}{2}$ in. When singing it perches on the dead branches of trees or on telegraph wires, swaying

1046

1047

about like a compass needle. It also sings during the courtship flight, making swooping turns like a bat. The note is long drawn-out and sounds like the creaking of an unoiled wheel. The European Serin's original home was the territory around the Mediterranean – north Africa, southern Europe and Asia Minor, whence, at the beginning of the 19th century, it suddenly spread over the Alps to the north and since then to the coast of the North and Baltic Seas all the way to the Gulf of Finland. It is found in the vicinity of human habitations, in villages and towns, in gardens, and at the edge of forests. In southern Europe it occurs high in the mountains. The nest is situated in tall trees and seeds are the mainstay of its diet. In northerly regions the Serin is migratory, flying to southern Europe in winter.

The **Gold-fronted Finch,** *Serinus pusillus* [1048, colour plate XL], is a handsomely coloured bird ranging from Asia Minor to Ladakh, where it is found in the mountains on the middle and upper slopes. It measures 5¼ in. The male has a black and grey head with a red cap on the forehead. The nest is built in rock crevices and on rock ledges.

Well known in all parts of the world is the Canary, a favourite cage-bird bred from Wild Canary stock, still to be found in the woods of the Canary Islands, as well as the Azores and Madeira islands. The **Wild Canary,** *Serinus canaria*, is olive-green above, greyish yellow below streaked with black. Among the domestic varieties birds whose plumage resembles

1048

that of their wild predecessors still occur. Since 1478, when the Canary Islands fell to the Spanish who introduced the first canaries to the European continent, many races and colour varieties have been produced by selective breeding. These include white, yellow and striped canaries [1049, 1050], birds of normal build and ones which have very long legs and unusual feather ornaments. Cross-breeding with *Carduelis cucullata* has even produced the pretty Red Canary. Most breeders, however, concentrate their efforts on song rather than colour. The best in this respect is the so-called Harz Mountain Roller bred in the Harz region of Germany.

1049

1050

1051

1052

1053

At first glance one would think the bird in the picture at top left was a Long-tailed Tit, but it is in fact the **Long-tailed Rosefinch,** *Uragus sibiricus* [1051]. However, the bill, resembling that of the Bullfinch, eliminates any possibility of its being related to the tits. The male is pink with dark wings and tail, the outer feathers of which are long and white. The back is streaked black, the wing quills are black. The female is brownish. It measures nearly 7 in. This species makes its home in the central part of Siberia, northern China, and Tibet. In the east it extends all the way to Sakhalin Island, north of Japan. The note resembles that of the Crossbill, but is rather more bell-like.

The nest is built in thickets alongside rivers and on bush-grown marshes. It is a compact structure placed in the twigs of a bush [1052]. The clutch consists of 3–6 speckled blue eggs. After the young have fledged the family forms an independent group or may join with others in small flocks which roam the countryside.

The **Isabelline Finch,** *Rhodospiza obsoleta* [1053], inhabits the dry plains of central Asia–Persia, Afghanistan, Turkestan and central Mongolia. It is also found in scrub country, oases and near human habitation. It is the colour of sand, the bill edged with black, the belly white, the wing and tail feathers black with broad white borders. It is a gregarious bird even during the breeding season, when pairs nest close to one another and fly in groups to drink and forage for food. The spacious nest has two layers, the inside layer often consisting of white tufts of cotton, and is placed in the branches of trees and bushes without any attempt at camouflage.

551

1054

The last family of passerine birds, the Ploceidae, shows great similarities to the Fringillidae, the evolution of the two being apparently parallel. The bill is conical and as in the preceding family is used to extract seeds. The majority of these birds make

1055

their home in the tropics of the Old World, from Africa to Australia; some are also widespread in Europe and Asia, and four genera have been introduced to the Americas. Most of them build domed nests with a side or bottom entrance, others weave complex structures with a long hollow tube for access, still others build large communal nests. Weaverbirds include some 260 species which are divided into several groups. Many are favourite cage-birds because of their lovely colouration. There is hardly need to describe what is perhaps the best known of all birds – the **House Sparrow**, *Passer domesticus* [1054]. The male has a dark grey crown, chestnut nape and black throat. The female is entirely brown without any black markings. The Sparrow nests in various places, under eaves, behind drain-pipes, in nestboxes, in the nests abandoned by House Martins and Swallows, and in trees. Some trees may contain dozens of the round, untidy nests –

a sort of weaver-bird colony. A native of North Africa, Europe and western Asia, the House Sparrow has been introduced to many parts of the world, including America, South Africa, Australia and also various islands; in North America, where it is now abundant, it is often called the **English Sparrow.** A much prettier bird is the **Eurasian Tree Sparrow,** *Passer montanus* [1056, 1057], which has a chocolate-brown crown, a black chin and a black patch on the cheek. It is somewhat smaller than the House Sparrow, and the young [1055] lack the black head markings. The nest is placed in the hollows of trees, in mud-banks and old, loose masonry; in many areas it has not the same close association with man as the House Sparrow. Compared to the House Sparrow, it has more limited area of distribution in Europe and western Asia; in North America there is a small introduced colony centred about East St Louis, Illinois.

1058

The group of typical weavers consists of 109 species, the **Red Bishop,** *Euplectes orix*, being one of the handsomest. The male has red upper parts, throat and under tail-coverts. The crown, sides of the head and underparts are black. This bird makes its home in Africa south of the Sahara, in savannahs and cultivated regions. The illustration [1058] shows a male of the race *Euplectes orix franciscana*, of central Africa, which has a red throat. The non-breeding plumage of both sexes is pale above, paler below, darkly streaked on the back and underparts and with a pale stripe over the eye [1060]. Termites form a large part of its diet, but the birds also feed in flocks on grain fields. The male's courtship antics, performed before his two or three mates, consist of undulating flights and a clapping sound produced

by the wings. He does not assist in the building of the nest. This round structure suspended in reeds or bushes is the work of the female alone. The **Red-billed Dioch** or **Quelea**, *Quelea quelea* [1059], 5 in. long, occurs in Africa south of the Sahara, where it is unpopular as the large flocks of tens of thousands of birds, which invade the country to breed immediately following the rainy season, cause damage to crops. They are such serious pests that chemicals sprayed from planes and flame-throwers have been used in attempts at mass extermination. The males build simple oval structures with a side entrance in trees or reeds, the females laying their eggs within a day or two after completion of the nest. Many thousands of nests may be placed close beside each other on a small area. Both sexes share the duties of incubation, which takes 13 days. The young fledge after 12 days and the whole flock, including the young, then set off again on their wanderings. The male has a red bill, the forehead, sides of the head and throat are black, the crown and underparts yellow-white.

1061

The **Black-headed** or **Village Weaver**, *Ploceus cucullatus* [1061], ranging from Senegal and Eritrea to Capetown, has a black head, white wings and upper parts, and yellow underparts; it measures 6½ in. The male builds a kidney-shaped nest which occasionally is furnished with an outside entrance tube. In exceptional circumstances he is capable of building it in a single day. The inside is lined with fine material by the female, who then lays 3 or 4 eggs which she alone incubates.

The excellent architectural ability of the weavers of the genus Ploceus is illustrated by the nest with entrance tube [1062] of the yellow-eyed **Vieillot's Black Weaver**, *Ploceus (Melanopteryx) nigerrima*,

of Nigeria to Uganda and north Angola, and that of the **Baya Weaver**, *Ploceus philippinus,* one of the 36 species of Asian weavers, widespread in India, Indochina and Malaya [1063]. The roughly woven unlined nest has an entrance tube and hangs from the branch of a tree; it is the work of the male.

The subfamily of waxbills (Estrildinae) consists of 107 species ranging from Africa to Australia, southern Asia and Micronesia. They are mostly small, brightly coloured birds. The nestlings have bright markings inside the mouth, sometimes also papillae at the gape which prompt the parents' instinct to feed the young by placing the morsels far down their gullets.

1063

The **Chestnut Mannikin,**
Lonchura ferruginosa [1064],
colour plate XLI], measuring
4½ in., has a black head, neck
and chest, white underparts
black in the centre, and cinnamon back, wings and flanks.
The sexes are alike in appearance. The range of distribution extends from India to
southern China and the
Philippines.

The **Striated Finch,**
Lonchura striata, is the wild
stock from which the do-
mestic cage-bird [1065] of
Japan and China was bred. It
occurs in many different
colour forms.

The **White-headed Munia,**
Lonchura maja [1066], also
of this group, measures 4¼
in. and is coloured chestnut
with a white head and neck.
The centre of the chest, the
belly and the under tail-
coverts are black. The sexes
are alike. It ranges from Siam
to Java and is a favourite
cage-bird.

Finches of the genera Granatina and Uraeginthus inhabit
the grassy country of Africa
where they occur in several
species. Extending from Senegal to Somaliland and the
Congo is the popular cage-
bird the **Cordon Bleu** or
Crimson-eared Waxbill,
Uraeginthus bengalus [1067],
measuring 5 in. with a longer,
pointed pale blue tail, blue
cheeks and throat, red-brown
underparts and a red bill. The
male has a red ear-patch.

The gaudy male **Red Avadavat,** *Amandava amandava*
[colour plate XLII], of India
and Ceylon has a dull non-
breeding plumage resembling
that of the female.

The **Cut-throat** or **Ribbon
Weaver-finch,** *Amadina fasciata* [1068], is remarkable for

1064

1065

its barred plumage. The pale yellow-brown upper parts are thickly barred with black, the sides of the head and throat are white with a glossy, carmine stripe extending on either side up to the ears. The underparts are pale yellow-brown with narrow bands, the middle of the belly is chestnut. The carmine throat-band and chestnut belly-patch are absent in the female. This species inhabits the whole of central and south-east Africa, frequenting the sparse woods of the savannahs. It is absent in the virgin forests and desert regions. The food consists of seeds, mainly grass seeds. As a rule it travels in larger groups, lone pairs being seen only rarely outside the nesting season.

Extremely attractive, though not so colourful, is the **Java Sparrow,** *Padda oryzivora* [1069], with its stout, reddish bill and white cheek-patches on either side of the black head, pearly grey upper parts, delicate grey underparts and black tail. Originally found only in the grassy, shrub-covered country of

1067

1068

xlii   **Red Avadavat** *Amandava amandava*

xliii   **Long-tailed Weaver-finch** *Poephila acuticauda*

xliv **Gouldian Finch**
Erythura gouldiae

xlv **Zebra Finch**
Taeniopygia guttata

Java and Bali, it became a popular cage-bird and has since been introduced to many parts of the world where it has gained a firm foothold. Today it occurs in southern Asia, China, parts of Africa, Hawaii and elsewhere. The male and female share the duties of nest-building, incubating and caring for the young. The 6–8 eggs are laid in an untidy domed nest resembling that of the sparrow. It is a favourite cage-bird in China and Japan. The note is a metallic chirping ending in a trill.

Of the species native to Australia, the one illustrated is the **Long-tailed** or **Shaft-tailed Weaver-finch** *Poephila acuticauda* [colour plate XLIII], with its graduated tail of pointed feathers up to 3 in. long. The head is ashy grey, the remaining plumage

cinnamon, white and black. The broad black patch on the chin is conspicuous and the bill is reddish yellow.

The related **Masked Weaver-finch,** *Poephila personata* [1070], inhabiting the grassland of north and north-west Australia, is distinguished from the preceding species by a cinnamon-brown head and black band encircling the base of the bill. It, too, has a long tail with pointed central feathers.

A jewel of a bird among those inhabiting northern Australia is the **Gouldian Finch,** *Erythura gouldiae* [colour plate XLIV], occurring in three colour variations—with black, red or yellow heads, the first of these being the most common and the third the rarest.

1072

Southern Australia is the home of the **Rufous-tailed** or **Red-faced Weaver-finch,** *Bathilda ruficauda* [1071], which can be found near rivers lined with lush vegetation, in reeds and low thickets. The male is olive yellow-brown above, with dark red upper tail-coverts. The forehead, the area round the eye, the cheeks and the chin are scarlet covered with tiny white dots, which are also present on the grey chest. The underparts are yellow. In the female the red colouring occurs only on the head; it is not as bright and there is less of it.

One of the most common cage-birds is the **Zebra Finch,** *Taeniopygia guttata* [1072, colour plate XLV], of Australia, where it occurs in great numbers especially in the interior. It keeps close to the ground in grasses and bushes and builds its flask-like nest in

shrubs or low trees, occasionally in cavities or even on dwellings. The throat and chest as well as the tail of the male are barred black and white like a zebra. It is grey above and white below; the flanks are reddish with white patches. A white band, bordered black on either side, runs down from the base of the red bill. The large chestnut ear-patch is separated from the grey crown by a white line. The female has a grey throat without the transverse bars. Zebra Finches multiply in captivity and can be bred in great numbers if suitable conditions are provided, nesting at any time of the year and laying 4–7 white, blue-tinged eggs which hatch after eleven days; both parents share the duties of incubation. The young leave the nest three weeks later and moult at about the age of eight weeks; they often start building

nests at this age. The selectively bred white form of the Zebra Finch retains its coral-red bill [1073].

The eight species of widowbirds or whydahs (subfamily Viduinae) inhabit the grasslands and savannahs of Africa south of the Sahara. They are fairly small birds, but the male has four long central tail feathers which play their role in the courtship performance, when he rises high up in the air flapping his wings and waving his tail and then rapidly coasts down to the female. The males are polygamous. Parasitism is another distinguishing feature of the widowbirds. The females do not rear their own offspring, each species laying its eggs in the nest of certain other birds, generally one or other of the closely related Estrildidae. The hosts are in no way harmed by this practice for the widowbirds do not throw out the host's eggs or nestlings as does the cuckoo. The foster-nestling gets along well with its fellow and is reared with them. An interesting feature is the fact that the eggs of the widowbirds are pure white and their offspring have markings inside their mouths the same as the young of their hosts.

The male **Shaft-tailed** or **Paradise Whydah,** *Vidua regia* [1075], of South Africa has four very long central tail feathers, without vanes except at the tips where they are slightly broadened. The bird's length, including the tail feathers, is 12 in. It is black above, reddish yellow-brown below, with red bill and feet. The female also has red feet, two dark bands on the head, brownish upper parts, yellow-brown breast and whitish underparts [1074]. The male has much the same colouration in his non-breeding plumage. The host in this instance is the **Violet-eared Wax-bill,** *Granatina granatina*.

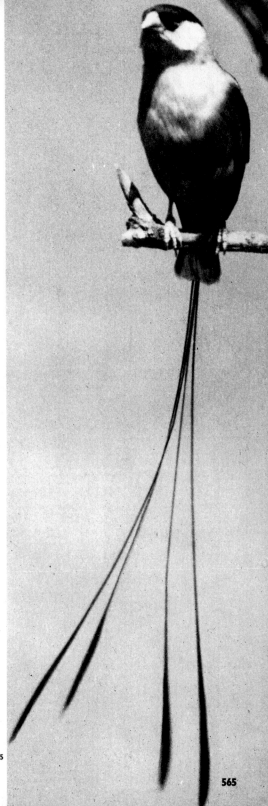

1075

Index

Picture Acknowledgements

A. W. Ambler (National Audubon Society), 803;
G. Ronald Austing, 752, 987, (National Audubon Society 989);
F. Balát;
S. Bártl;
Des Bartlett (Armand Denis Productions), 484, 485, 756;
P. Beretzk;
Allan D. Cruikshank (National Audubon Society), 584, 584A;
P. Čtyřoký;
Jack Dermid (Photo Researchers), 887;
I. Eibel-Eibelsfeldt;
J. Felix;
V. Fiala;
William L. Finley, 242;
J. Formánek;
C. A. W. Guggisberg (Photo Researchers), 598;
Hugh M. Halliday (Annan Photo Features), 988;
J. Hanzák;
J. Janalík;
K. A. Judin;
N. N. Kartaschev;
A. Keppert;
Russ Kinne (Photo Researchers), 704, 741;
B. K. Kinský;
Z. Klůz;
P. Kramer;

A. V. Kretschmar;
Loke Wan-Tho, 878;
A. G. Luchtanov;
G. C. Madoc, 748;
L. Marek;
John Markham, 65, 365, 751;
Karl H. Maslowski (Photo Researchers Inc.), 466, 886;
H. Moll;
R. R. Monro (Camera Press Ltd.), 742;
A. Mošanský;
I. A. Neifeldt;
P. Pavlík;
L. A. Portenko;
Royal Zoological Society, London, 986;
J. Rys;
J. Sálek;
J. Seget;
M. F. Soper, 805;
J. Svoboda
Barrie Thomas (Photo Researchers), 46;
John Warham, 44, 49, 965;
Won-Chon-Gu;
Zentrale Farbbild–Agentur.

Drawings: A. Pospíšil